Scott, Foresman and Company

Introduction to Statistics

Frank W. Carlborg
Northern Illinois University

Library of Congress Catalog Number 68-11978
Copyright © 1968 by Scott, Foresman and Company, Glenview, Illinois 60025.
All rights reserved. Printed in the United States of America.
Regional offices of Scott, Foresman are located in Atlanta,
Dallas, Glenview, Palo Alto, and Oakland, N.J.

Preface

Most important human activities involve complex situations with many factors. Statistical methods were created for some of these multi-factor situations. Many of the most powerful methods, such as the analysis of variance, were developed in particular fields of scientific research, such as agriculture and medicine. These methods are used widely now in other fields, for example, in market research.

The primary purpose of this book is to survey the statistical methods for multi-factor situations in an introductory manner. Specifically, this purpose is to survey multiple regression and the analysis of variance. The intended reader seeks a general knowledge of these methods. After reading the book, he should be able to identify a statistical situation, to look in the right place for more theoretical or applied information, and to use the suggestions of a statistical consultant.

In the allowed space, it is impossible to discuss these statistical methods for multi-factor situations and to include all the usual introductory topics. Probability receives a brief treatment. Nonparametric methods, for example, are omitted completely.

The book is designed for a three-hour, one-semester introductory course. About ninety per cent of the material, including all the important statistical topics, can be read with a mathematical background of college algebra. The other ten per cent requires a background of some calculus. A section, paragraph, or exercise requiring calculus is starred (*). The starred material is supplementary, but not essential, to the unstarred material.

Johannes Venter, Potchefstroom University, South Africa, read an early version of the book and gave many valuable criticisms of the statistical material. Many students used the early version and made suggestions. All the suggestions were appreciated. At every step in the process of converting a set of class notes into a published textbook, some person at Scott, Foresman was helpful, especially Susan Hastings with her editorial assistance.

Frank W. Carlborg

Saint Charles, Illinois
March 1968

Contents

Introduction I

1
Statistics

Definitions of statistics tend to have meanings only to those who already know what the subject is. It seems more valuable to describe a few of the situations which usually require statistics. Then the contribution of a statistician to these situations can be indicated.

Games of Chance. Dice are rolled according to some specified procedure. The number of spots on the upward faces varies from roll to roll.

Opinion Survey. Members of a population are asked questions about a current issue. If the issue is controversial, the answers vary from person to person.

Traffic Engineering. Automobile trips between two particular points in a city are timed. If the trip is typical of urban travel, the time required varies from trip to trip.

Agriculture. The owners of farms in a region plant the same crop on their fields. At harvest there is a variation in yields among the fields.

Biology. Many persons with a certain disease take the same drug. Recoveries from the disease vary from person to person.

Census. After identifying a household, the census taker records the number of residents. The number varies from household to household within a community.

Military. Each recruit is trained to operate the same type of rifle. At the end of basic training, there is a variation in the marksmanship record attained by the recruits.

As you can see, statistical situations are characterized by variation. Statisticians are active in all these situations—except games of chance—because of their inherent variation. Remove the variation, and you remove the need for a statistician.

The variation in a statistical situation has a particular pattern. That is, one pair of dice gives outcomes according to one pattern; another pair may have a slightly different pattern. Citizens of one population show one pattern to their opinions on an issue; they may have a different pattern for another issue; or another population may have a different pattern for the same issue. Similar cases exist for the other examples.

The goal of an investigation into a statistical situation is to find the pattern of variation. When the investigator finds this pattern, he has described the situation as completely as possible. Since long investigations are usually expensive, the investigator wants to find the pattern quickly. Identifying the pattern of variation from a small investigation is the job of a statistician.

2
Random Experiments

An activity that satisfies the following two general requirements is an *experiment:* There is a clear description of how to perform the activity, and there is a clear description of how to observe the outcome. Some examples are

Experiment A. A player rolls a six-sided die. The rules require that the die hit a vertical board before coming to rest in a level position. The number of spots on the upward face of the die is the outcome.

Experiment B. According to some well-defined procedure, a citizen is selected from a particular community and asked to give his opinion of the United Nations. The outcome of this experiment is the citizen's exact reply.

Experiment C. A motorist drives to work every morning by the same route. He leaves home at about the same time and passes one traffic light on his trip. On some of the trips the light is red, and he must wait. The outcome of the experiment is his waiting time in minutes. If the light is green, the experiment is not performed.

In a *random experiment*, the outcome varies from performance to performance. This variation is inherent in the experiment; it is not the effect of a procedural mistake. The random experiment is the formal analog of the statistical situation which was informally discussed in section 1. In most contexts the three experiments of the preceding paragraph are random. Many of the experiments performed in a student's laboratory are not random. For example, hydrogen burns in oxygen to produce water. Another outcome would be unacceptable; and should it occur, some procedural mistake would be sought. When properly performed, nonrandom experiments always yield the same outcome.

In many random experiments the outcome may be described by one or more real numbers. These are *numerical-valued* random experiments. Example A, the rolled die, is a numerical-valued random experiment. Only the number of spots on the upward face is important to the experimenter. Other aspects of the outcome, such as the player's reaction, are ignored. Example C, the delayed motorist, is also a numerical-valued random experiment. Only the waiting time is important to the experimenter. The statistical situations discussed in the introduction to this chapter suggest many more numerical-valued random experiments.

Example B, the citizen's response, is not numerically valued. If the experimenter is interested in the citizen's exact opinion of the UN, then there is no way to make this a numerical-valued random experiment. However, suppose he is interested only in whether the reply is favorable or not. He may assign the number 1 to a favorable reply and the number 0 to every other reply. He now has defined a numerical-valued random experiment in which the outcome is the number (0 or 1) of favorable responses. This device is often used to make a random experiment numerically valued. In this book we will be discussing numerical-valued random experiments. The above device extends the application of statistical theories to situations similar to the citizen's evaluation of the UN.

When the outcome of a numerical-valued random experiment can be described by only one real number, the experiment is *one-dimensional*. Example A, the rolled die, is one-dimensional, because the outcome is 1, 2, 3, 4, 5, or 6. The modified version of example B is one-dimensional, because the outcome is 0 or 1. Example C is also one-dimensional. When the outcome of a numerical-valued random experiment requires more than one number to describe it, the experiment is *multi-dimensional*. For the example of the delayed motorist, suppose the experimenter is interested in the waiting time, and in the number of delayed cars ahead of his particular motorist. In this case, two numbers are required to describe the outcome. The pair (0.7, 2) might mean that he waits 0.7 minutes and that there are 2 cars ahead of him. The dimensionality of the experiment depends primarily on the interests of the experimenter.

The set of all outcomes for a random experiment is the *space* for that experiment. Every random experiment has its space, but a given set of numbers can be the space for more than one random experiment. For example A, the usual space is {1, 2, 3, 4, 5, 6}. For example B, the space is {0, 1}. This set happens to be the space for many other random experiments. In example C, if the light is red for two minutes, the space is the interval of real numbers from 0 to 2, or {0 to 2}. From this point of view, a numerical-valued, nonrandom experiment has a space of one number; it is a degenerate form of a random experiment.

When the space contains a finite number of outcomes, the random experiment is *discrete*. In the examples, the space for A contains 6 outcomes, and it is discrete; the space for B contains 2 outcomes, and it is discrete. When the space is an interval of real numbers, the random experiment is *continuous*. The space for example C is the interval from 0 to 2, and C is continuous. The space for a continuous random experiment is frequently an interval of infinite length.

A subset of the space is an *event*. For example A, {2} is the event of 2 spots on the upward face of the die; {1, 2} is the event of 1 or 2 spots; {2, 4, 6} is the event of an even number of spots. If the outcome is 1, event

{1, 2} occurs, and events {2} and {2, 4, 6} do not occur. Notice that there is a difference between an outcome, such as 2, and a single-outcome event, such as {2}. For example B, {1} is the event that the chosen citizen favors the UN. For example C, {0 to 1.5} is the event that the motorist waits at most 1.5 minutes. If he waits 1.7 minutes, the event {0 to 1.5} does not occur.

A random experiment has one space and many events from that space. On one trial of the experiment, a particular event either occurs or it does not. In several trials of the experiment, the event occurs on some proportion of the total number of trials. This proportion is an important feature of the event. In symbols, let G be the particular event. For several trials this proportion or relative frequency is

$$\frac{\text{number of trials on which } G \text{ occurs}}{\text{total number of trials}}.$$

As the total number of trials increases, we assume the relative frequency for G approaches a limit in some sense. This limit is the *probability* of the event G. The probability of G is a number between 0 and 1. If the probability is near 0, then G tends to occur rarely. If the probability is near 1, then G tends to occur very often. If the probability is near .50, then G tends to occur on one-half the trials. The patterns of variation discussed in section 1 will be identified through the probabilities of events. In example A, take the event {1, 2}. To find the probability of {1, 2} according to this definition, one would roll the die a large number of times. The probability would be approximately

$$\frac{\text{number of trials on which } \{1, 2\} \text{ occurred}}{\text{total number of trials}}.$$

There is no hope for verifying the assumption that every event for every experiment has a probability according to this definition. Only in simple experiments like those involving dice and cards is it possible to repeat the experiment many times and observe the relative frequency of an event. Indeed, the profits of large gambling casinos offer some evidence to support the assumption for these cases. In the more important applications of probability, many repetitions are either impossible or too expensive.

Summary. The outcome of a numerical-valued random experiment is described by a number. The set of all possible outcomes is the space for that experiment. A discrete random experiment has a finite number of outcomes in its space; a continuous random experiment has an interval for its space. The probability of an event is the long-term relative frequency of the event's occurrences. Thus, the probability of an event is a number between 0 and 1. We assume that every event for every random experiment has a unique probability.

EXERCISES

1. The following may be considered as numerical-valued random experiments. Suggest a possible space for each. State whether it is discrete or continuous.
   a) The number of hits on the target for a marksman's next 10 rounds.
   b) The speed of the next car to pass a given place on a highway.
   c) The actual net weight of a can of soup from the grocer's shelf.
   d) The number of months that a dealer holds a new car before selling it.
   e) The time required for a particular baseball player to run to first base.
   f) The number of hits by a baseball player in his next time at bat.
   g) The number of Democrats found in questioning one voter.

2. Describe the event {1} for a), d), f), and g) in exercise 1.

3. Describe the event {3, 4} for a) and d) in exercise 1.

4. Describe the event {0 to 40} for b) in exercise 1.

3
Random Variables

In mathematical discussions a variable is a letter that takes the place of a number from some set. In probabilistic discussions, the letter is a *random variable*, and it takes values from the space of a random experiment. In slightly different words, a random variable is an outcome of a random experiment. Capital letters, especially X and Y, are used for random variables. Each random experiment has an associated random variable. For examples, associate the random variables A, B, and C with the corresponding random experiments discussed in section 2.

Random variables are introduced for convenience only; there is really nothing new here. Each random variable is only a shorthand reference to an experiment. In complicated situations, possibly involving several different random experiments, it is very convenient to use random variables instead of verbal descriptions and references. Suppose there is a discussion involving the three random experiments of section 2. By itself, the symbol $\{1\}$ may refer to the event of 1 spot on the die, a citizen's favorable response, or a delay of 1 minute for the motorist. Using a random variable clears this up, as in $\{A = 1\}$, $\{B = 1\}$, or $\{C = 1\}$. Some other events are $\{A = 1, 2\}$, $\{A = 2, 4, 6\}$, and $\{0 \leq C \leq 1.5\}$. When a simple random experiment is repeated many times, the basic random variable with a subscript is often used. For example, A_9 might refer to the ninth roll of the die. Similarly, $A_1 + A_2 + \cdots + A_9$ might refer to the sum of the spots on the first nine rolls.

If X is defined as the random variable for some particular random experiment, then X is one-dimensional or multi-dimensional and discrete or continuous according to the corresponding random experiment. In the examples, the random variables A and B are one-dimensional and discrete; the random variable C is one-dimensional and continuous. There is one difference in usage: the experimenter performs the random experiment, but he observes the random variable.

4
Relation Between
Probability and Statistics

Probability is deductive; statistics is inductive. To illustrate this, take experiment B, the citizen's response. In some ways this is the simplest possible type of random experiment, because there are only four possible events: the empty set $\emptyset$, the event of a favorable response $\{1\}$, the event of an unfavorable response $\{0\}$, and the space itself $\{0, 1\}$. Suppose the experimenter knows the corresponding four probabilities. That is, he has as complete a knowledge of the experiment as is possible. The experiment is now performed 25 times to obtain the reactions of 25 citizens. What is the probability that exactly 20 of the 25 citizens favor the UN? This is a typical problem in probability. On the other hand, suppose that the four basic probabilities are unknown. The experiment is performed 25 times, and exactly 20 of the 25 citizens favor the UN. What now are the four probabilities in the basic experiment? This is a typical problem in statistics.

This illustration suggests the need for some study of probability before statistics. In Chapter II we will discuss probability for one-dimensional random experiments. Chapters III and IV will discuss statistics for these experiments. We will study probability for multi-dimensional random experiments in the first part of Chapter V. The second part of Chapter V, Chapters VI, VII, and VIII will discuss statistics for these experiments. Most of the discussions will be in terms of random variables.

Probability *II*

1
Discrete
Random Variables

Recall that the space for a discrete random variable is a finite set of numbers. In most of the illustrations of this section, the spaces are sets of integers. Simplicity, not necessity, is the reason for this.

1.1 PROBABILITY FUNCTION

To every outcome in the space of a discrete random variable, there is the corresponding single-outcome event. Each single-outcome event has a probability. This defines the *probability function* which associates a probability with every outcome. In symbols, let X be the random variable and let x be a particular outcome in the space for X. Then, $\{x\}$ is the corresponding single-outcome event with probability $\Pr\{x\}$. The probability function associates $\Pr\{x\}$, a real number between 0 and 1, with every x, an outcome in the space.

By its definition, the probability function gives the probabilities for all single-outcome events. It also gives the probabilities for all other events. To see this, consider first two outcomes in the space, x and x'. The corresponding event is $\{x, x'\}$, and the symbol for the desired probability is $\Pr\{x, x'\}$. Imagine a large number of trials of the experiment. $\Pr\{x, x'\}$ is related to the probability function by

$$\Pr\{x, x'\} = \frac{\text{number of occurrences of } x \text{ or } x'}{\text{total number of trials}}$$

$$= \frac{\text{number of occurrences of } x}{\text{total number of trials}} + \frac{\text{number of occurrences of } x'}{\text{total number of trials}}$$

$$= \Pr\{x\} + \Pr\{x'\}.$$

That is, the probability of $\{x, x'\}$ is the sum of the probabilities of $\{x\}$ and $\{x'\}$. This shows how to find the probabilities of all the two-outcome events. To complete the demonstration, let G be any event. The previous discussion generalizes to

$$\Pr G = \sum_{x \in G} \Pr \{x\},$$

where $\sum\limits_{x \in G} \Pr\{x\}$ is the sum of values of the probability function for all the outcomes in G.

Mathematically, the probability function needs to satisfy only two conditions:

1) It must be non-negative.

$$\Pr\{x\} \geq 0 \text{ for all } x \text{ in the space.}$$

2) The sum over the whole space must be 1.

$$\sum\limits_{\text{Space}} \Pr\{x\} = 1.$$

The necessity of the first condition comes from the fact that $\Pr\{x\}$ is a probability and cannot be negative. To see the second condition, consider the whole space as an event. According to the relative-frequency definition of probability, the probability of the space is 1 because it is certain to occur.

$$1 = \Pr \text{ Space.}$$

The probability of the whole space is also

$$\Pr \text{ Space} = \sum\limits_{\text{Space}} \Pr\{x\}.$$

Therefore,

$$1 = \Pr \text{ Space} = \sum\limits_{\text{Space}} \Pr\{x\},$$

and the necessity of the second condition is established. These two conditions are also sufficient. For a space with n outcomes, the x's, any n numbers that are non-negative and add to 1 can be the values of the probability function, the $\Pr\{x\}$'s, for that space.

For an illustration, return to the experiment in which the player rolls one die and counts the number of spots on the upward face. The space is $\{1, 2, 3, 4, 5, 6\}$. The probability function associates a probability with each of these six outcomes. Formally, any six non-negative numbers that add to 1 form a possible probability function for this experiment. Of course, there is only one correct probability function for a particular experiment with a particular die. If the die is "fair" and the roll is "honest," the following function might be anticipated:

$$\Pr\{1\} = \Pr\{2\} = \Pr\{3\} = \Pr\{4\} = \Pr\{5\} = \Pr\{6\} = 1/6 = .167.$$

In this case, the probability of a 1 or a 2 is

$$\Pr\{1, 2\} = \Pr\{1\} + \Pr\{2\} = 1/6 + 1/6 = 1/3 = .333.$$

The probability of an even outcome is

$$\Pr\{2, 4, 6\} = \Pr\{2\} + \Pr\{4\} + \Pr\{6\} = 1/6 + 1/6 + 1/6 = 1/2 = .500.$$

In total, there are $2^6 = 64$ possible events:

$$\emptyset, \{1\}, \{2\}, \ldots, \{1, 2\}, \{1, 3\}, \ldots, \{1, 2, 3\}, \ldots, \{1, 2, 3, 4, 5, 6\}.$$

The probability of each can be calculated from the probability function. Let A be the random variable for this die with the distribution of probability over $\{1, 2, 3, 4, 5, 6\}$. The corresponding symbol for an outcome is a; the single-outcome event is $\{a\}$; and the probability function is $\Pr\{a\} = 1/6$ for $a = 1, 2, 3, 4, 5, 6$.

Table 1

Outcome	U $\Pr\{u\}$	V $\Pr\{v\}$	W $\Pr\{w\}$	A $\Pr\{a\}$
1	.10	.40	.05	.167
2	.40	.05	.05	.167
3	.20	.05	.40	.167
4	.10	.05	.40	.167
5	.10	.05	.05	.167
6	.10	.40	.05	.167

For comparisons, imagine three other experiments with three other dice. Each has the same space $\{1, 2, 3, 4, 5, 6\}$. Let the random variables be U, V, and W; let typical outcomes in their spaces be u, v, and w; let the three probability functions be $\Pr\{u\}$, $\Pr\{v\}$, and $\Pr\{w\}$. Table 1 gives some drastic probability functions for U, V, W, and A. Figure 1 gives the graphs of these four functions. For the event $\{5, 6\}$, the probabilities are

$$\text{for } U: \ \Pr\{5, 6\} = \Pr\{5\} + \Pr\{6\} = .20,$$

$$\text{for } V: \ \Pr\{5, 6\} = \Pr\{5\} + \Pr\{6\} = .45,$$

$$\text{for } W: \ \Pr\{5, 6\} = \Pr\{5\} + \Pr\{6\} = .10,$$

$$\text{for } A: \ \Pr\{5, 6\} = \Pr\{5\} + \Pr\{6\} = .33.$$

Summary. For a discrete random variable X, the probability function $\Pr\{x\}$ gives the probability of every single-outcome event $\{x\}$. The probability of any event G is the sum $\sum_{x \in G} \Pr\{x\}$ over all the outcomes x in G. Mathematically, the only requirements for $\Pr\{x\}$ are: (1) $\Pr\{x\} \geq 0$ for each x in the space, and (2) $\Pr \text{Space} = \sum_{\text{Space}} \Pr\{x\} = 1$.

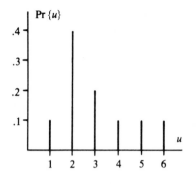

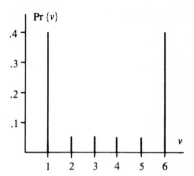

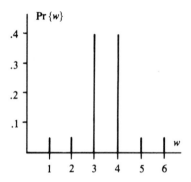

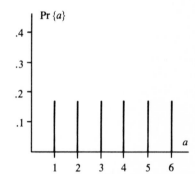

Figure 1

EXERCISES

1. Let X be the number of months a dealer holds a new car before selling it. Suppose the probability function is

$$x = \quad 1 \quad 2 \quad 3 \quad 4$$
$$\Pr\{x\} = \quad .20 \quad .40 \quad .30 \quad .10$$

a) What is the space?

b) How many events are there for this experiment?

c) How many single-outcome events are there?

d) Find the following probabilities: $\Pr\{3\}$, $\Pr\{X = 3\}$, $\Pr\{3, 4\}$, $\Pr\{2 \leq X \leq 4\}$, and $\Pr\{X \leq 3\}$.

2. In Table 1, find the probability of $\{1, 2, 6\}$
   a) for U.
   b) for V.
   c) for W.
   d) for A.

3. X is a discrete random variable with the following space and probability function:

$$\Pr\{x\} = kx^2 \quad \text{for} \quad x = 1, 2, 3.$$

   Find k.

4. X is a discrete random variable with space $\{1, 2, 3, \ldots, n\}$ and probability function

$$\Pr\{x\} = kx \quad \text{for} \quad x = 1, 2, 3, \ldots, n$$

   Find k.

5. In the context of exercise 1, suppose the dealer profits \$400 if he sells the car in 1 month and \$300 if he sells it in more than 1 month. Let Y be the dealer's profit on the car.
   a) What is the space for Y?
   b) Find $\Pr\{y\}$.

1.2 EXPECTED VALUE

A probability function describes the variation of a random variable. *Parameters* are used to identify and classify probability functions. A particular parameter associates a real number with each probability function. In this sense, a parameter is a function of the probability function.

Table 2

Outcome	Frequency
1	100
2	400
3	200
4	100
5	100
6	100

One of the most important parameters is the *expected value*. It indicates a typical value for a probability function. Suppose random variable U

of Table 1 were observed 1000 times. Any distribution of the 6 outcomes would be possible, but the underlying probabilities make some more likely than others. According to the relative-frequency interpretation of probability, the 1000 outcomes which are most representative of $\Pr\{u\}$ are in Table 2. A common "average" of a set of numbers is the sum of the numbers divided by the total number of numbers:

$$\frac{1 \times 100 + 2 \times 400 + 3 \times 200 + 4 \times 100 + 5 \times 100 + 6 \times 100}{1000} = \frac{3000}{1000}$$
$$= 3.0.$$

This operation can be rewritten as

$$1 \times \frac{100}{1000} + 2 \times \frac{400}{1000} + 3 \times \frac{200}{1000} + 4 \times \frac{100}{1000}$$

$$+ 5 \times \frac{100}{1000} + 6 \times \frac{100}{1000} = 3.0,$$

or

$$1\Pr\{1\} + 2\Pr\{2\} + 3\Pr\{3\} + 4\Pr\{4\} + 5\Pr\{5\} + 6\Pr\{6\} = 3.0,$$

or

$$\sum u\Pr\{u\} = 3.0,$$

where the sum is over all the outcomes in the space. The last expression shows that it was not necessary to go through the fictitious observations of U. The desired typical value can be computed from $\Pr\{u\}$ directly. For a general discrete random variable, the *expected value* of X is

$$E(X) = \sum x\Pr\{x\},$$

where the sum is over every x in the space. Table 3 gives the expected values for the random variables of Table 1.

Table 3

Random variable	Expected value
U	3.0
V	3.5
W	3.5
A	3.5

Important decisions involving random experiments frequently are made only on the expected value. That is, the decision maker ignores the complete probability function and looks only at this one parameter. A very simple illustration follows. Every year a dealer sells Christmas trees at the same location. From past experience, he knows that his total demand will be exactly 2000, 3000, or 4000 trees. The probabilities are

Total demand	Probability
2000	.50
3000	.40
4000	.10

He must order now for the coming season. He can order 2000 trees at a cost of $3.00 per tree, 3000 trees at $2.50 per tree, or 4000 trees at $2.00 per tree. All trees are sold at $4.00 per tree. Unsold trees are a total loss. The dealer's problem is to choose from the three possible orders. The solution is to compute the expected profit for each possible order and maximize it. To illustrate, consider an order of 3000 trees at a cost of $7500. If the demand is 2000, he sells 2000 and throws 1000 away; the profit is $4.00 \times 2000 - 7500 = 500$. If the demand is 3000 or 4000, he sells 3000; the profit is $4.00 \times 3000 - 7500 = 4500$. Therefore, the space for his profit is $\{500, 4500\}$, and the probability function is $\Pr\{500\} = \Pr\{4500\} = .50$. The parameter is

$$\text{Expected profit} = 500 \times .50 + 4500 \times .50 = 2500.$$

The expected profit for an order of 2000 trees is $2000. The expected profit for an order of 4000 trees is $2400. Therefore, he maximizes his expected profit by ordering 3000 trees.

Summary. A parameter measures the probability function of a random variable. One parameter, the expected value, indicates a typical value. For a discrete X, the definition is

$$E(X) = \sum x \Pr\{x\},$$

where the sum is over the whole space.

EXERCISES

6. The dealer described in exercise 1 of this chapter holds a car X months, where

$x =$	1	2	3	4
$\Pr\{x\} =$	.20	.40	.30	.10

a) Find $E(X)$.

b) If the inventory cost is $10 for each month (or part of a month), how much should the dealer allocate to inventory for each new car?

7. What is wrong with the following answer to part b) of exercise 6? The average car is held 2.3 months; the inventory cost for a car held 2.3 months is $30; this is the proper amount to allocate.

8. Find $E(X)$ for the variable of exercise 3:

$$Pr\{x\} = \frac{x^2}{14} \quad \text{for} \quad x = 1, 2, 3.$$

9. Find $E(X)$ for the variable of exercise 4:

$$Pr\{x\} = \frac{2x}{n(n+1)} \quad \text{for} \quad x = 1, 2, 3, \ldots, n.$$

Use

$$\sum_{i=1}^{n} i^2 = \frac{n(n+1)(2n+1)}{6}.$$

10. Verify the other two expected profits for the example of the Christmas trees.

11. A realtor who takes the listing on a house to be sold knows that he will spend $300 trying to sell the house. If he sells it himself, he will earn 6 per cent of the selling price. If another realtor sells a house from his list, he will earn only 3 per cent of the price. If the house is unsold in 6 months, he will lose the listing. Suppose the probabilities are

	Probability
sell himself	.50
sell by another realtor	.30
not sell in 6 months	.20

What is the expected profit for listing a $25,000 house?

12. A small rental company has three cars to rent on a day-to-day basis. The number of cars rented on any one day X is a random variable with the following probability function:

x	0	1	2	3
$Pr\{x\}$	.10	.10	.20	.60

When a car is rented for a day, the net profit is $20 on that car; when a car is not rented, the net loss is $5 on that car.
a) What is the expected daily net profit for the company?
b) A study of actual demand per day Y indicates the following probability function:

y	0	1	2	3	4	5
$\Pr\{y\}$	.10	.10	.20	.30	.20	.10

How many more cars should the company buy?

1.3 VARIANCE AND STANDARD DEVIATION

A second important parameter is the *variance*. It measures spread in the probability function of a discrete random variable. Variables V and W of Table 1 have the same space $\{1, 2, 3, 4, 5, 6\}$ and the same expected value 3.5, but still the probability is spread differently over the space. Variable V tends to yield separated observations (1's and 6's); variable W tends to yield close observations (3's and 4's). The variance indicates this difference.

Consider random variable U of Table 1, with $E(U) = 3.0$. A way to measure the spread in $\Pr\{u\}$ is to measure deviations from $E(U)$, $u - E(U)$. Numerically, these are $-2, -1, 0, 1, 2$, and 3. Their corresponding probabilities are $\Pr\{1\}, \Pr\{2\}, \ldots, \Pr\{6\}$. Note that the expected deviation is zero:

$$\sum [u - E(U)]\Pr\{u\} = (-2)(.1) + (-1)(.4) + (0)(.2) +$$
$$(1)(.1) + (2)(.1) + (3)(.1) = 0.$$

This is always true. One way to get a measure that is not always zero is to take the expected value of the absolute value of the deviation:

$$\sum |u - E(U)| \Pr\{u\} = |-2|(.1) + |-1|(.4) + |0|(.2) +$$
$$|1|(.1) + |2|(.1) + |3|(.1) = 1.2.$$

Another way to get a measure that is not always zero is to take the expected value of the squared deviation:

$$\sum [u - E(U)]^2 \Pr\{u\} = (-2)^2(.1) + (-1)^2(.4) + (0)^2(.2) +$$
$$(1)^2(.1) + (2)^2(.1) + (3)^2(.1) = 2.2.$$

The first may seem more reasonable, but the second is more useful and leads to the general definition.

For a general discrete random variable X, the *variance* is the expected squared deviation. In symbols, this is

$$V(X) = \text{Var}(X) = \sum[x - E(X)]^2 \text{Pr}\{x\},$$

where the sum is over the whole space. For the variable U of Table 1, $V(U) = 2.2$ as shown in the above paragraph.

The square root of the variance is the *standard deviation* which is also a parameter. For a discrete random variable X, the standard deviation is

$$D(X) = [V(X)]^{1/2} = \left\{ \sum[x - E(X)]^2 \text{Pr}\{x\} \right\}^{1/2}.$$

The standard deviation is expressed in the same units as the random variable, but the variance is expressed in the square of these units. Table 4 gives the variances and the standard deviations for the four variables of Table 1. Compare especially the variances and standard deviations of variables V, W, and A which have the same expected values.

Table 4

Random variable	Expected value	Variance	Standard deviation
U	3.0	2.20	1.48
V	3.5	5.25	2.29
W	3.5	1.05	1.02
A	3.5	2.92	1.71

Summary. The variance and the standard deviation are parameters that measure the spread in the probability function of a discrete random variable. If the variable is X, their definitions are

$$V(X) = \sum[x - E(X)]^2 \text{Pr}\{x\},$$
$$D(X) = [V(X)]^{1/2},$$

where the sum is over the whole space.

EXERCISES

13. The dealer of exercises 1 and 6 holds a car X months, where

x	1	2	3	4
$\text{Pr}\{x\}$	.2	.4	.3	.1

Find $V(X)$ and $D(X)$.

14. In many gambling games a player wins a dollar with probability θ and loses a dollar with probability $1 - \theta$. Let $W = 1$ for a win and $W = -1$ for a loss. Find $E(W)$ and $V(W)$ in terms of θ.

1.4 PROPERTIES OF EXPECTED VALUE AND VARIANCE

If the numerical outcome of a random experiment is transformed in some prescribed manner, then the transformed outcomes form a space with a transformed probability function. This new probability function has a new expected value and a new variance of its own. Often the new expected value and variance are simply related to the original expected value and variance. In symbols, let X be the random variable for the original space, and let g be the prescribed transformation. If Y is the random variable for the transformed space, then $Y = g(X)$. $E(Y)$ and $V(Y)$ may be simply related to $E(X)$ and $V(X)$ in ways that depend on g.

Expected Value

Let the transformation g be one-to-one. That is, to every x in the space for X, there is one and only one $y = g(x)$ in the space for Y. Then for each y, $\Pr\{y\}$ equals $\Pr\{x\}$ for the one x such that $y = g(x)$. Also, $y\Pr\{y\}$ equals $g(x)\Pr\{x\}$ for the corresponding y and x. Therefore,

$$E(Y) = \sum y \Pr\{y\} = \sum g(x) \Pr\{x\},$$

where the sums are over the corresponding spaces. That is, $E(Y)$ may be found from $\Pr\{x\}$ without knowing $\Pr\{y\}$. Define $E[g(X)]$ by

$$E[g(X)] = E(Y) = \sum g(x) \Pr\{x\}.$$

The same result holds when $g(x)$ is not one-to-one. The details of the proof are omitted. For an illustration, take variable U of Table 1 again:

u	1	2	3	4	5	6
$\Pr\{u\}$	.1	.4	.2	.1	.1	.1

Let the transformation be $Y = g(U) = U^2$. The space and probability function for Y are easy to find, but they are not needed to obtain the expected value:

$$E(Y) = E(U^2) = \sum u^2 \Pr\{u\} = (1^2)(.1) + (2^2)(.4) + \cdots + (6^2)(.1)$$

$$= 11.2.$$

An important special case is

$$Y = aX + b,$$

where a and b are constants. The derivation for $E(Y)$ is

$$E(Y) = E(aX+b) = \sum(ax+b)\Pr\{x\} = a\sum x\Pr\{x\} + b\sum\Pr\{x\} = aE(X)+b.$$

To illustrate, take variable U of Table 1 again. Let

$$Y = 2U^2 - 3.$$

With $a = 2$, $b = -3$, and $X = U^2$, the special case applies to give

$$E(Y) = E(2X - 3) = 2E(X) - 3.$$

Replacing X by U^2 gives

$$E(Y) = 2E(U^2) - 3 = 2(11.2) - 3 = 19.4.$$

If X_1 and X_2 are any two random variables and a, b, and c are constants, then $Y = aX_1 + bX_2 + c$ defines a new random variable. This is a generalization of the special case $Y = aX + b$. The expected value of Y is

$$E(Y) = aE(X_1) + bE(X_2) + c;$$

but the proof, which involves two-dimensional random variables, must wait until Chapter V. To illustrate, let

$$Y = 2U + 3U^2 - 7,$$

where U again is taken from Table 1. The expected value of Y is

$$E(Y) = 2E(U) + 3E(U^2) - 7 = 32.6.$$

These results lead to a very useful fact about the variance of X, the original variable. Note that the variance of X is an expectation with respect to $\Pr\{x\}$:

$$V(X) = \sum[x - E(X)]^2\Pr\{x\} = E[X - E(X)]^2.$$

Squaring and applying the result of the above paragraph gives

$$V(X) = E[X^2 - 2E(X)X + E^2(X)] = E(X^2) - 2E(X)E(X) + E^2(X),$$
$$= E(X^2) - E^2(X),$$

where $E^2(X)$ is the square of $E(X)$. This is usually the efficient way to calculate a variance. It avoids the calculations for the deviations, $x - E(X)$. For the illustrative variable U,

$$V(U) = E(U^2) - E^2(U) = 11.20 - (3.0)^2 = 2.20.$$

Variance

For the special transformation $Y = g(X) = aX + b$, the variance of Y is related simply to the variance of X. The derivation is

$$V(Y) = E[Y - E(Y)]^2 = E[aX + b - aE(X) - b]^2 = a^2E[X - E(X)]^2$$

$$= a^2V(X).$$

For an example, let $Y = 3U + 7$. Then

$$V(Y) = 3^2V(U) = 19.8.$$

Finally, consider the variance of Y for the transformation $Y = aX_1 + bX_2 + c$. Sometimes the above result generalizes to

$$V(Y) = a^2V(X_1) + b^2V(X_2);$$

sometimes it does not. Some intuitive explanation is necessary here. When the outcome of X_1 is unknown, there is one probability function for X_2. When the outcome of X_1 is known, there is another probability function for X_2. If these two probability functions are always the same, X_1 and X_2 are *independent*. If there is a difference, X_1 and X_2 are *dependent*. In other words, X_1 and X_2 are independent when knowing the outcome of X_1 does not change the probabilities of events for X_2. If X_1 and X_2 are independent,

$$V(Y) = a^2V(X_1) + b^2V(X_2).$$

A more comprehensive discussion of independence, which involves two-dimensional random variables, appears in Chapter V. For an example, let U_1 and U_2 refer to two independent rolls of the die. If $Y = U_1 + U_2$, then

$$V(Y) = V(U_1) + V(U_2) = 2.20 + 2.20 = 4.40.$$

Summary. For a discrete random variable X, let $Y = g(X)$ define a new random variable. Then

$$E(Y) = E[g(X)] = \sum g(x)\Pr\{x\}.$$

This suggests an efficient way to calculate $V(X)$:

$$V(X) = E[X - E(X)]^2 = E(X^2) - E^2(X)$$

$$= \sum x^2\Pr\{x\} - [\sum x\Pr\{x\}]^2.$$

If X_1 and X_2 are random variables and $Y = aX_1 + bX_2 + c$, then

$$E(Y) = aE(X_1) + bE(X_2) + c.$$

If X_1 and X_2 are also independent, then

$$V(Y) = a^2 V(X_1) + b^2 V(X_2).$$

EXERCISES

15. Using $\mathrm{Var}(V) = E(V^2) - E^2(V)$, verify that 5.25 is the variance of variable V of Table 1.

16. Using $V(W) = E(W^2) - E^2(W)$, verify that 1.05 is the variance of variable W of Table 1.

17. Let A_1 and A_2 correspond to two independent rolls of the die described in Table 1.
    a) Interpret $Y = A_1 + A_2$.
    b) Find $E(Y)$ and $V(Y)$.

18. For the variable U of Table 1, let $Y = 2U^2 - 3$ as in this section. Find the variance of Y according to

$$V(Y) = 4V(U^2) = 4[E(U^4) - E^2(U^2)].$$

19. Suppose U_1, U_2, and U_3 are independent random variables, and each has the probability function of U in Table 1. Let $Y = 3U_1 + U_2 - 2U_3 + 2$.
    a) Find $E(Y)$.
    b) Find $V(Y)$.

20. For the random variable W of exercise 14, let $Y = \dfrac{1}{W}$.
    a) Find the space for Y.
    b) Find $\Pr\{y\}$.
    c) Find $E(Y)$.
    d) Is it true that $E(Y) = \dfrac{1}{E(W)}$?

21. The dealer mentioned in exercises 1, 6, and 13 holds a car X months, where

x	1	2	3	4
$\Pr\{x\}$	.2	.4	.3	.1

    a) Find $E(X^2)$ and $V(X)$.
    b) If each month of inventory costs \$10, interpret $Y = 10X$.
    c) Find $E(Y)$, $V(Y)$, and $D(Y)$.

22. Find $E(X^2)$ and $V(X)$ for the variable of exercise 3:

$$\Pr\{x\} = \frac{x^2}{14} \text{ for } x = 1, 2, 3.$$

23. Find $E(X^2)$ and $V(X)$ for the variable of exercise 4:

$$\Pr\{x\} = \frac{2x}{n(n+1)} \text{ for } x = 1, 2, \ldots, n.$$

Use

$$\sum_{i=1}^{n} i^3 = \left[\frac{n(n+1)}{2}\right]^2.$$

24. X has the following probability function:

x	0	1	2
$\Pr\{x\}$	.6	.3	.1

Let $Y = 2X + 3$.
a) Find $E(X)$.
b) Find $V(X)$.
c) Find the space for Y.
d) Find $\Pr\{y\}$.
e) Using $\Pr\{y\}$, find $E(Y)$.
f) Using $\Pr\{y\}$, find $V(Y)$.
g) Verify numerically that $E(Y) = 2E(X) + 3$ and $V(Y) = 4V(X)$.

25. A small company makes a product which sells for $2000. Sales are made by only three salesmen. The number of sales per week by each salesman is a random variable X with

x	0	1	2	3	4
$\Pr\{x\}$	.1	.2	.4	.2	.1

a) Find the expected weekly gross sales for the company.
b) Find the standard deviation of the weekly gross sales. Assume independent performances for the salesmen. What do you think of this assumption?

1.5 BERNOULLI DISTRIBUTION

A very simple space for a random variable is $\{0, 1\}$. Only one kind of probability function on this space is possible. It is the *Bernoulli probability function*, or the *Bernoulli distribution* of probability. Since a space with only one outcome corresponds to a nonrandom experiment, this is one of the simplest possible random experiments. Examples are numerous:

Opinion Survey. According to a well-defined procedure, a citizen is selected from a particular community and asked his opinion of the United Nations. The number of favorable responses (0 or 1) is the outcome.

Biology. From some population of diseased persons, a person is chosen and given a new drug. The number of recoveries (0 or 1) in a prescribed time period is the outcome.

Quality Control. One cake from a bakery's recent production is chosen at random. The number of defective cakes (0 or 1) is the outcome.

There are only four possible events from the space $\{0, 1\}$. They are the empty set $\emptyset$, $\{0\}$, $\{1\}$, and the space itself $\{0, 1\}$. The probability of the empty set is always 0, and the probability of the space itself is always 1. Since

$$\Pr\{0\} + \Pr\{1\} = \Pr\{0, 1\} = 1,$$

only one of the two remaining probabilities can be arbitrary. Let

$$\Pr\{1\} = \theta \text{ and } \Pr\{0\} = 1 - \theta.$$

Knowledge of θ then, completely describes the probabilities for the random experiment. θ is the *proportion* for the Bernoulli distribution. In the example of the citizen's opinion of the UN, $\theta = .80$ means that 80 per cent of the persons in the community favor the UN. In the bakery example, $\theta = .01$ means that 1 per cent of the cakes are defective.

The expected value, variance, and standard deviation are simple functions of θ. If X is the random variable, then

$$E(X) = \sum x \Pr\{x\} = (0)(1 - \theta) + (1)(\theta) = \theta,$$

$$E(X^2) = \sum x^2 \Pr\{x\} = (0^2)(1 - \theta) + (1^2)(\theta) = \theta,$$

$$V(X) = E(X^2) - E^2(X) = \theta - \theta^2 = \theta(1 - \theta),$$

$$D(X) = [\theta(1 - \theta)]^{1/2}.$$

A random variable X with a Bernoulli distribution frequently is observed several times. If $X_1, X_2, \ldots, X_n$ refer to n independent observations of X and if $Y = X_1 + X_2 + \ldots + X_n$, then the parameters for Y are

$$E(Y) = E(X_1) + E(X_2) + \cdots + E(X_n) = n\theta,$$

$$V(Y) = V(X_1) + V(X_2) + \cdots + V(X_n) = n\theta(1 - \theta).$$

Let B be the random variable for the citizen's opinion of the UN, and let $\theta = .80$. If 10 citizens are independently asked, then $Y = B_1 + B_2 + \cdots + B_{10}$ is the total number of the 10 who favor the UN. The expected value and variance for Y are

$$E(Y) = n\theta = 8,$$

$$V(Y) = n\theta(1 - \theta) = 1.6.$$

Summary. If the space for a random variable X is $\{0, 1\}$, then X has a Bernoulli distribution. The proportion θ is $\Pr\{1\}$. The parameters are

$$E(X) = \theta \quad \text{and} \quad V(X) = \theta(1 - \theta).$$

EXERCISES

26. Suppose 30 per cent of the customers in a market favor a certain brand of potato chip. In a sample of 100 customers independently chosen,
   a) what is the expected number who prefer the brand?
   b) what is the variance of the number who prefer the brand?

27. If X has a Bernoulli distribution with parameter θ, graph $V(X)$ as a function of θ.

28. As a promotion device, 100 persons on the street will be stopped independently and asked for the name of the sponsor of a television program. If the first person knows, he will receive 1 dollar; if not, he will receive nothing. If the second knows, he will receive 2 dollars. If the nth person knows, he will receive n dollars. Suppose 50 per cent of the population actually knows the sponsor's name. What are the expected value and standard deviation of the cost for this promotion device?

2
Continuous
Random Variables

Recall that the space for a continuous random variable is an interval of real numbers. Events are usually subintervals from this space.

2.1 DENSITY FUNCTION

The *density function* is to the continuous random variable what the probability function is to the discrete random variable. That is, the density function describes the variation in a continuous random variable. In particular, the probabilities of events are calculated from the density function.

We can illustrate with an example. Let X be the continuous random variable for some particular random experiment. Suppose the space is the interval of real numbers between 0 and 2, $\{0 \leq X \leq 2\}$. Consider the event $\{0 \leq X \leq 0.5\}$. Why not use the procedure for discrete random variables to get the probability of this event? That is, use the probabilities of the single-outcome events, and find the probability of an event G by summing over the outcomes in G.

$$\text{Pr } G = \sum_{x \in G} \text{Pr}\{x\}.$$

For an interval such as $G = \{0 \leq X \leq 0.5\}$, calculating this sum is impossible, because there are too many outcomes in the interval. Some other procedure must be used.

For the same variable X, the space itself has a probability of 1,

$$\text{Pr}\{0 \leq X \leq 2\} = 1.$$

Figure 2(a), on page 28, corresponds to this. There is a rectangle with the event as the base and with an area equal to the probability of the event. There is, however, no way to use this figure to find the probability of $\{0 \leq X \leq 0.5\}$.

Consider next the two events $\{0 \leq X \leq 1\}$ and $\{1 < X \leq 2\}$. Their probabilities add to 1,

$$\text{Pr}\{0 \leq X \leq 1\} + \text{Pr}\{1 < X \leq 2\} = 1.$$

Figure 2(b) corresponds to this. There is a rectangle with the event $\{0 \leq X \leq 1\}$ as the base and with an area that is supposed to be equal to the event's probability; there is also a rectangle with the event $\{1 < X \leq 2\}$ as the base and with an area equal to the probability of this event. The sum of the two areas is again 1, but there is still no way to find $\text{Pr}\{0 \leq X \leq 0.5\}$ from the graph.

Figures 2(c) and 2(d) correspond to finer subdivisions of the space. In each case, the space is partitioned into subintervals. The area over a subinterval equals the probability of that subinterval, and the sum of the areas is 1. The probability of $\{0 \leq X \leq 0.5\}$ is now available in each graph; it is the shaded area. As the number of subdivisions increases, the rectangles become indistinguishable, and a smooth curve like that of Figure 3 is the limiting graph. The total area under this curve is still 1. $\text{Pr}\{0 \leq X \leq 0.5\}$

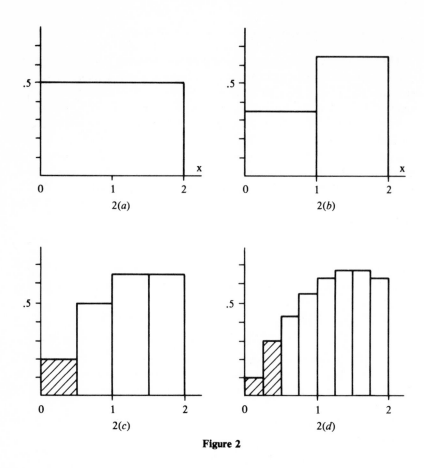

Figure 2

is the shaded area. Similarly, the probability of any other event must be the area determined by the event and the curve of Figure 3.

There is a similar limit curve for every continuous random variable X. The height of this curve defines a function, which assigns a non-negative number $f(x)$ to every outcome x in the space of X. This function is the *density function* for the random variable. The probabilities of all events can be calculated as areas under the curve of the density function. In this sense, the density function completely describes the variation in a continuous random experiment. Table 5 gives four density functions for the space $\{0 \text{ to } 2\}$. The random variables are U, V, W, and A. Particular outcomes in the space are u, v, w, and a. The density functions are $f(u)$, $f(v)$, $f(w)$, and $f(a)$. Figure 4 shows the graphs of these four density functions.

By the geometry of rectangles, triangles, and trapezoids, the probabilities of {0 to 0.5} may be found for U, V, and A. $\Pr\{0 \leq W \leq 0.5\}$ is not as simple to find. These probabilities are also in Table 5.

Table 5

Random variable	Density function	Pr{0 to .5}
U	$f(u) = 1/2$	.25
V	$f(v) = v/2$	.06
W	$f(w) = \frac{3}{4}w(2 - w)$	.16
A	$f(a) = \begin{cases} 1 - a \text{ for } 0 \leq a \leq 1 \\ a - 1 \text{ for } 1 \leq a \leq 2 \end{cases}$	.38

One surprising consequence is that the probability of a single-outcome event is zero, the area above a point. Since we associate a zero probability with an impossible event, this seems to say that every outcome in the space is impossible. The contradiction is less upsetting when we admit that the random experiments of the practical world are all discrete. No measurement actually can be made with the accuracy assumed by a continuous space. For some very small number ϵ which is related to the accuracy of measurement, the single-outcome event $\{x\}$ of the practical world is the interval $\{x - \epsilon, x + \epsilon\}$ for the continuous random variable.

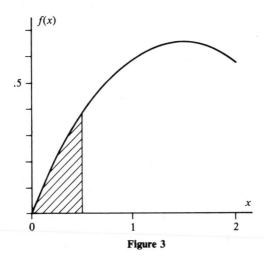

Figure 3

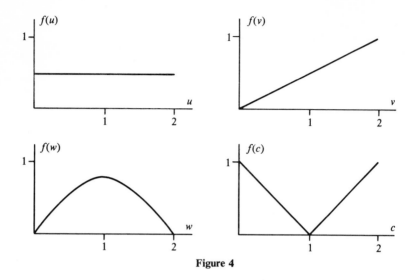

Figure 4

Since $\Pr\{x\} = 0$ for all outcomes, all the intervals determined by two numbers have the same probability, with or without the endpoints. For example, the following events have the same probability:

$$\{0 < X < 0.5\}, \ \{0 < X \le 0.5\}, \ \{0 \le X < 0.5\}, \ \{0 \le X \le 0.5\}.$$

Summary. For every continuous random variable X, there is a density function defined over the space for X. The probability of an event equals the area determined by curve of the density function and the event on the x-axis. Mathematically, there are only two restrictions on the density function: (1) It is non-negative; (2) the area determined by the curve of the function and the whole space equals 1.

* With the aid of calculus, another introduction to the density function and its properties is possible. The discussion begins with a related function. Let X be the continuous random variable for some experiment; let $\{a \text{ to } b\}$ be the space; and let x be an outcome in the space. $\{a \le X \le x\}$ or $\{X \le x\}$ is an event with some probability $\Pr\{X \le x\}$, which depends only on x. That is, $\Pr\{X \le x\}$ defines a function on the space for X. This is the *distribution function* for the random variable. The symbol is

$$F(x) = \Pr\{X \le x\}.$$

*Indicates that the material in the paragraph requires calculus for complete comprehension.

Every random variable has a distribution function. For a continuous random variable, the distribution function is a continuous function over the space. That is, there are no jumps or breaks in the curve of the function.
* Since b is the largest outcome in the space, $F(b)$ equals 1. [If $b = +\infty$, take $F(+\infty)$ to mean $\lim_{x\to+\infty} F(x)$.] Also, $F(a)$ equals 0. [If $a = -\infty$, take $F(-\infty)$ to mean $\lim_{x\to-\infty} F(x)$.] Suppose x' and x'' are in the space, and $x' < x''$. When the event $\{X \le x'\}$ occurs, so does the event $\{X \le x''\}$, but not conversely. The relative-frequency interpretation of probability suggests

$$F(x') = \Pr\{X \le x'\} \le \Pr\{X \le x''\} = F(x'').$$

Therefore, F is an increasing function of x with $F(a) = 0$ and $F(1) = 1$.
* When probability was introduced as area under a curve, a single-outcome event $\{x\}$ received zero probability. The continuous distribution function also demands this. If c and x are outcomes in the space such that $c < x$, the relative-frequency interpretation of probability establishes

$$\Pr\{X \le c\} + \Pr\{c < X \le x\} = \Pr\{X \le x\}.$$

When rearranged, this is

$$\Pr\{c < X \le x\} = \Pr\{X \le x\} - \Pr\{X \le c\} = F(x) - F(c).$$

Whatever value $\Pr\{x\}$ has, $\Pr\{c < X \le x\}$ must approach it as c approaches x. Therefore, the desired result is

$$\Pr\{x\} = \lim_{c\to x} \Pr\{c < X \le x\}$$

$$= \lim_{c\to x} [F(x) - F(c)]$$

$$= F(x) - \lim_{c\to x} F(c) = 0,$$

where $\lim_{c\to x} F(c) = F(x)$ by the continuity of F.
* To verify the concept of probability as area, suppose F is differentiable except possibly at a few isolated points. Let the derivative be f, where

$$\frac{dF(x)}{dx} = f(x)$$

for every outcome x in the space. Let $\{c \text{ to } d\}$ be an interval-event for X. As in the preceding paragraph with "x" replaced by "d", the probability of $\{c \text{ to } d\}$ is

$$\Pr\{c \le X \le d\} = F(d) - F(c).$$

The Fundamental Theorem of Integral Calculus gives

$$F(d) - F(c) = \int_c^d f(x)\,dx.$$

Since the definite integral $\int_c^d f(x)\,dx$ is usually introduced as a measure of the area under the curve of f between c and d, the desired verification is complete; and f is identified as the density function.

Table 6

Random variable	Distribution function
U	$F(u) = u/2$
V	$F(v) = v^2/4$
W	$F(w) = \dfrac{3}{4}\left[w^2 - \dfrac{w^3}{3}\right]$
A	$F(a) = \begin{cases} a - \dfrac{a^2}{2} & \text{for } 0 \le a \le 1 \\[2mm] 1 - a + \dfrac{a^2}{2} & \text{for } 1 \le a \le 2 \end{cases}$

* Since $\int_a^x f(x)\,dx$ equals $F(x)$, there is essentially a one-to-one correspondence between density functions and distribution functions. Knowledge of either one is a complete description of the related random experiment. Table 6 gives the distribution functions for the four random variables of Table 5. Figure 5 gives the corresponding pictures.

* **Summary.** For a continuous random variable X, the distribution function is defined by $F(x) = \Pr\{X \le x\}$. F is continuous, and it is related to the density function f by

$$\frac{dF(x)}{dx} = f(x).$$

The probability of an event G is the definite integral of f over G.

$$\Pr G = \int_G f(x)\,dx.$$

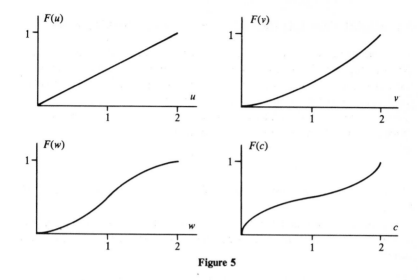

Figure 5

EXERCISES

29. For the continuous random variables of Table 5, find
    a) $\Pr\{1 \le U \le 2\}$,
    b) $\Pr\{1 \le V \le 2\}$,
    c) $\Pr\{V \le 1 \text{ or } 1.5 \le V\}$,
    d) $\Pr\{U = 1\}$.

30. For the variables of Table 5, find the value of c such that
    a) $\Pr\{U \le c\} = .75$,
    b) $\Pr\{c \le U \le 2 - c\} = .90$,
    c) $\Pr\{V \le c \text{ or } 2 - c \le V\} = .10$.

* 31. For the variable W of Table 5, find $\Pr\{W \le 0.5\}$.

* 32. Find k for the continuous random variable X which has the following density function and space:

$$f(x) = k e^{-\theta x} \quad \text{for} \quad 0 \le x < \infty \quad \text{and} \quad 0 < \theta.$$

* 33. Find the distribution function for the random variable of exercise 32.

* 34. Suppose the length (in minutes) of the telephone calls at a switchboard has the density function of exercise 32. If $\theta = 1$, what is the probability of
    a) the next call lasting more than 2 minutes?
    b) the next call lasting between 1 and 2 minutes?

2.2 EXPECTED VALUE, VARIANCE, AND PROPERTIES

A continuous random variable also has an expected value and a variance. Without the use of calculus, however, they are usually difficult to find. In the non-calculus part of this section, these two parameters are calculated for a very simple continuous random variable.

A random variable X has a *uniform* distribution of probability, if the space is $\{0 \text{ to } \theta\}$ and the density function is

$$f(x) = \frac{1}{\theta},$$

where θ is a positive constant. Variable U of Table 5 is an example, with $\theta = 2$.

A procedure for calculating the expected value of X is to refer the problem back to a related discrete case. Divide the space $\{0 \text{ to } \theta\}$ into n equal subintervals:

$$\left\{0 \text{ to } \frac{1\theta}{n}\right\}, \left\{\frac{1\theta}{n} \text{ to } \frac{2\theta}{n}\right\}, \cdots, \left\{\frac{(n-1)\theta}{n} \text{ to } \frac{n\theta}{n}\right\}.$$

Think of a related discrete random variable X' with space

$$\left\{\frac{1\theta}{n}, \frac{2\theta}{n}, \cdots, \frac{n\theta}{n}\right\}.$$

Assign probabilities to X' according to

$$\Pr\left\{0 \le X \le \frac{1\theta}{n}\right\} \text{ to } \Pr\left\{X' = \frac{1\theta}{n}\right\},$$

$$\Pr\left\{\frac{1\theta}{n} \le X \le \frac{2\theta}{n}\right\} \text{ to } \Pr\left\{X' = \frac{2\theta}{n}\right\},$$

$$\cdot \quad \cdot \quad \cdot$$

$$\Pr\left\{\frac{(n-1)\theta}{n} \le X \le \frac{n\theta}{n}\right\} \text{ to } \Pr\left\{X' = \frac{n\theta}{n}\right\}.$$

All of these probabilities are $1/n$ for this uniform distribution. $E(X')$ now can be calculated (all summations are for $i = 1, 2, \ldots, n$).

$$E(X') = \sum \frac{i\theta}{n} \frac{1}{n} = \frac{\theta}{n^2} \frac{n(n+1)}{2} = \frac{\theta}{2}\left(1 + \frac{1}{n}\right).$$

As n becomes larger, the quality of this approximation to the continuous distribution should improve. Therefore, let

$$E(X) = \lim_{n \to \infty} E(X') = \frac{\theta}{2}.$$

To find the variance of X', first calculate $E(X'^2)$.

$$E(X'^2) = \sum\left(\frac{i\theta}{n}\right)^2 \frac{1}{n} = \frac{\theta^2}{n^3}\sum i^2 = \frac{\theta^2}{n^3}\left[\frac{n(n+1)(2n+1)}{6}\right]$$

$$= \frac{\theta^2}{6}\left[2 + \frac{3}{n} + \frac{1}{n^2}\right].$$

Similarly, let

$$E(X^2) = \lim_{n\to\infty} E(X'^2) = \frac{\theta^2}{3},$$

and let

$$V(X) = \lim_{n\to\infty} V(X')$$

$$= \lim_{n\to\infty} [E(X'^2) - E^2(X')]$$

$$= \frac{\theta^2}{3} - \frac{\theta^2}{4} = \frac{\theta^2}{12}.$$

For random variable U of Table 5, θ is 2. The parameters are

$$E(U) = \frac{\theta}{2} = 1.00,$$

$$V(U) = \frac{\theta^2}{12} = .33.$$

This procedure works fairly well for the other random variables of Table 5, but one further approximation must be made. If X' is the related discrete variable again, approximate $\Pr\left\{X' = \frac{i\theta}{n}\right\}$ by $\frac{\theta}{n} \cdot f\left(\frac{i\theta}{n}\right)$. With this change in the procedure, the expected values and variances can be computed. Table 7 gives the results.

Table 7

Random variable	Density function	Expected value	Variance	Standard deviation
U	$f(u) = 1/2$	1.00	.33	.57
V	$f(v) = v/2$	1.33	.22	.47
W	$f(w) = \frac{3}{4}w(2-w)$	1.00	.20	.45
A	$f(a) = \begin{cases} 1 - a \text{ for } 0 \le a \le 1 \\ a - 1 \text{ for } 1 \le a \le 2 \end{cases}$	1.00	.50	.71

It is of small value to pursue this discussion, since we are merely calculating definite integrals by a hard method. For the non-calculus reader, three results should be observed: (1) Some meaning has been attached to $E(X)$ and $V(X)$ for a continuous X. (2) The expected value and variance of the uniform distribution have been calculated. (3) Since a continuous X has a closely related discrete X', one should be willing to assume the important properties of expected value and variance for the continuous case. Specifically, these are

$$E(aX_1 + bX_2 + c) = aE(X_1) + bE(X_2) + c$$

for all variables, and

$$V(aX_1 + bX_2 + c) = a^2V(X_1) + b^2V(X_2)$$

for independent variables X_1 and X_2.

* The *expected value* of a continuous random variable X is defined as

$$E(X) = \int x f(x)\, dx,$$

where f is the density function, and the definite integral is over the entire space. The motivation for such a definition was given in the derivation of $E(X)$ for the uniform distribution, but it is repeated here. For a space which is a finite interval and for a continuous density function, the essential sequence of steps is as follows:

1) Approximate the continuous space with a discrete space $\{x_1, x_2, \ldots, x_n\}$ of n outcomes.
2) Approximate the corresponding n probabilities with $f(x_i)\Delta x_i$, where Δx_i is a subinterval associated with x_i.
3) Calculate the expected value for the discrete case.

$$\sum_i x_i f(x_i)\Delta x_i.$$

4) Take the limit of this as $n \to \infty$.
5) Observe that the result is the definite integral of $xf(x)$, as stated in the definition.

For the example of a uniform distribution on the space $\{0 \text{ to } \theta\}$, the calculation is

$$E(X) = \int x f(x)\ dx = \int_0^\theta x \frac{1}{\theta}\, dx = \frac{\theta}{2}.$$

For variable W of Table 5, the calculation is

$$E(W) = \int_0^2 w \frac{3}{4} w(2 - w)\, dw = \frac{3}{4}\left[\frac{2w^3}{3} - \frac{w^4}{4}\right]_0^2 = 1.$$

* The *variance* of a continuous random variable X is defined similarly as

$$V(X) = \int [x - E(X)]^2 f(x) \, dx.$$

The motivation of the above paragraph applies with obvious changes of words and symbols.

* If X is a continuous random variable with known density function f_X and g is a continuous function defined on the space of X, then $Y = g(X)$ is a new continuous random variable. It has some density function f_Y and some expected value $E(Y)$. We assume, as in the discrete case, that $E(Y)$ may be found without f_Y.

$$E(Y) = \int y f_Y(y) \, dy = \int g(x) f_X(x) \, dx = E[g(X)],$$

where the last equality defines $E[g(X)]$. An important particular case is $Y = aX + b$.

$$E(Y) = E(aX + b) = \int (ax + b) f_X(x) \, dx = aE(X) + b.$$

A second important particular case is $Y = [X - E(X)]^2$:

$$E(Y) = V(X) = E[X - E(X)]^2 = E(X^2)$$

$$- E^2(X) = \int x^2 f_X(x) \, dx - [\int x f_X(x) \, dx]^2.$$

As in the discrete case, it is almost always easier to calculate $V(X)$ from $E(X^2) - E^2(X)$. For the example of uniform distribution with space $\{0$ to $\theta\}$ and $E(X) = \theta/2$, the calculation for the variance is

$$E(X^2) = \int_0^\theta x^2 \frac{1}{\theta} \, dx = \frac{\theta^2}{3},$$

$$V(X) = E(X^2) - E^2(X) = \frac{\theta^2}{3} - \frac{\theta^2}{4} = \frac{\theta^2}{12}.$$

* **Summary.** For a continuous random variable X with density function f, the expected value and variance are

$$E(X) = \int x f(x) \, dx,$$

$$V(X) = \int [x - E(X)]^2 f(x) \, dx = \int x^2 f(x) \, dx - E^2(X),$$

where all integrals are over the whole space for X.

EXERCISES

35. Using $\sum_{i=1}^{n} i^2 = \dfrac{n(n+1)(2n+1)}{6}$, verify that $E(V)$ is 1.33 in Table 7.

36. Using $\sum_{i=1}^{n} i^3 = \left[\dfrac{n(n+1)}{2} \right]^2$, find $E(V^2)$ and verify that the variance of V is .22 in Table 7.

* 37. Using the definite integral, verify the expected value and variance for V in Table 7.

* 38. Verify $E(W)$ and $V(W)$ in Table 7.

* 39. Verify $E(A)$ and $V(A)$ in Table 7.

* 40. For the following density function, find $E(X)$ and $V(X)$.

$$f(x) = \theta e^{-\theta x} \quad \text{for} \quad 0 \leq x < \infty \quad \text{and} \quad 0 < \theta.$$

2.3 THE NORMAL DISTRIBUTION

The density function completely describes a continuous random experiment. The number of different density functions is infinite. Mathematically, any non-negative function with unit area over the space qualifies. Statistically, one density function is far more important than the others. It is the *normal* density function, or *normal distribution* of probability. A normal distribution has described the variation in such unrelated situations as the heights of persons in a population, the errors in laboratory measurements, and the times required by various workers to perform a particular job.

The continuous random variable Z has a *unit-normal* distribution of probability, if the density function is

$$f(z) = \frac{1}{\sqrt{2\pi}} e^{-\frac{z^2}{2}}.$$

The space is the set of all real numbers $\{-\infty \text{ to } +\infty\}$. The number e (2.718...) is the base of the natural logarithms. This density function is positive over the whole space. It is symmetric about the origin. Figure 6 is a graph of the function. It requires calculus to verify that the area under the curve is 1, that $E(Z) = 0$, and that $V(Z) = D(Z) = 1$. The letter Z is reserved for a random variable with a unit-normal density function. Table II in the Appendix gives a few thousand random observations of Z.

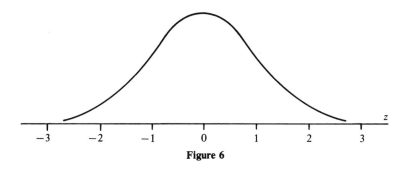

Figure 6

Even with the aid of calculus, it is not easy to find areas under this curve directly. Table III in the Appendix is useful for this purpose. For each positive z, Table III gives the area under the curve and to the right of z. For example, the area to the right of $z = 1.23$, or $\Pr\{1.23 \leq Z\}$, is .1093. By symmetry, the area to the left of -1.23, or $\Pr\{Z \leq -1.23\}$, is also .1093. $\Pr\{0 \leq Z \leq 1.23\}$ is $.5000 - .1093 = .3907$. The probability of any interval may be obtained by suitable use of this table. For a slightly more complex example,

$$\Pr\{0.87 \leq Z \leq 1.23\} = \Pr\{0.87 \leq Z\} - \Pr\{1.23 \leq Z\}$$

$$= .1922 - .1093 = .0829.$$

It is just as common to use this table in the other direction; that is, to find the outcome corresponding to a given probability. In terms of a convenient notation, let α be the given probability, and let $z(\alpha)$ be the outcome such that $\Pr\{z(\alpha) \leq Z\} = \alpha$. For example, take $\alpha = .10$ and find the outcome $z(.10)$ such that $\Pr\{z(.10) \leq Z\} = .10$. $z(.10)$ is such that the area to the right of it and under the curve is .1000. In the columns of Table III, .1003 is closest to the given probability. Without interpolation the corresponding outcome $z(.10)$ is 1.28.

The density function for the general normally distributed, random variable X is

$$f(x) = \frac{1}{\sqrt{2\pi}\,\sigma}\,e^{-\frac{1}{2}\left(\frac{x-\mu}{\sigma}\right)^2},$$

where μ and σ are constants. μ can be any real number, and σ can be any positive real number. The space, like that for the unit normal, is $\{-\infty \text{ to } +\infty\}$. Figure 7 gives the graph. The expected value of X is μ; the variance is σ^2; and the standard deviation is σ. Since μ and σ are the only constants in the density function, knowledge of these two parameters is a complete description of the corresponding experiment. In particular, the unit normal is merely a special case with $\mu = 0$ and $\sigma = 1$. These two Greek letters will be reserved for the parameters of a normal distribution.

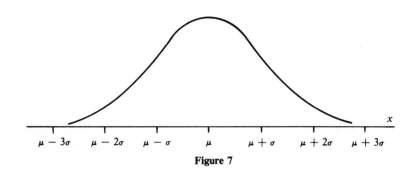

Figure 7

To discuss probability for the general case, suppose X has a normal distribution with parameters μ and σ^2. If Z is the unit normal, consider the variable $\sigma Z + \mu$. In a later discussion using calculus, we will prove that such a linear combination of Z still has a normal distribution of probability. The parameters of the new variable $\sigma Z + \mu$ are

$$E(\sigma Z + \mu) = \sigma E(Z) + \mu = \mu,$$

$$V(\sigma Z + \mu) = \sigma^2 V(Z) = \sigma^2.$$

Therefore, X and $\sigma Z + \mu$ have the same normal distribution. For probabilistic discussions, they are the same.

$$X = \sigma Z + \mu \quad \text{or} \quad Z = \frac{X - \mu}{\sigma}.$$

Now let $\{c \leq X \leq d\}$ be an event for X, and consider its probability.

$$\Pr\{c \leq X \leq d\} = \Pr\left\{\frac{c - \mu}{\sigma} \leq \frac{X - \mu}{\sigma} \leq \frac{d - \mu}{\sigma}\right\}$$

$$= \Pr\left\{\frac{c - \mu}{\sigma} \leq Z \leq \frac{d - \mu}{\sigma}\right\}.$$

The conclusion is that the probability of an event for X, such as $\{c \leq X \leq d\}$, can be calculated from the probability of a related event for Z. Therefore, Table III for the unit normal is sufficient for all normal distributions. For a numerical example, suppose the parameters of X are

$$E(X) = \mu = 100,$$

$$V(X) = \sigma^2 = 400.$$

$\{90 \leq X \leq 125\}$ is an event for X, and its probability is

$$\Pr\{90 \leq X \leq 125\} = \Pr\left\{\frac{90 - 100}{20} \leq \frac{X - 100}{20} \leq \frac{125 - 100}{20}\right\}$$

$$= \Pr\{-.50 \leq Z \leq 1.25\} = .5840.$$

There is one more important property of the normal distribution. The sum of two (or more) normal random variables is itself normally distributed. The proof is beyond the level of this book. To summarize this and previous properties let X_1 and X_2 have normal distributions, and let a, b, and c be constants. Then $Y = aX_1 + bX_2 + c$ has a normal distribution with

$$E(Y) = aE(X_1) + bE(X_2) + c.$$

If X_1 and X_2 are also independent, then

$$V(Y) = a^2V(X_1) + b^2V(X_2).$$

For an illustration, take the mixing of concrete. In each concrete batch of one cubic yard, let

$$X_1 = \text{pounds of cement,}$$
$$X_2 = \text{pounds of water,}$$
$$X_3 = \text{pounds of dry sand,}$$
$$X_4 = \text{pounds of gravel.}$$

Assume the X_i's are normally distributed according to

$E(X_1) = \mu_1 = 470,$	$D(X_1) = \sigma_1 = 5,$
$E(X_2) = \mu_2 = 234,$	$D(X_2) = \sigma_2 = 50,$
$E(X_3) = \mu_3 = 1440,$	$D(X_3) = \sigma_3 = 100,$
$E(X_4) = \mu_4 = 1890,$	$D(X_4) = \sigma_4 = 200.$

It is probably unrealistic, but assume the X_i's are independent. What is the probability that a batch weighs more than 4100 pounds? If $Y = X_1 + X_2 + X_3 + X_4$ is the total weight, then

$$E(Y) = \mu_1 + \mu_2 + \mu_3 + \mu_4 = 4034,$$
$$V(Y) = \sigma_1^2 + \sigma_2^2 + \sigma_3^2 + \sigma_4^2 = 52,525,$$
$$D(Y) = 229.2.$$

The desired probability is

$$\Pr\{4100 \leq Y\} = \Pr\left\{\frac{4100 - 4034}{229.2} \leq \frac{Y - 4034}{229.2}\right\}$$

$$= \Pr\{.29 \leq Z\} = .39.$$

Next suppose that a batch makes poor concrete, if the weight of the sand and gravel is more than 8 times the weight of the cement. The event corresponding to a poor batch is

$$\{8X_1 \leq X_3 + X_4\} = \{0 \leq X_3 + X_4 - 8X_1\}.$$

$Y = X_3 + X_4 - 8X_1$ has a normal distribution with

$$E(Y) = \mu_3 + \mu_4 - 8\mu_1 = -430,$$
$$V(Y) = \sigma_3^2 + \sigma_4^2 + 64\sigma_1^2 = 51,600,$$
$$D(Y) = 227.2.$$

The probability is

$$\Pr\{0 \leq Y\} = \Pr\left\{\frac{0 + 430}{227.2} \leq \frac{Y + 430}{227.2}\right\} = \Pr\{1.90 \leq Z\} = .03.$$

That is, about 3 per cent of the batches make this type of poor concrete under the present conditions.

* With the aid of calculus, most of the properties of the normal distribution are easily proved. The first proof is that the unit normal density function integrates to 1.

$$\int \frac{1}{\sqrt{2\pi}} e^{-\frac{z^2}{2}} dz = 1.$$

Since the integrand is always positive, the integral is some positive number I. The trick is to show that $I^2 = 1$ by means of familiar operations with double integrals. This will establish $I = 1$. All integrals are from $-\infty$ to $+\infty$ in

$$I^2 = I \cdot I = \left[\int \frac{1}{\sqrt{2\pi}} e^{-\frac{z^2}{2}} dz\right]\left[\int \frac{1}{\sqrt{2\pi}} e^{-\frac{y^2}{2}} dy\right].$$

Assume that this product may be written as a double integral,

$$I^2 = \int\int \frac{1}{2\pi} e^{-\frac{z^2 + y^2}{2}} dz dy,$$

where the double integral is evaluated over the entire z, y plane. In the usual transformation to polar coordinates, the new variables are

$$z = r \cos \theta,$$

$$y = r \sin \theta.$$

The integral becomes

$$I^2 = \frac{1}{2\pi} \int \int e^{-\frac{r^2}{2}} r \, dr \, d\theta,$$

where the limits on r are 0 to $+\infty$ and the limits on θ are 0 to 2π. When treated as an iterated integral, this becomes

$$I^2 = \frac{1}{2\pi} \int_0^{2\pi} \left[\int_0^\infty e^{-\frac{r^2}{2}} r \, dr \right] d\theta = \frac{1}{2\pi} \int_0^{2\pi} 1 \, d\theta = 1.$$

* The proofs that $E(Z) = 0$ and $V(Z) = 1$ are left to the exercises. To prove that the general normal density function integrates to one is not difficult; the only step is to transform the integral to the unit-normal case. The same step is required to prove that the expected value and variance are μ and σ^2 for the general normal case.

* To show that a linear function of a normal random variable is still normal, let X have parameters μ and σ. Let $Y = aX + b$, where a and b are constants. The problem is to prove Y is normal. Let $\{c \leq Y \leq d\}$ be any event for Y. If we can show that $\Pr\{c \leq Y \leq d\}$ is the integral from c to d of some normal density function, then we will have proved that Y is normal.

$$\Pr\{c \leq Y \leq d\} = \Pr\{c \leq aX + b \leq d\} = \Pr\left\{\frac{c-b}{a} \leq X \leq \frac{d-b}{a}\right\}$$

$$= \int_{\frac{c-b}{a}}^{\frac{d-b}{a}} \frac{1}{\sqrt{2\pi}} e^{-\frac{1}{2}\left(\frac{x-\mu}{\sigma}\right)^2} dx.$$

Now, transform the variable in the integral by $y = ax + b$ and obtain

$$\Pr\{c \leq Y \leq d\} = \int_c^d \frac{1}{\sqrt{2\pi} \, a\sigma} e^{-\frac{1}{2}\left[\frac{y-(a\mu+b)}{a\sigma}\right]^2} dy.$$

The result is of the desired normal form with expected value $a\mu + b$ and variance $a^2\sigma^2$. Therefore, Y has a normal distribution. The proof was given for a positive value of a. Modifying the proof for a negative value of a is a good exercise.

EXERCISES

41. For the unit normal Z, find the following probabilities:
    a) $\Pr\{0 \leq Z\}$.
    b) $\Pr\{1.65 \leq Z\}$.
    c) $\Pr\{Z \leq -0.80\}$.
    d) $\Pr\{-0.80 \leq Z \leq 1.65\}$.
    e) $\Pr\{Z \leq -1.96 \text{ or } 1.96 \leq Z\}$.
    f) $\Pr\{-1.96 \leq Z \leq -0.80\}$.
    g) $\Pr\{Z = 1.00\}$.

42. For the unit normal, find the value of c (to the nearest tabular value)
    in the following:
    a) $\Pr\{c \leq Z\} = .20$.
    b) $\Pr\{Z \leq -c \text{ or } c \leq Z\} = .05$.
    c) $\Pr\{Z \leq c\} = .75$.
    d) $\Pr\{-c \leq Z \leq c\} = .90$.
    e) $\Pr\{Z \leq c\} = .005$.

43. For $\alpha = .05$ and $\alpha = .01$, find
    a) $z(\alpha)$.

    b) $z\left(\dfrac{\alpha}{2}\right)$.

    c) $z\left(1 - \dfrac{\alpha}{2}\right)$.

44. X has a normal distribution with $E(X) = \mu = 50$ and $V(X) = \sigma^2 = 25$. Find
    a) $\Pr\{50 \leq X\}$.
    b) $\Pr\{55 \leq X\}$.
    c) $\Pr\{42 \leq X \leq 55\}$.
    d) $\Pr\{X \leq 40\}$.
    e) the value of c such that $\Pr\{c \leq X\} = .025$.
    f) the values of c_1 and c_2 such that

    $$\Pr\{X \leq c_1\} = \Pr\{c_2 \leq X\} = .005.$$

45. Scores for a population of students on a certain aptitude test have a
    normal distribution with an expected value of 100 and a standard
    deviation of 20. If a student scores 135, what per cent of the popu-
    lation would score less than he?

46. In the example of mixing the concrete, suppose a bad batch results when 8 per cent or more of the total mix is water. What is the probability of this?

* 47. For the unit normal Z, prove
   a) $E(Z) = 0.$
   b) $V(Z) = 1.$

* 48. If X has a general normal density function with parameters μ and σ^2, prove

   a) $\int_{-\infty}^{+\infty} f(x)\, dx = 1.$

   b) $E(X) = \mu.$
   c) $E(X^2) = \sigma^2 + \mu^2.$
   d) $V(X) = \sigma^2.$

3
Statistics

A *statistic* is a number that characterizes a sequence of numbers. That is, a statistic for a sequence of numbers is a function of those numbers. A statistic is to a sequence of numbers what a parameter is to a probability distribution. The probability distribution describes completely the corresponding random experiment. Parameters give simplified descriptions: the expected value indicates a typical value; the variance measures the spread. Similarly, the sequence of numbers completely describes itself. However, one statistic, the *mean*, indicates a typical value for the sequence; another, the *variance*, indicates the spread in the sequence.

Let the sequence of n numbers be $x_1, x_2, \ldots, x_n$. This is not to be thought of as the space for some discrete random experiment. Some of the x_i's can even be the same number. For example, suppose the salaries of the top 10 executives of some company are of interest:

20,000	30,000
20,000	35,000
25,000	40,000
25,000	50,000
25,000	70,000

The *mean* of the n numbers, which indicates a typical value, is the quotient of the sum and n. The symbol is $\bar{x}$,

$$\bar{x} = \frac{\sum x_i}{n},$$

where the sum is for $i = 1, 2, \ldots, n$. In many contexts, $\bar{x}$ is also called the *sample mean*. The mean salary for the 10 executives is

$$\bar{x} = \frac{\sum x_i}{n} = \frac{340{,}000}{10} = 34{,}000.$$

The *variance* s^2 of the n numbers is (almost) the mean of the squared deviations from the mean. In symbols,

$$s^2 = \frac{\sum (x_i - \bar{x})^2}{n - 1},$$

where the sum is for $i = 1, 2, \ldots, n$. In most contexts, s^2 is also called the *sample variance*. This name avoids the possibility of confusing the variance of a sequence of numbers with the variance of a probability distribution. It is almost never a good idea to compute s^2 from the definition. The best computing formula is

$$s^2 = \frac{\sum x_i^2 - \dfrac{\left(\sum x_i\right)^2}{n}}{n - 1},$$

where the sum is over $i = 1, 2, \ldots, n$. For the 10 executives' salaries, the variance is

$$s^2 = \frac{13{,}800{,}000{,}000 - \dfrac{(340{,}000)^2}{10}}{9} = 248{,}888{,}889.$$

The square root of the variance is the *standard deviation s*. In some contexts, s is also called the *sample standard deviation*. For the 10 executives' salaries, $s = 15{,}776$.

The sample mean and the sample variance have some of the same properties as the expected value and the variance. To illustrate, suppose each number x_i in the sequence is transformed to $y_i = ax_i + b$. The new sequence of numbers $y_1, y_2, \ldots, y_n$ has a mean $\bar{y}$ and a variance s_y^2. The relations between the two sets of statistics are

$$\bar{y} = a\bar{x} + b,$$
$$s_y^2 = a^2 s_x^2,$$
$$s_y = |a| s_x.$$

These relations can be very useful when one has to make the calculations by hand. The idea is to transform the data to simpler, smaller numbers, compute the mean and variance for the collection of simpler numbers, and then transform the computed mean and variance back to the original data. For the numerical example with the salaries, let

$$y_i = \frac{1}{5000}(x_i - 20{,}000) \quad \text{or} \quad x_i = 5000y_i + 20{,}000.$$

The y_i's are

0	2
0	3
1	4
1	6
1	10

For these, the calculations are

$$\bar{y} = \frac{\sum y_i}{n} = \frac{28}{10} = 2.8,$$

$$s_y^2 = \frac{\sum y_i^2 - \dfrac{\left(\sum y_i\right)^2}{n}}{n-1} = \frac{168 - \dfrac{(28)^2}{10}}{9} = 9.9556,$$

$$s_y = 3.155.$$

The transformation back is

$$\bar{x} = 5000\bar{y} + 20{,}000 = 34{,}000,$$

$$s_x = 5000 s_y = 15{,}776.$$

The wide availability of calculators and computers has decreased the general value of these numerical techniques, and we shall not discuss them further.

Summary. If $x_1, x_2, \ldots, x_n$ is a sequence of n numbers, the mean $\bar{x}$ is

$$\bar{x} = \frac{\sum x_i}{n}.$$

The sample variance s^2 is

$$s^2 = \frac{\sum (x_i - \bar{x})^2}{n-1} = \frac{\sum x_i^2 - \dfrac{\left(\sum x_i\right)^2}{n}}{n-1},$$

and the sample standard deviation is the square root of the sample variance. If $y_i = ax_i + b$ for all i, then

$$\bar{y} = a\bar{x} + b,$$

$$s_y^2 = a^2 s_x^2,$$

$$s_y = |a| s_x.$$

EXERCISES

49. Verify the computing formula for the sample variance by showing

$$\sum(x_i - \bar{x})^2 = \sum x_i^2 - \frac{\left(\sum x_i\right)^2}{n}.$$

50. Compute the mean and the standard deviation for the following numbers:

$$1, 5, 2, 3, 1.$$

51. Use the result of exercise 50 to compute easily the mean and standard deviation of the following:

$$1100, 1500, 1200, 1300, 1100.$$

52. If $y_i = ax_i + b$, verify that $\bar{y} = a\bar{x} + b$ and $s_y^2 = a^2 s_x^2$.

53. Each of the 10 executives in the example of this section receives two salary adjustments: a 30 per cent reduction followed by a $5000 raise. What are the final mean and standard deviation?

54. Each of the 10 executives in the example receives two salary adjustments: a $5000 raise followed by a 30 per cent reduction. What are the final mean and standard deviation?

4

The Central Limit Theorem

When the same random experiment is to be performed several times, the result will be a sequence of outcomes. This sequence of numbers will have a mean, which will be a random variable with a probability distribution of its own. The Central Limit Theorem identifies the probability distribution of the mean. It is the most important theorem in probability.

Let X be the random variable for some experiment. A *random sample* for X is a sequence of independent random variables X_1, X_2, ..., X_n, each with the probability distribution of X. That is, a basic random experiment is performed n times under the same conditions. The outcomes are x_1, x_2, ..., x_n. The same term, random sample, will be used for the n random variables, the X_i's, and for the n outcomes, the x_i's.

For one example, recall the experiment of the citizen's response:

Experiment B. According to a well defined procedure, a citizen is selected from a particular community and asked his opinion of the United Nations. The number of favorable responses (0 or 1) is the outcome. Let B be the random variable.

If $n = 5$, a possible random sample is 1, 1, 0, 1, 0. This corresponds to favorable responses from the 1st, 2nd, and 4th citizens and unfavorable responses from the 3rd and 5th citizens.

For a second example, recall

Experiment C. A motorist drives to work every morning by the same route. He leaves home at about the same time and passes one traffic light on his trip. On some of the trips the light is red, and he must wait. The outcome of the experiment is his waiting time in minutes. If the light is green, the experiment is not performed. Let C be the random variable.

A possible random sample of size 5 is

$$0.12, 1.34, 0.79, 0.91, 1.83,$$

where these are the waiting times in minutes on five delayed trips past the light.

Obtaining a random sample for some experiment usually raises practical difficulties. In fact, performing the experiment only once according to the probability model raises most of these difficulties. Take experiment B, the citizen's opinion of the UN. Let θ be the proportion favoring the UN in the community. To perform the experiment once, the experimenter asks a citizen his opinion; but how does he choose the citizen? One idealized method is to put each citizen's name on a separate, small piece of paper; put the papers in a large bowl; mix thoroughly; select one paper blindly; find the selected citizen; get his opinion of the UN. By this procedure, each citizen has an equal chance to be chosen. In many repetitions of this procedure, the long-term relative frequency of favorable responses would be θ. That is, this process gives $\Pr\{B = 1\} = \theta$, as desired.

This procedure is an ideal way to perform the experiment, but it is usually a practical impossibility. For example, getting a complete list of citizens can be a very expensive job. For much less money, a fairly complete list may be available. The experimenter may wish to choose from this incomplete population. Strictly speaking, his inferences apply only to the incomplete population, although he may hope $\Pr\{B = 1\}$ is still θ. Several other compromises with the ideal procedure may be necessary. To obtain a random sample of size n, the experimenter independently repeats whatever practical procedure he used the first time.

Part of the Central Limit Theorem is based on familiar properties of the expected value and the variance. For a random sample of a random variable X, consider the sample mean

$$\bar{X} = \frac{X_1 + X_2 + \cdots + X_n}{n} = \frac{\sum X_i}{n}.$$

Since the individual X_i's are random, $\bar{X}$ is also a random variable. This means that $\bar{X}$ has a probability distribution with the usual parameters. The expected value, variance, and standard deviation are

$$E(\bar{X}) = E\left(\frac{\sum X_i}{n}\right) = \frac{1}{n}E\left(\sum X_i\right) = \frac{1}{n}\sum E(X_i) = \frac{1}{n}\sum E(X) = E(X),$$

$$V(\bar{X}) = V\left(\frac{\sum X_i}{n}\right) = \frac{1}{n^2}V\left(\sum X_i\right) = \frac{1}{n^2}\sum V(X_i) = \frac{1}{n^2}\sum V(X) = \frac{1}{n}V(X),$$

$$D(\bar{X}) = \frac{1}{\sqrt{n}}D(X).$$

These results are based on the previously assumed and proved properties of $E(\ )$ and $V(\ )$.

The profound part of the Central Limit Theorem says that the distribution of $\bar{X}$ approaches a normal distribution as n increases. This means that probabilities for $\bar{X}$ can be approximated by using only

$$E(X), \ D(X)/\sqrt{n}$$

and the normal tables. The remarkable point is that the distribution of the original X is not used; it may be anything, discrete or continuous. The quality of this approximation, however, depends on the event in question, the distribution of the original X, and the size of n. The proof of this theorem is beyond the level of this book.

At one extreme, suppose the original variable X has a normal distribution. The Central Limit Theorem says nothing new in this case. $\bar{X}$, which is a linear combination of the X_i's, has an exact normal distribution for any sample size.

Near the other extreme is a random variable X with a Bernoulli distribution. At least the spaces are as different as possible: $\{0, 1\}$ vs. $\{-\infty$ to

$+\infty$ }. To show the approach to normal for $\bar{X}$, take the non-symmetric case $\theta = .80$. For each n, the space for $\bar{X}$ is

$$\left\{\frac{0}{n}, \frac{1}{n}, \frac{2}{n}, \ldots, \frac{n}{n}\right\}.$$

Of course, no outcomes in this space are ever smaller than zero or larger than one, but the outcomes become dense as n increases. In this sense, the space approaches that of a continuous variable. Figure 8 shows the approach for the probability functions for $\bar{X}$ with $n = 5$, 10, 15, and 20. The probability functions seem to be approaching the general shape of a normal distribution with

$$E(\bar{X}) = E(X) = \theta = .80.$$

When θ is very near 0 or 1, .01 or .99 for example, a very large n is required for a good approximation. Otherwise n of about 30 is usually sufficient for $.10 \le \theta \le .90$.

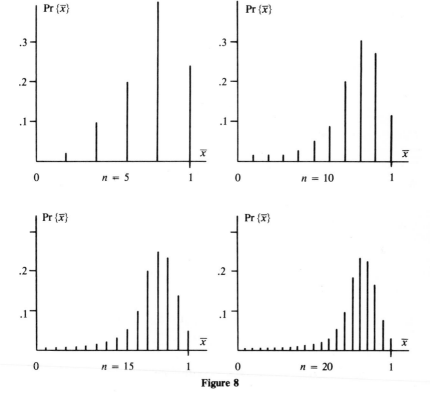

Figure 8

To illustrate the calculations, first take experiment B with probability function

$$\Pr\{B = 0\} = 1 - \theta = .20,$$

$$\Pr\{B = 1\} = \theta = .80.$$

.80 is the proportion of citizens in the population who favor the UN. The parameters for B are

$$E(B) = \theta = .80,$$

$$V(B) = \theta(1 - \theta) = .16,$$

$$D(B) = \sqrt{\theta(1 - \theta)} = .40.$$

In a random sample of $n = 100$, $\bar{B}$ is the sample proportion favoring the UN. The parameters for $\bar{B}$ are

$$E(\bar{B}) = E(B) = \theta = .80,$$

$$V(\bar{B}) = \frac{V(B)}{n} = \frac{\theta(1 - \theta)}{n} = .0016,$$

$$D(\bar{B}) = \frac{D(B)}{\sqrt{n}} = \sqrt{\frac{\theta(1 - \theta)}{n}} = .04.$$

Consider some event for $\bar{B}$, such as $\{.85 \leq \bar{B}\}$. Then,

$$\Pr\{.85 \leq \bar{B}\} = \Pr\left\{\frac{.85 - .80}{.04} \leq \frac{\bar{B} - .80}{.04}\right\} = \Pr\{1.25 \leq Z\} = .11.$$

That is, if 80 per cent of the population favor the UN, there is approximately an .11 probability that at least 85 per cent favor the UN in a random sample of 100 citizens.

For a second illustration, take experiment C, the delayed motorist. On his next 30 delayed trips, what is the probability that his total delay is between 24 and 36 minutes? This is equivalent to a mean delay between $24/30 = .80$ and $36/30 = 1.20$ minutes. The desired probability is $\Pr\{.80 \leq \bar{C} \leq 1.20\}$. Suppose the density function for the original variable C is the uniform distribution with $\theta = 2$.

$$f(c) = \frac{1}{\theta} = \frac{1}{2} \quad \text{for } 0 \leq c \leq 2.$$

The parameters are

$$E(C) = \frac{\theta}{2} = \frac{2}{2} = 1.00,$$

$$V(C) = \frac{\theta^2}{12} = \frac{4}{12} = 0.3333,$$

$$D(C) = 0.577.$$

According to the Central Limit Theorem, $\bar{C}$ is normally distributed with

$$E(\bar{C}) = E(C) = 1.00,$$

$$V(\bar{C}) = \frac{V(C)}{n} = 0.0111,$$

$$D(\bar{C}) = \frac{D(C)}{\sqrt{n}} = 0.105.$$

The required calculation is

$$\Pr\{.80 \le \bar{C} \le 1.20\} = \Pr\left\{\frac{.80 - 1.00}{.105} \le \frac{\bar{C} - 1.00}{.105} \le \frac{1.20 - 1.00}{.105}\right\}$$

$$= \Pr\{-1.90 \le Z \le 1.90\} = .94.$$

That is, the event of waiting between 24 and 36 minutes on the next 30 delayed trips has an approximate probability of .94.

Summary. For a random variable X, a random sample is a sequence of independent random variables $X_1, X_2, \ldots, X_n$, each with the probability distribution of X. The sample mean $\bar{X}$ is also a random variable with

$$E(\bar{X}) = E(X), \quad V(\bar{X}) = \frac{V(X)}{n}, \quad \text{and} \quad D(\bar{X}) = \frac{D(X)}{\sqrt{n}}.$$

As the sample size increases, the distribution for $\bar{X}$ approaches a normal distribution.

EXERCISES

55. Scores on an aptitude test have a normal distribution with $\mu = 100$ and $\sigma = 20$. If X is the variable corresponding to the experiment of selecting a person at random and giving him the test, find
a) $\Pr\{110 \le X\}$.
In a random sample of 10 people, let $\bar{X}$ be the sample mean. Find
b) $E(\bar{X})$.
c) $V(\bar{X})$.
d) $D(\bar{X})$.
e) $\Pr\{110 \le \bar{X}\}$.

56. Suppose a batter has a probability of .300 to get a hit each time at bat. If successive times at bat are independent experiments (very unlikely), what is the probability of his getting an average of at least .330 in his next 200 times at bat?

57. A company has 20 per cent of the available market. A market survey of 400 consumers is taken. What is the probability that at least 25 per cent of those in the survey use the company's product?

58. In the context of exercises 1, 6, and 13, with $E(X) = 2.30$ and $D(X) = .90$, suppose the dealer independently handles 25 cars. Let $X_1, X_2, \ldots, X_{25}$ be the corresponding random variables. Consider $W = \sum X_i$, which is the number of car-months of inventory. Find
    a) $\Pr\{50 \le W \le 65\} = \Pr\{2.00 \le \bar{X} \le 2.60\}$.
    b) If each car-month costs $10 in inventory, what is the probability of a total inventory cost of less than $500?

59. For the situation in exercise 58, let $\bar{X}$ be the mean for a random sample of size 25. Verify the probabilities of the following events:

Event	Probability
$\{\bar{X} \le 1.94\}$	.02
$\{1.94 \le \bar{X} \le 2.12\}$	.14
$\{2.12 \le \bar{X} \le 2.30\}$	.34
$\{2.30 \le \bar{X} \le 2.48\}$	.34
$\{2.48 \le \bar{X} \le 2.66\}$	.14
$\{2.66 \le \bar{X}\}$	.02

60. Simulate the experiment in exercise 58 by making a deck of 10 cards with 2 aces, 4 two's, 3 three's, and 1 four. Draw (with replacement and shuffling) 25 cards. Compute the sample mean $\bar{x}$ and sample standard deviation s. Compare your $\bar{x}$ to $E(X) = 2.30$ and your s to $D(X) = .90$. If several people do this simulation, complete the following frequency table and compare the last column to the probabilities in exercise 59:

Class	Number of $\bar{x}$'s in each class	Per cent of the $\bar{x}$'s in each class
below 1.94		
1.94 to 2.12		
2.12 to 2.30		
2.30 to 2.48		
2.48 to 2.66		
2.66 and over		

61. Fifty people take the aptitude test in exercise 55. What is the probability that at least 18 of them score 110 or more?

ADDITIONAL READINGS

Feller, W. *An Introduction to Probability Theory and Its Applications.* 2nd ed. New York: John Wiley & Sons, Inc., 1957.

Mosteller, F., R. Rourke, and G. Thomas, Jr. *Probability and Statistics.* Reading, Massachusetts: Addison-Wesley Publishing Co., Inc., 1961.

Parzen, E. *Modern Probability Theory and Its Applications.* New York: John Wiley & Sons, Inc., 1960.

Problems

1. The price of a stock on the exchange varies from day to day. Let Y be this change in dollars. Suppose the probability function is

y	$=$	-2	-1	0	1	2
$\Pr\{y\}$	$=$	.10	.20	.35	.25	.10

a) What is the space?
b) What is the probability of a rise in price next Tuesday?
c) What is the expected value of Y?
d) What is the variance of Y?
e) An investor buys the stock today but must sell it after exactly 100 days of trading on the market. What is the probability that he will take a loss? Assume successive daily changes are independent.

2. A prisoner plans to escape by climbing a fence at a particular spot. It will take him one-half minute to get over the fence. He knows that a guard passes the spot every five minutes, but he doesn't know the exact times. If he starts his climb within one minute of the guard's last passage, he will be caught. If he is in the act of climbing and the guard is within two minutes of his next passage, he will be caught.

Let X be the time since the last passage at the start of his climb.
a) What is the space for X?
b) What is the density function for X?
c) What is the event of his escape?
d) What is the probability of this event?

3. Calderwood has a system for determining the probability of a given horse winning a race. Just prior to the first race at the track, the situation for a win bet is

Horse	Calderwood's probabilities	Equal odds for one dollar
A	.40	.70
B	.25	3.25
C	.15	16.00
D	.10	4.70
E	.10	6.50

That is, horse A returns $3.40 on a two-dollar bet.
a) If he believes in his system, how should Calderwood bet his two dollars, and what is his expected profit?
b) What per cent of the total amount bet is returned to the bettors by the track?

* 4. A supplier has 0.5 thousand items in inventory and cannot get more in the next month. His total demand for the next month is a random variable X (in thousands) which has the following density function:

$$f(x) = 3(1 - x)^2 \quad \text{for} \quad 0 \le x \le 1.$$

a) Find the expected demand.
b) Find the expected number of items to be sold.

5. Johnson sells deluxe swimming pools. He makes a $600 profit on each sale. For the coming season, the number of sales in his territory is a random variable X with

$$\Pr\{x\} = \frac{2}{n+1}\left(1 - \frac{x}{n}\right) \quad \text{for} \quad x = 1, 2, \ldots, n.$$

The amount spent on promotion c and the potential market size n are related by $c = 2n^2$.
a) How large should Johnson make his market size n to maximize his expected net profit?
b) How much should be spent on promotion for the optimal market size?

c) What is the maximum expected net profit?

d) What is the corresponding probability that Johnson will actually lose money this season?

e) If he makes a net profit of at least $10,000, his wife gets a trip to Hawaii. What is the probability of this?

6. A truck must deliver a piano in town A, drive to town B, deliver a chair in town B, and return to town A. Let W be the time to deliver the piano, X be the one-way time between towns, and Y be the time to deliver the chair. Assume normal distributions for W, X, and Y, which are measured in minutes:

variable	μ	σ^2
W	30	50
X	15	10
Y	10	11

Assume independence as needed.

a) What is the probability that the total time for the job is less than one hour?

b) What is the probability that the time traveling between towns exceeds the time for the two deliveries?

7. Sixty per cent of the car owners in a community have garages. In a sample of 48 car owners, what is the probability that at least 55 per cent own garages?

8. A continuous random variable U has the space $\{0 \text{ to } \theta\}$ and the density function

$$f(u) = \frac{2u}{\theta^2} \quad \text{for} \quad 0 \le u \le \theta \quad \text{and} \quad 0 < \theta.$$

Show that $E(U) = \frac{2\theta}{3}$ and $V(U) = \frac{\theta^2}{18}$.

9. Mrs. Campbell will attempt to sell greeting cards to her neighbors. The probability of making a sale to any neighbor is .25, and the neighbors behave independently. If she contacts 100 neighbors, what is the probability that Mrs. Campbell will sell to at most 20 neighbors?

10. As in problem 9, Mrs. Elliott will attempt to sell cards in her neighborhood. If she also calls on 100 neighbors and if .25 is the probability of a sale, what is the probability that Mrs. Elliott will make at least 10 more sales than Mrs. Campbell?

Testing Hypotheses *III*

A statistical hypothesis is a statement about the unknown value of a parameter for a random experiment. The statement is either true or false. As an introductory explanation, one can think of a statistical test as a procedure for evaluating the truth or falsity of the hypothesis. The test is usually based on the outcomes of several trials of the experiment. Other factors, such as the cost of making a wrong evaluation and the experimenter's subjective feelings about the hypothesis, can be involved in the test. The statement $\mu = 80$, for example, might be a statistical hypothesis about the expected value for a random experiment with a normal distribution of probability. If three trials of the experiment produce outcomes 81, 89, and 87, a statistical test uses these outcomes to evaluate the hypothesis $\mu = 80$.

The four major testing procedures are: significance tests, decision procedures, minimax procedures, and Bayes procedures. To some extent, they complement each other, but they are also partially contradictory. Statisticians occasionally disagree over the best procedure for testing a hypothesis. The plan for this chapter is to discuss significance tests in detail and to indicate briefly the other three procedures.

1

Significance Tests

If the statistical hypothesis for a random experiment is true, then some outcomes for the random experiment are more likely to occur than others. If the random experiment is actually performed and if unlikely outcomes occur, then the hypothesis is rejected as false. A *significance test* is a rule for identifying the outcomes which reject the hypothesis. That is, it is primarily concerned with detecting a false hypothesis, not with verifying a true hypothesis.

A significance test is an extension of traditional logic. To illustrate this, we start with a review of logic and the scientific method. Let H and C be two statements. Since each is either true or false, there are four possible combinations. Consider the conditional statement, if H, then C. The conditional statement is either true or false, depending on the truth or falsity of H and C. The truth table which corresponds to common usage of the conditional is

H	C	If H, then C.
true	true	true
true	false	false
false	true	true
false	false	true

This means that the conditional, if H, then C, is false when H is true and C is false; the conditional is true for the three other combinations. Now suppose the conditional is known to be true, and the status of H is desired. If C is also known to be true, then H can be true or false. That is, no definite decision about H is logically possible. If C is known to be false, however, then H must be false. That is, a definite decision about H is possible.

The scientific method is only an application of this logical structure. The statement H is usually a very general hypothesis or theory about nature. It is either completely true, or else it is false. In the important situations, H is so general that its truth or falsity cannot be established directly. By assuming H is true and using accepted steps, the scientist derives a necessary conclusion C. That is, a true conditional statement, if H, then C, is formed. The conclusion C is a specific statement (prediction). By a suitable experiment, the truth or falsity of C is determined. Suppose the experiment shows that C is true. Then H was useful in making a prediction, and the scientist's faith in H may be increased. Logically, however, H remains unproved; it can still be true or false. Even centuries of successful predictions do not prove completely that H is true. Suppose the experiment shows that C is false. One honest disagreement like this proves that H is false. It must be abandoned or modified to account for the disagreement. The history of science provides many examples of this sequence of hypothesis, experiment, and modification. Newton's laws of motion, for example, had to be modified after centuries of use when they failed to lead to a correct prediction of the speed of light in the famous Michaelson-Morley experiment.

Significance tests are based on a modification of the scientific method. The hypothesis H concerns a parameter of a random experiment. By assuming the truth of H, the experimenter uses probability to derive a conclusion C. At this point, the random aspects enter. A completely true conditional statement of the form, if H, then C, usually contains a prediction C which is so general that all experimental outcomes agree with it.

In significance testing, the conditional statement is formulated so that it is "almost true." If the experimental outcomes agree with C, then nothing definite can be said about H. If the experimental outcomes disagree with C, then H is rejected as false.

In a significance test, there is a small, predetermined chance of rejecting a true hypothesis H. The probability of this is the *significance level* of the test. It is the "almost-true" nature of the conditional statement that introduces the new concept. Four of the most important testing situations are discussed in the following subsections.

EXERCISES

1. Suppose the following conditional statement is true:
   If Selleg is talented, then he will be successful.
   a) Suppose it is also true that Selleg succeeds. Does it follow that he is talented?
   b) He is talented. Does it follow that he will be successful?
   c) He does not succeed. Does it follow that he is not talented?
   d) He is not talented. Does it follow that he will not succeed?
   e) If Selleg does not become wealthy, then he will not be successful. He is talented. Does it follow that he will become wealthy?

1.1 EXPECTED VALUE FOR A NORMAL DISTRIBUTION

A random experiment with normal distribution has two parameters, μ and σ^2. Testing situations with hypotheses about the expected value μ arise frequently. The variance σ^2 may be known or unknown. When σ^2 is known, the significance test is slightly simpler.

Known Variance

The random variable X has a normal distribution with unknown expected value μ and known variance σ^2. A frequently encountered hypothesis for μ is $\mu = \mu_0$, where μ_0 is a known number. If the hypothesis is not true, μ is smaller or larger than μ_0.

Agricultural Example. A certain variety of wheat is widely grown in some geographical region. Many fields in the region are usually planted in this variety. The yield, measured in bushels per acre, varies from field to field in any year. Suppose the distribution of yields is normal with an expected value of 80 and a standard deviation of 15. For simplicity, assume the same distribution of yields for every year. That is, a particular field may not always have the same yield every year, but the total distribution remains the same. An experimenter develops a new variety of wheat and wants to evaluate it. One of the first questions might be, "Does it differ in yield from the old variety?" Consider the following idealized experiment: select a field at random from the region; induce the owner to plant the new variety; raise and harvest the crop in the usual manner; and measure the yield. Let Y be the corresponding random variable for the yield. Assume Y has a normal distribution and assume $D(Y)$ is 15, as for the old variety. In this context, the new variety gives the same yield, if the hypothesis $E(Y) = 80$ is true. If the hypothesis is false, the new variety gives a different yield.

Physiological Example. A pharmaceutical company develops a new drug which affects blood pressure. Consider the following idealized experiment: Select a person at random from some particular population; measure his blood pressure; assume this is constant with no day-to-day variation; administer the drug to the person; measure his new blood pressure which is also assumed constant; record the change P in blood pressure. Assume P has a normal distribution of probability. Since a person may react sharply to the drug, suppose $D(P) = 10$. The company might be interested in the hypothesis $E(P) = 0$. If this hypothesis is true, the expected change for the population is zero; if it is false, there is an expected change for the population as a whole.

For the random variable X, suppose only one observation is to be made. We seek a conclusion to the conditional statement about x, the observed outcome of X. To make the conditional statement completely true, the conclusion must be $-\infty < x < +\infty$. This conditional statement

$$\text{if } \mu = \mu_0, \text{ then } -\infty < x < +\infty$$

is useless, because the experimental outcome always agrees with the conclusion. There is no way to reject the hypothesis $\mu = \mu_0$. A more useful conditional statement results from lowering our logical standards and looking for a conclusion that is more closely related to the hypothesis. Since the hypothesis says that μ_0 is a typical value for X, such a conclusion might be of the general form

$$x \text{ is near } \mu_0.$$

In terms of some temporarily unspecified constants, this conclusion is

$$c_1 < x < c_2,$$

where μ_0 lies in the interval from c_1 to c_2. The conditional statement is now

$$\text{if } \mu = \mu_0, \text{ then } c_1 < x < c_2.$$

If the observed outcome x is less than c_1 or greater than c_2, the hypothesis is rejected as false. Therefore, particular values for c_1 and c_2 define a significance test for the hypothesis $\mu = \mu_0$, because they provide a rule for rejecting the hypothesis.

This conditional statement is no longer completely true. If the hypothesis $\mu = \mu_0$ is true, there is only a high probability that the experimental outcome will be consistent with the conclusion $c_1 < x < c_2$. Let this probability be $1 - \alpha$, where

$$\Pr\{c_1 < X < c_2\} = 1 - \alpha,$$

when $\mu = \mu_0$. A restatement of this is

$$\Pr\{X \leq c_1 \text{ or } c_2 \leq X\} = \alpha,$$

when $\mu = \mu_0$. This identifies α as the significance level for the significance test determined by c_1 and c_2. That is, α is the probability of rejecting a true hypothesis.

In the usual sequence, the experimenter chooses his significance level α first, and lets this determine the significance test, c_1 and c_2. Recall the relation between them,

$$\Pr\{X \leq c_1 \text{ or } c_2 \leq X\} = \alpha,$$

when $\mu = \mu_0$. For each α, there is an infinite number of choices for c_1 and c_2, but the conventional choice is according to

$$\Pr\{X \leq c_1\} = \Pr\{c_2 \leq X\} = \frac{\alpha}{2},$$

when $\mu = \mu_0$. Since the standard deviation σ is assumed known, transform to the unit normal variable Z of Table III by

$$\Pr\{c_2 \leq X\} = \Pr\left\{\frac{c_2 - \mu_0}{\sigma} \leq \frac{X - \mu_0}{\sigma}\right\} = \Pr\left\{\frac{c_2 - \mu_0}{\sigma} \leq Z\right\} = \frac{\alpha}{2}.$$

Therefore,

$$\frac{c_2 - \mu_0}{\sigma} = z\left(\frac{\alpha}{2}\right) \quad \text{and} \quad c_2 = \mu_0 + z\left(\frac{\alpha}{2}\right)\sigma.$$

Similarly,

$$\Pr\{X \leq c_1\} = \Pr\left\{\frac{X - \mu_0}{\sigma} \leq \frac{c_1 - \mu_0}{\sigma}\right\} = \Pr\left\{Z \leq \frac{c_1 - \mu_0}{\sigma}\right\} = \frac{\alpha}{2},$$

and

$$\frac{c_1 - \mu_0}{\sigma} = z\left(1 - \frac{\alpha}{2}\right) = -z\left(\frac{\alpha}{2}\right) \quad \text{and} \quad c_1 = \mu_0 - z\left(\frac{\alpha}{2}\right)\sigma.$$

In summary, the conditional statement for the hypothesis $\mu = \mu_0$ is

$$\text{if } \mu = \mu_0, \text{ then } \mu_0 - z\left(\frac{\alpha}{2}\right)\sigma < x < \mu_0 + z\left(\frac{\alpha}{2}\right)\sigma.$$

If the outcome is less than $\mu_0 - z\left(\frac{\alpha}{2}\right)\sigma$ or greater than $\mu_0 + z\left(\frac{\alpha}{2}\right)\sigma$, then the hypothesis is rejected as false. The significance level for this significance test is α.

The two examples provide numerical illustrations. The experimenter with the new variety of wheat wants to test the hypothesis $E(Y) = 80$. The standard deviation is known to be 15. At a significance level of $\alpha = .05$, the cut-off points for the test based on one observation of Y are

$$c_1 = \mu_0 - z\left(\frac{\alpha}{2}\right)\sigma = 80 - (1.96)(15) = 50.6,$$

$$c_2 = \mu_0 + z\left(\frac{\alpha}{2}\right)\sigma = 80 + (1.96)(15) = 109.4.$$

If the observed yield y lies in the interval 50.6 to 109.4, the hypothesis $E(Y) = 80$ may be true or false. That is, $E(Y)$ may or may not equal 80. If the observed yield y is less than 50.6 or greater than 109.4, the hypothesis $E(Y) = 80$ is rejected. That is, the experimenter concludes that $E(Y)$ is not 80. Since this test is at the .05 significance level, he knows there is a 5 per cent chance of concluding $E(Y)$ is not 80, when $E(Y)$ is, in fact, 80.

Suppose the pharmaceutical company wants to test the hypothesis $E(P) = 0$ at a significance level α of .01. Since $D(P) = 10$, the cut-off points for the test based on an observation of one person are

$$c_1 = \mu_0 - z\left(\frac{\alpha}{2}\right)\sigma = 0 - (2.58)(10) = -25.8,$$

$$c_2 = \mu_0 + z\left(\frac{\alpha}{2}\right)\sigma = 0 + (2.58)(10) = 25.8.$$

If the observed change in blood pressure lies in the interval -25.8 to 25.8, then the drug may or may not affect $E(P)$ for the whole population. If the observed change in blood pressure is less than -25.8 or greater than 25.8, the company concludes at the .01 level that the drug affects $E(P)$ for the whole population.

It appears that the experimenter should be hoping for a false conclusion, since this leads to the more definite belief concerning the hypothesis. This often is the experimenter's position, especially when it is possible to state the hypothesis so that it is the negative of some statement of interest. If the test rejects the hypothesis, then the interesting statement is established. This might be the position of the developer of the new variety of wheat. He might like to prove that the new variety differs from the old. To do it, he attempts to disprove the hypothesis $E(Y) = 80$. Similarly, the pharmaceutical company might wish to prove that the new drug does affect $E(P)$ by disproving the hypothesis $E(P) = 0$.

A slightly different hypothesis for the expected value μ is that it is less than or equal to a given number. In symbols, $\mu \leq \mu_0$ is this hypothesis, where μ_0 is known. The variance σ^2 is assumed known, and there is only one observation of X. We seek a new conclusion to follow this new hypothesis in a conditional statement. Since the hypothesis says that a typical value for X is less than or equal to μ_0, a conclusion might be of the general form,

$$x \text{ is not too large.}$$

In terms of a temporarily unspecified constant, this conclusion is $x < c$. The conditional statement is now

$$\text{if } \mu \leq \mu_0, \text{ then } x < c.$$

A particular value for c determines a significance test, because an outcome x greater than c rejects the hypothesis $\mu \leq \mu_0$.

Identifying the significance level is slightly different. When $\mu = \mu_0$, let $1 - \alpha$ be the probability.

$$\Pr\{X < c\} = 1 - \alpha.$$

A restatement of this is

$$\Pr\{c \leq X\} = \alpha,$$

when $\mu = \mu_0$. When $\mu < \mu_0$, the corresponding statements are

$$\Pr\{X < c\} > 1 - \alpha \quad \text{and} \quad \Pr\{c \leq X\} < \alpha.$$

Therefore, when $\mu \leq \mu_0$,

$$\Pr\{X < c\} \geq 1 - \alpha \quad \text{and} \quad \Pr\{c \leq X\} \leq \alpha.$$

The significance level is defined as the largest probability of rejecting a true hypothesis; this is still α.

When the experimenter selects the significance level α, he again selects the test c. The relation between them is

$$\Pr\{c \leq X\} = \Pr\left\{\frac{c - \mu_0}{\sigma} \leq \frac{X - \mu_0}{\sigma}\right\} = \Pr\left\{\frac{c - \mu_0}{\sigma} \leq Z\right\} = \alpha,$$

when $\mu = \mu_0$. Therefore,

$$\frac{c - \mu_0}{\sigma} = z(\alpha) \quad \text{and} \quad c = \mu_0 + z(\alpha)\sigma.$$

When the observed outcome x is greater than $c = \mu_0 + z(\alpha)\sigma$, the hypothesis $\mu \le \mu_0$ is rejected.

There is a similar discussion for the hypothesis that μ is greater than or equal to a given number μ_0. That is, $\mu_0 \le \mu$ is the hypothesis. A level α significance test rejects, if the outcome x is less than $c = \mu_0 - z(\alpha)\sigma$.

Hypotheses of this one-sided form might be reasonable for the examples of this section. Suppose the developer of the new variety of wheat is interested in selling it only if it gives a greater yield than the old variety. To prove the superiority he formulates the hypothesis $E(Y) \le 80$ that it is inferior, and he tries to disprove it. At a significance level of $\alpha = .05$, the cut-off point for this test is

$$c = \mu_0 + z(\alpha)\sigma = 80 + (1.65)(15) = 104.75.$$

If the observed yield y is less than 104.75, the new variety may or may not be inferior. If the observed yield is greater than 104.75, the hypothesis is rejected; and the superiority of the new variety is established.

The pharmaceutical company might want to prove that the new drug reduces the expected blood pressure for the whole population. The company assumes the negative hypothesis $E(P) \ge 0$ and tries to disprove it. At a significance level of $\alpha = .01$, the cut-off point for this test is

$$c = \mu_0 - z(\alpha)\sigma = 0 - (2.33)(10) = -23.3.$$

If the blood pressure of the one person in the experiment drops more than 23.3, the hypothesis is rejected, and the company concludes that the drug lowers the expected blood pressure for the population as a whole.

A significance test for $\mu = \mu_0$ is *two-sided*, because this hypothesis is rejected when the outcome is too small or too large. A test for $\mu \le \mu_0$ (or $\mu \ge \mu_0$) is *one-sided*, because this hypothesis is rejected only when the outcome is too large (or small).

To construct either a two-sided or a one-sided significance test for some hypothesis H, the experimenter first selects a significance level α. From this, he calculates directly the cut-off points, or the cut-off point, for the test. Clearly, the choice of significance level α is important for the final decision about H. Since rejection of H is usually the experimenter's desire and since a large α makes rejection easier, the experimenter feels some pressure to select a large α. On the other hand, a large significance level α leads to a test with a high probability of rejecting H when it is actually true. The possibility of this error creates pressure to select a small α. The proper α depends on the particular experiment and the contemplated actions following the test. In general discussions, it is conventional to pick .05 or .01 for α. With $\alpha = .05$, for example, a true H is rejected about one time in twenty tests. Later sections of this chapter return to this problem.

These significance tests are easily modified to use the outcomes from a random sample of size n. To illustrate for the hypothesis $\mu = \mu_0$, let $x_1, x_2, \ldots, x_n$ be the outcomes of the random sample. The variable X has a normal distribution with known variance σ^2. We seek a conclusion for the conditional statement. Consider the random properties of the sample mean:

$$E(\bar{X}) = E(X) = \mu,$$

$$V(\bar{X}) = \frac{V(X)}{n} = \frac{\sigma^2}{n},$$

$$D(\bar{X}) = \frac{D(X)}{\sqrt{n}} = \frac{\sigma}{\sqrt{n}}.$$

From this point on, the discussion with $\bar{x}$ is almost identical to the previous case with x. If $\mu = \mu_0$, then μ_0 is a typical value for $\bar{X}$. Again, a conclusion might be of the form

$$c_1 < \bar{x} < c_2,$$

where

$$\Pr\{c_1 < \bar{X} < c_2\} = 1 - \alpha,$$

and

$$\Pr\{\bar{X} \leq c_1\} = \Pr\{c_2 \leq \bar{X}\} = \frac{\alpha}{2}.$$

Therefore,

$$\frac{c_2 - \mu_0}{\sigma/\sqrt{n}} = z\left(\frac{\alpha}{2}\right) \quad \text{and} \quad c_2 = \mu_0 + z\left(\frac{\alpha}{2}\right)\frac{\sigma}{\sqrt{n}}.$$

Similarly,

$$c_1 = \mu_0 - z\left(\frac{\alpha}{2}\right)\frac{\sigma}{\sqrt{n}}.$$

The resulting significance test of level α is

$$\text{reject if } \bar{x} \leq \mu_0 - z\left(\frac{\alpha}{2}\right)\frac{\sigma}{\sqrt{n}} \quad \text{or} \quad \mu_0 + z\left(\frac{\alpha}{2}\right)\frac{\sigma}{\sqrt{n}} \leq \bar{x}.$$

One-sided tests are simple modifications of this test.

For a numerical illustration, assume the developer of the new variety of wheat is interested in the hypothesis $E(Y) = 80$. The yield Y has a normal distribution with $D(Y) = 15$. Take a random sample of 9 fields. If $\alpha = .05$, the cut-off points for the test are

$$c_1 = \mu_0 - z\left(\frac{\alpha}{2}\right)\frac{\sigma}{\sqrt{n}} = 80 - (1.96)\left(\frac{15}{\sqrt{9}}\right) = 70.2,$$

$$c_2 = \mu_0 + z\left(\frac{\alpha}{2}\right)\frac{\sigma}{\sqrt{n}} = 80 + (1.96)\left(\frac{15}{\sqrt{9}}\right) = 89.8.$$

If the observed sample mean $\bar{y}$ is less than 70.2 or greater than 89.8, the developer concludes that the new variety differs from the old.

For a second numerical illustration, assume the pharmaceutical company is interested in the hypothesis $E(P) \geq 0$. The change in a person's blood pressure P has a normal distribution with $D(P) = 10$. Take a random sample of 50 persons from the population. If $\alpha = .01$, the cut-off point for the test is

$$c = \mu_0 - z(\alpha)\frac{\sigma}{\sqrt{n}} = 0 - (2.33)\left(\frac{10}{\sqrt{50}}\right) = -3.30.$$

If the mean change of the 50 persons is a drop of more than 3.30, the company concludes that the expected blood pressure is lower for the new drug.

EXERCISES

2. X has a normal distribution with $\sigma = 2$. A hypothesis is $\mu = 10$.
   a) For one observation of X, a test is

   $$\text{reject if } x \leq 8 \text{ or } 12 \leq x.$$

   What is the significance level of this test?
   b) For a random sample of size 4, a test is

   $$\text{reject if } \bar{x} \leq 8 \text{ or } 12 \leq \bar{x}.$$

   What is the significance level of this test?

3. X is a continuous random variable with a uniform distribution. The density function is

$$f(x) = \frac{1}{\theta} \quad \text{for } 0 \leq x \leq \theta.$$

A hypothesis is $\theta = 2$. For one observation of X, a test is

$$\text{reject if } x \leq 0.8 \text{ or } 2 \leq x.$$

What is the significance level of this test?

4. X has a normal distribution with $\sigma = 10$. A hypothesis is $\mu \leq 100$.
   a) For one observation of X, a significance test is

   $$\text{reject if } c \leq x.$$

   Find c if $\alpha = .05$.
   b) For a random sample of $n = 25$, a significance test is

   $$\text{reject if } c \leq \bar{x}.$$

   Find c if $\alpha = .05$.

5. X has a uniform distribution with density function

   $$f(x) = \frac{1}{\theta} \quad \text{for} \quad 0 \leq x \leq \theta.$$

   A hypothesis is $\theta \leq 2$. For one observation of X, a test is

   $$\text{reject if } c \leq x.$$

   Find c if $\alpha = .10$.

6. X has a normal distribution with $\sigma = 10$. The hypothesis is $90 \leq \mu \leq 100$. For one observation of X, a significance test is

   $$\text{reject if } x \leq 70 \text{ or } 120 \leq x.$$

   What is the significance level of this test?

Unknown Variance

In the more realistic significance testing situations for the expected value, the variance is also unknown. That is, the random variable X has a normal distribution with both parameters, μ and σ^2, unknown. A hypothesis about μ, such as $\mu = \mu_0$, is of interest. The previous test, which used σ, must be modified to account for this additional ignorance about X. The agricultural example is the same, except $D(Y)$ is now unknown. In the physiological example, $D(P)$ is unknown.

To prepare for the significance test we must discuss a new distribution. X has a normal distribution with parameters μ and σ^2. From a random sample of size n, $\bar{X}$ is the sample mean, and S is the sample standard deviation. Both are random variables with distributions of their own, which depend on σ. Define a new variable T by

$$T = \frac{\bar{X} - \mu}{S/\sqrt{n}}.$$

T is continuous with space $\{-\infty \text{ to } +\infty\}$. The density function for T is symmetric about the origin and looks like a normal density function. There is only one parameter ν for the distribution. The variable has a *t-distribution* with ν *degrees of freedom*. Numerically, ν equals $n - 1$ for this situation. Some critical values for significance tests appear in Table IV of the Appendix. The values are indicated by $t(\alpha, \nu)$, where

$$\Pr\{t(\alpha, \nu) \leq T\} = \alpha.$$

For example, $t(.05, 4) = 2.132$. By symmetry, $t(1 - \alpha, \nu) = -t(\alpha, \nu)$. Therefore, $t(.95, 4) = -t(.05, 4) = -2.132$. Also, note in Table IV that $t(\alpha, \nu)$ approaches $z(\alpha)$ as ν increases. This is shown in the last row as $t(\alpha, \infty) = z(\alpha)$.

With this new tool, let us return to the construction of a significance test for the hypothesis $\mu = \mu_0$, where μ_0 is a known number. From a random sample of size n, the conditional statement again might be

$$\text{if } \mu = \mu_0, \text{ then } c_1 < \bar{x} < c_2.$$

Let $1 - \alpha$ be the probability.

$$\Pr\{c_1 < \bar{X} < c_2\} = 1 - \alpha,$$

when $\mu = \mu_0$. The restatement is

$$\Pr\{\bar{X} \leq c_1\} = \Pr\{c_2 \leq \bar{X}\} = \frac{\alpha}{2},$$

when $\mu = \mu_0$. The calculation for c_2 is

$$\Pr\{c_2 \leq \bar{X}\} = \Pr\left\{\frac{c_2 - \mu_0}{S/\sqrt{n}} \leq \frac{\bar{X} - \mu_0}{S/\sqrt{n}}\right\} = \Pr\left\{\frac{c_2 - \mu_0}{S/\sqrt{n}} \leq T\right\} = \frac{\alpha}{2},$$

or

$$\frac{c_2 - \mu_0}{S/\sqrt{n}} = t\left(\frac{\alpha}{2}, n - 1\right).$$

The cut-off point C_2 is a function of S and is itself a random variable

$$C_2 = \mu_0 + t\left(\frac{\alpha}{2}, n - 1\right)\frac{S}{\sqrt{n}}.$$

By the symmetry of the *t*-distribution,

$$C_1 = \mu_0 - t\left(\frac{\alpha}{2}, n - 1\right)\frac{S}{\sqrt{n}}.$$

After the experiment, $S = s$ is observed, and the level α test is

$$\text{reject if } \bar{x} \le \mu_0 - t\left(\frac{\alpha}{2}, n-1\right)\frac{s}{\sqrt{n}} \quad \text{or} \quad \mu_0 + t\left(\frac{\alpha}{2}, n-1\right)\frac{s}{\sqrt{n}} \le \bar{x}.$$

One-sided tests are obvious modifications of this test.

For the first numerical illustration, suppose the developer of the new variety of wheat is interested in the hypothesis $E(Y) = 80$. In a random sample of 9 fields, let the results be $\bar{y} = 91.0$ and $s = 11.0$. If $\alpha = .05$, the cut-off points are

$$c_1 = \mu_0 - t\left(\frac{\alpha}{2}, n-1\right)\frac{s}{\sqrt{n}} = 80 - (2.306)\left(\frac{11}{\sqrt{9}}\right) = 71.5,$$

$$c_2 = \mu_0 - t\left(\frac{\alpha}{2}, n-1\right)\frac{s}{\sqrt{n}} = 80 + (2.306)\left(\frac{11}{\sqrt{9}}\right) = 88.5.$$

Since $\bar{y} = 91.0$ is greater than 88.5, the hypothesis is rejected, and the difference of the new variety is established.

In the second numerical example, suppose the company is interested in the hypothesis $E(P) \ge 0$. In a random sample of 50 persons, let the results be $\bar{p} = -7.7$ and $s = 11.0$. If $\alpha = .01$, the cut-off point is

$$c = \mu_0 - t(\alpha, n-1)\frac{s}{\sqrt{n}} = 0 - (2.33)\left(\frac{11}{\sqrt{50}}\right) = -3.62.$$

Since $\bar{p} = -7.7$ is less than -3.62, the hypothesis is rejected.

Throughout this discussion, it is assumed that the basic random variable X has a normal distribution. When this is true, the tests of this section are strictly correct. These tests, however, are widely used even when X is not normal. If X is not normal, the Central Limit Theorem says that $\bar{X}$ is approximately normal, when n is large. It is primarily the normality of $\bar{X}$ that justifies the derivations of these tests.

Summary. Let X be a normally distributed random variable with expected value μ and variance σ^2. A hypothesis for the expected value is $\mu = \mu_0$, where μ_0 is a known number. If σ^2 is unknown, a level α significance test from a random sample of size n is

$$\text{reject if } \bar{x} \le \mu_0 - t\left(\frac{\alpha}{2}, n-1\right)\frac{s}{\sqrt{n}} \quad \text{or} \quad \mu_0 + t\left(\frac{\alpha}{2}, n-1\right)\frac{s}{\sqrt{n}} \le x.$$

If n is large (greater than 30), replace $t\left(\dfrac{\alpha}{2}, n-1\right)$ by $z\left(\dfrac{\alpha}{2}\right)$. If σ is known, replace $t\left(\dfrac{\alpha}{2}, n-1\right)$ by $z\left(\dfrac{\alpha}{2}\right)$ and s by σ. For one-sided tests, use only one of the inequalities and replace $\dfrac{\alpha}{2}$ by α.

EXERCISES

7. X has a normal distribution with unknown μ and unknown σ. A hypothesis for μ is $\mu = 100$. In a random sample of size $n = 16$, the results are $\bar{x} = 112$ and $s = 28$.
   a) At the .01 level, what is the significance test?
   b) Do the experimental results reject the hypothesis?

8. A company manufactures one type of automobile tire and tests it in the laboratory. In the test, the tire rolls continuously in a small circle. The life of the tire X, in miles, is a random variable. Suppose the distribution is normal with $\mu = 25{,}000$ and $\sigma = 2000$.
   a) Discuss some of the possible physical problems involved in defining and measuring the life of one particular tire.
   b) How do you think the distribution for the laboratory would compare to the distribution for all actual users on the road?
   A modification in the tire manufacturing process, which might change μ, is proposed.
   c) Discuss two possible testing situations for the new process.

   $$\text{hypothesis: } \mu = 25{,}000 \qquad\qquad \text{hypothesis: } \mu \leq 25{,}000$$

   d) Speculate on the difficulties of actually getting a random sample produced by the new process and tested in the laboratory.
   e) Does it seem reasonable to assume $\sigma = 2000$ for the new process? Why would one like to make this assumption?
   f) For a very small significance level, the company is very unlikely to make a certain incorrect decision. Interpret this error in the one-sided situation.

9. For the one-sided situation with $\sigma = 2000$ in exercise 8 c), construct a significance test at the .05 level. Take $n = 6$.

10. For the two-sided situation with unknown σ in exercise 8 c), do $n = 6$, $\bar{x} = 30{,}000$ and $s = 2200$ reject the hypothesis at the .01 level?

11. At what significance level does $\bar{x} = 27{,}000$ reject the hypothesis for the one-sided situation with $\sigma = 2000$ in exercise 8 c)? Take $n = 6$ again.

12. Suppose the I.Q.'s of the students at Colwell College have a normal distribution. It is claimed that the average I.Q. is at least 120. A random sample of 16 students showed

$$\text{sample mean} = 110,$$

$$\text{sample standard deviation} = 12.$$

Is this difference significant at the .05 level?

13. The Houlahan brothers made 500 sales in their used-car business last year. They claimed gross sales of not more than $500,000. A tax investigator wants to check their claim and makes a spot check of 36 sales:

$$\text{mean sale price} = \$1{,}080,$$

$$\text{standard deviation} = \$\ 400.$$

At the .05 level, should the investigator, who seeks fraudulent claims, begin legal proceedings against the Houlahan brothers?

14. A machine puts cereal in boxes. The net weight in the boxes has a normal distribution with $\sigma = 0.4$ ounces. The operator of the machine claims $\mu = 12$ ounces. If he is right, the operation should continue. If he is wrong, the machine should be stopped and adjusted. The decision is to be made from a sample of four boxes.
a) What is the significance test of the claim at the .01 level?
b) What two errors can be made in this situation?
c) Which of the errors in b) is considered in the test in a)?
d) Which of the errors in b) is not considered in the test in a)?

15. Professor Kopcha has developed a new method for teaching sixth-grade arithmetic. Sixth-grade classes in his state take an achievement test. Each class is graded as a group. Every year, the state-wide average is 75 on the test. Kopcha and his three associates select four sixth grades at random and teach the arithmetic this year. The scores for their classes are 90, 85, 92, and 93.
a) At the .01 level, are these results significantly better than past performances with the old method?
b) Based on the result in a), Professor Kopcha claims his new method is superior. Comment.

1.2 PROPORTION FOR A BERNOULLI DISTRIBUTION

A random experiment with a Bernoulli distribution has essentially only one parameter, the proportion θ. A common statistical hypothesis is $\theta = \theta_0$, where θ_0 is a known number. If X is the corresponding random variable, recall that the space is $\{0, 1\}$, $\Pr\{1\} = \theta$, $\Pr\{0\} = 1 - \theta$, $E(X) = \theta$, $V(X) = \theta(1 - \theta)$, and $D(X) = \sqrt{\theta(1 - \theta)}$.

Gambling Example. A roulette player suspects that a certain wheel is unbalanced. To prove it to himself he sets up a hypothesis that it is not, and tries to disprove it. If the wheel is perfectly balanced, red and black should come up equally often in the long run. If the wheel has another possible outcome, he wants to ignore it. Let $R = 1$ for a red outcome and $R = 0$ for a black. Then for a balanced wheel, the hypothesis is $E(R) = .50$. If the wheel is unbalanced, the hypothesis $E(R) = .50$ is false.

With the outcomes $x_1, x_2, \ldots, x_n$ of a random sample for X, we seek a conclusion to follow the hypothesis $\theta = \theta_0$. Consider the sample mean $\bar{x}$:

$$E(\bar{X}) = E(X) = \theta,$$

$$V(\bar{X}) = \frac{V(X)}{n} = \frac{\theta(1 - \theta)}{n},$$

$$D(\bar{X}) = \frac{D(X)}{\sqrt{n}} = \sqrt{\frac{\theta(1 - \theta)}{n}}.$$

If the hypothesis $\theta = \theta_0$ is true, θ_0 is a typical value for $\bar{X}$. The conclusion might be of the general form

$$c_1 < \bar{x} < c_2,$$

where θ_0 lies in the interval from c_1 to c_2. The conditional statement is now

$$\text{if } \theta = \theta_0, \text{ then } c_1 < \bar{x} < c_2.$$

If the observed $\bar{x}$ is less than c_1 or greater than c_2, the hypothesis is rejected as false.

The significance level α and the cut-off points are related by

$$\Pr\{c_1 < \bar{X} < c_2\} = 1 - \alpha,$$

$$\Pr\{\bar{X} \leq c_1\} = \Pr\{c_2 \leq \bar{X}\} = \frac{\alpha}{2},$$

when $\theta = \theta_0$. To solve for c_2, use the Central Limit Theorem and

$$\Pr\{c_2 \le \bar{X}\} = \Pr\left\{\frac{c_2 - \theta_0}{D(\bar{X})} \le \frac{\bar{X} - \theta_0}{D(\bar{X})}\right\} = \Pr\left\{\frac{c_2 - \theta_0}{D(\bar{X})} \le Z\right\} = \frac{\alpha}{2}$$

to get

$$\frac{c_2 - \theta_0}{D(\bar{X})} = z\left(\frac{\alpha}{2}\right) \text{ or } c_2 = \theta_0 + z\left(\frac{\alpha}{2}\right)D(\bar{X}) = \theta_0 + z\left(\frac{\alpha}{2}\right)\sqrt{\frac{\theta_0(1 - \theta_0)}{n}}.$$

Similarly,

$$c_1 = \theta_0 - z\left(\frac{\alpha}{2}\right)\sqrt{\frac{\theta_0(1 - \theta_0)}{n}}.$$

Note that a discussion of the t-distribution for an unknown variance is not relevant here, because the assumed value of θ determines the variance of $\bar{X}$.

The roulette player watches the next 89 spins of the wheel and observes 54 red outcomes. Does this prove the wheel is unbalanced at the .01 level? The observed sample mean is $\bar{r} = 54/89 = .61$. The cut-off points are

$$c_1 = \theta_0 - z\left(\frac{\alpha}{2}\right)\sqrt{\frac{\theta_0(1 - \theta_0)}{n}} = .50 - (2.58)\sqrt{\frac{(.5)(.5)}{89}} = .36,$$

$$c_2 = \theta_0 + z\left(\frac{\alpha}{2}\right)\sqrt{\frac{\theta_0(1 - \theta_0)}{n}} = .50 + (2.58)\sqrt{\frac{(.5)(.5)}{89}} = .64.$$

The player cannot conclude the wheel is unbalanced at $\alpha = .01$.

Summary. Let X be a random variable with a Bernoulli distribution with proportion $\theta = \Pr\{1\} = E(X)$. A hypothesis for the proportion is $\theta = \theta_0$, where θ_0 is a known number. For a random sample of size n, the significance test of level α is (approximately)

reject if
$$\bar{x} \le \theta_0 - z\left(\frac{\alpha}{2}\right)\sqrt{\frac{\theta_0(1 - \theta_0)}{n}}$$

or
$$\theta_0 + z\left(\frac{\alpha}{2}\right)\sqrt{\frac{\theta_0(1 - \theta_0)}{n}} \le \bar{x}.$$

For one-sided tests, use only one of the inequalities and replace $\frac{\alpha}{2}$ by α.

EXERCISES

16. It is well known that 60 per cent of the people with a certain disease recover in a one-month period without any treatment. A pharmaceutical company has a new drug that might be effective for the disease. Let X be the random variable for the number of recoveries

(0 or 1) in less than one month when a diseased person is given the drug. X has a Bernoulli distribution, and a hypothesis for the proportion θ who recover with the new drug is $\theta \leq .60$. Twenty people are given the drug.

a) At the .01 level, how large must $\bar{x}$ be to reject the hypothesis?

b) Suppose the authorities require significance at the .01 level to allow public sales, and suppose $\bar{x} = .75$. What can the company do?

17. Wesner Foods has been getting 20 per cent of the potato chip market for many months. An advertising agency was retained, and a campaign was conducted. Wesner wants to evaluate the campaign quickly. A sample of 50 customers shows 38 per cent buying Wesner's chips now. Set up the hypothesis that the campaign had no positive effect. At the .10 level, does the campaign appear to have had a positive effect?

18. A marketing firm claims that exactly 1/3 of the TV viewers watch a given program. To test the claim, a sample of 100 viewers is taken. Set up the significance test at the .01 level. Contemplate the difficulties of getting a random sample.

19. Harvey, the quarterback on a professional football team, claims to complete at least 50 per cent of his passes. He is paid accordingly. In his first 120 tries, he completes 50. At what significance level can the management conclude Harvey is overpaid?

20. For a certain large population of couples, suppose 25 per cent of the marriages end in divorce in the first two years. Forty typical couples from this population will spend the first two years of their marriage in unusual conditions in a foreign country. At the .05 level, how many divorces will it take to suggest that the unusual conditions affect the divorce rate?

1.3 VARIANCE FOR A NORMAL DISTRIBUTION

Although interest in the expected value is more common, hypotheses concerning the variance do arise. Let X be the corresponding normally distributed random variable with unknown expected value μ and unknown variance of σ^2. Consider the hypothesis $\sigma^2 = \sigma_0^2$, where σ_0^2 is a known number. If the statement is not true, σ^2 is smaller or larger than σ_0^2. This hypothesis about the variance is equivalent to the hypothesis $\sigma = \sigma_0$ for the standard deviation. A significance test for one is easily modified to suit the other.

To prepare for the significance test, we must discuss a new distribution. Let X have a normal distribution with parameters μ and σ^2. From a random sample of size n, S^2 is the sample variance. Define a new variable K by $K = (n-1)S^2/\sigma^2$. K is continuous with the space $\{0 \text{ to } +\infty\}$. There is one parameter ν. The variable has a *chi-square* distribution with ν *degrees of freedom*. Figure 1 is a graph of the density function for $\nu = 8$. Some critical values for significance tests appear in Table V of the Appendix. These values are indicated by $\chi^2(\alpha, \nu)$, where $\Pr\{\chi^2(\alpha, \nu) \leq K\} = \alpha$. For example, $\chi^2(.975, 8) = 2.18$ and $\chi^2(.025, 8) = 17.5$. These two points are marked on the horizontal axis of Figure 1.

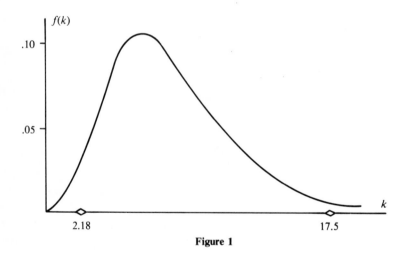

Figure 1

The chi-square distribution leads to a significance test for the hypothesis $\sigma^2 = \sigma_0^2$. From a random sample of size n, the conditional statement for the test might be

$$\text{if } \sigma^2 = \sigma_0^2, \text{ then } c_1 < s^2 < c_2,$$

where σ_0^2 lies in the interval from c_1 to c_2 and s^2 is the observed sample variance. As usual, let $1 - \alpha$ be the probability.

$$\Pr\{c_1 < S^2 < c_2\} = 1 - \alpha,$$

when $\sigma^2 = \sigma_0^2$. A restatement is

$$\Pr\{S^2 \le c_1\} = \Pr\{c_2 \le S^2\} = \frac{\alpha}{2}.$$

The derivation for c_2 is

$$\Pr\{c_2 \le S^2\} = \Pr\left\{\frac{(n-1)c_2}{\sigma_0^2} \le \frac{(n-1)S^2}{\sigma_0^2}\right\} = \Pr\left\{\frac{(n-1)c_2}{\sigma_0^2} \le K\right\} = \frac{\alpha}{2},$$

or

$$\frac{(n-1)c_2}{\sigma_0^2} = x^2\left(\frac{\alpha}{2}, n-1\right) \quad \text{and} \quad c_2 = \frac{x^2\left(\frac{\alpha}{2}, n-1\right)\sigma_0^2}{n-1}.$$

Similarly,

$$c_1 = \frac{x^2\left(1 - \frac{\alpha}{2}, n-1\right)\sigma_0^2}{n-1}.$$

If the observed sample variance s^2 is less than c_1 or greater than c_2, the hypothesis $\sigma^2 = \sigma_0^2$ is rejected as false at a significance level of α. The equivalent hypothesis $\sigma = \sigma_0$ is rejected, if the observed sample standard deviation s is less than $\sqrt{c_1}$ or greater than $\sqrt{c_2}$. One-sided tests are simple modifications of this two-sided test.

For the developer of the new variety of wheat, suppose he is interested in the hypothesis $V(Y) = 225$ or $D(Y) = 15$. If this is true, the new variety has the same variance as the old. If the hypothesis is false, the new variety has more or less variation in the region. At the .05 level, the cut-off points for $n = 9$ are

$$c_1 = \frac{x^2\left(1 - \frac{\alpha}{2}, n-1\right)\sigma_0^2}{n-1} = \frac{x^2(.975, 8)(225)}{8} = 61.3,$$

$$c_2 = \frac{x^2\left(\frac{\alpha}{2}, n-1\right)\sigma_0^2}{n-1} = \frac{x^2(.025, 8)(225)}{8} = 492.2.$$

If, for example, $s^2 = 121$, then the hypothesis cannot be rejected; $V(Y)$ may or may not be 225. The cut-off points for $D(Y) = 15$ are the square roots of 61.3 and 492.2. They are 7.8 and 22.2.

Summary. Let X be a normally distributed random variable with unknown expected value μ and unknown variance σ^2. A hypothesis for the variance is $\sigma^2 = \sigma_0^2$, where σ_0^2 is a known number. A level α significance test from a random sample of size n is

reject if $\quad s^2 \leq \dfrac{\chi^2\left(1 - \dfrac{\alpha}{2}, n - 1\right)\sigma_0^2}{n - 1} \quad$ or $\quad \dfrac{\chi^2\left(\dfrac{\alpha}{2}, n - 1\right)\sigma_0^2}{n - 1} \leq s^2.$

For one-sided tests, use only one of the inequalities and replace $\dfrac{\alpha}{2}$ by α.

EXERCISES

21. A random variable X has a normal distribution. From a sample of size $n = 5$, a significance test for the hypothesis $\sigma^2 = 100$ is

    reject if $s^2 \leq 17.8$ or $237.2 \leq s^2$.

    What is the significance level for this test?

22. A random variable X has a normal distribution. Construct a significance test at the .05 level for the hypothesis $\sigma^2 \geq 30$ from a random sample of size 10.

23. As in exercise 14 of this chapter, a machine fills cereal boxes. When it operates in the customary way, the weight in a box W has a normal distribution with $E(W) = 12$ ounces and $D(W) = 0.4$ ounces. If it is not operating in the customary way, the operator wants to stop the machine and find out why.
    a) From a random sample of four boxes, construct a test for the hypothesis $D(W) = 0.4$. Use $\alpha = .01$.
    b) For the test in a), .01 is the probability of making what mistake for the operator?
    c) What does $D(W) < 0.4$ mean to the operation?
    d) What does $D(W) > 0.4$ mean to the operation?

24. For a fixed setting on one of the army's cannons, the actual range of the projectile in yards has a normal distribution with a standard deviation of 60. A new type of ammunition is being considered. The army wants to know if the variation in range is smaller for the new ammunition. Twenty rounds will be fired at the fixed setting on the cannon. At the .05 level, set up the test that attempts to prove that the variation in range is smaller for the new ammunition.

1.4 EXPECTED VALUES FOR TWO NORMAL DISTRIBUTIONS

Scientific investigations frequently require complex experiments that are composed of more than one simple random experiment. In this subsection, the complex experiment consists of two single-valued random experiments, each with a normal distribution of probability. Some hypothesis about the two expected values is usually associated with the experiment. Let X_1 be the normally distributed random variable which is associated with one of the simple random experiments. The parameters are μ_1 and σ_1^2. Let X_2 be the other normally distributed random variable with parameters μ_2 and σ_2^2. X_1 and X_2 are independent. The hypothesis is usually a statement about $\mu_1 - \mu_2$, such as $\mu_1 - \mu_2 = 0$ or $\mu_1 - \mu_2 \leq 0$. The notation differs from some of the previous discussions, because X_1 and X_2 are not two observations of the same basic random variable X. Two familiar examples can be modified to illustrate these situations.

Agricultural Example. The developer of a new variety of wheat wants to compare it to the old variety in a particular geographic region. He does not know the distribution of yields for either variety. Let Y_1 refer to the experiment of picking a field at random from the region, planting the old variety, raising the crop, harvesting it, and measuring the yield per acre on the field. Y_2 is defined similarly for the new variety. If the varieties have the same expected yield, the hypothesis $E(Y_1) = E(Y_2)$ is true. If they have different expected yields, the hypothesis is false. An equivalent form of the hypothesis is $E(Y_1) - E(Y_2) = 0$.

Physiological Example. The pharmaceutical company wants to evaluate the effect of a new drug on blood pressure. Human beings may react to the drug, but they may also react to the ritual of receiving a drug. To separate these reactions, consider the experiment of selecting a person from some hypertensive population and giving him a placebo. The outcome is his change in blood pressure. Let P_1 be the corresponding random variable, where P_1 has a normal distribution. For the second experiment, a selected person is given the active drug. P_2 is the normally distributed variable corresponding to his change in blood pressure. Note that P_1 and P_2 are negative for a decrease in blood pressure. If the hypothesis $E(P_1) \leq E(P_2)$ is true, the placebo lowers expected blood pressure at least as much as the drug. If the hypothesis is false, the drug lowers expected blood pressure more than the placebo. To establish the efficacy of the drug for hypertension, the pharmaceutical company might want to disprove the hypothesis. An equivalent form for the hypothesis is $E(P_1) - E(P_2) \leq 0$.

We seek a significance test for the hypothesis $\mu_1 - \mu_2 = \mu_0$, where μ_0 is a known number. For the random variable X_1, a random sample of size n_1 is $x_{11}, x_{12}, x_{13}, \ldots, x_{1n_1}$. For X_2, a random sample of size n_2 is $x_{21}, x_{22}, x_{23}, \ldots, x_{2n_2}$. The two sample means are

$$\bar{x}_1 = \frac{\sum_{j=1}^{n_1} x_{1j}}{n_1} \quad \text{and} \quad \bar{x}_2 = \frac{\sum_{j=1}^{n_2} x_{2j}}{n_2}.$$

The random variable $\bar{X}_1 - \bar{X}_2$ is the difference of two normally distributed variables; thus it also has a normal distribution. The parameters are

$$E(\bar{X}_1 - \bar{X}_2) = E(\bar{X}_1) - E(\bar{X}_2) = \mu_1 - \mu_2,$$

$$V(\bar{X}_1 - \bar{X}_2) = V(\bar{X}_1) + V(\bar{X}_2) = \frac{\sigma_1^2}{n_1} + \frac{\sigma_2^2}{n_2}.$$

Since $\mu_1 - \mu_2$ is a typical value for $\bar{X}_1 - \bar{X}_2$, the conditional statement for the significance test might be of the form

$$\text{if } \mu_1 - \mu_2 = \mu_0, \text{ then } c_1 < \bar{x}_1 - \bar{x}_2 < c_2,$$

where μ_0 lies in the interval from c_1 to c_2. As usual, take $1 - \alpha$ to be the probability.

$$\Pr\{c_1 < \bar{X}_1 - \bar{X}_2 < c_2\} = 1 - \alpha,$$

or

$$\Pr\{\bar{X}_1 - \bar{X}_2 \le c_1\} = \Pr\{c_2 \le \bar{X}_1 - \bar{X}_2\} = \frac{\alpha}{2},$$

when $\mu_1 - \mu_2 = \mu_0$.

The relation between a significance test, the values of c_1 and c_2, and the significance level α depends on the sample sizes and the experimenter's knowledge of the variances of X_1 and X_2. Three cases are considered in this book.

CASE 1. The variances, σ_1^2 and σ_2^2, are both known. This is the simplest and least practical case. The calculation for c_2 is

$$\Pr\{c_2 \le \bar{X}_1 - \bar{X}_2\} = \Pr\left\{\frac{c_2 - \mu_0}{D(\bar{X}_1 - \bar{X}_2)} \le Z\right\} = \frac{\alpha}{2},$$

and

$$c_2 = \mu_0 + z\left(\frac{\alpha}{2}\right)D(\bar{X}_1 - \bar{X}_2) = \mu_0 + z\left(\frac{\alpha}{2}\right)\sqrt{\frac{\sigma_1^2}{n_1} + \frac{\sigma_2^2}{n_2}}.$$

Similarly,

$$c_1 = \mu_0 - z\left(\frac{\alpha}{2}\right)\sqrt{\frac{\sigma_1^2}{n_1} + \frac{\sigma_2^2}{n_2}}.$$

CASE 2. The variances, σ_1^2 and σ_2^2, are both unknown, but the sample sizes, n_1 and n_2, are both large; each is about 30 or more. When the sample sizes are this large, s_1^2 and s_2^2 are adequate approximations to σ_1^2 and σ_2^2. The cut-off points, c_1 and c_2, are as in case 1, with σ_1^2 replaced by s_1^2 and σ_2^2 replaced by s_2^2.

CASE 3. The variances are unknown, but they are known to be equal; that is, $\sigma_1^2 = \sigma_2^2$. See Chapter VII.

For a numerical illustration of the one-sided test for case 2, take the physiological example. The hypothesis $E(P_1) - E(P_2) \leq 0$ is rejected if

$$c = \mu_0 + z(\alpha)\sqrt{\frac{s_1^2}{n_1} + \frac{s_2^2}{n_2}} \leq \bar{p}_1 - \bar{p}_2,$$

where $\mu_0 = 0$. Take $\alpha = .01$, and suppose the two random samples yield

$$n_1 = 40 \qquad\qquad n_2 = 50$$

$$\bar{p}_1 = -4.1 \qquad\qquad \bar{p}_2 = -7.7$$

$$s_1 = 6.0 \qquad\qquad s_2 = 11.0$$

The cut-off point is

$$c = 0 + (2.33)\sqrt{\frac{(6.0)^2}{40} + \frac{(11.0)^2}{50}} = +4.25.$$

Since the observed $\bar{p}_1 - \bar{p}_2 = 3.6$, the experiment does not prove that the drug is more effective than a placebo. The data for P_2, the drug, are as in section 1.1 of this chapter. In that discussion, the hypothesis $E(P_2) \geq 0$ is disproved by these data. That is, the drug and the ritual of taking the drug do reduce the expected blood pressure for the population. The efficacy of the drug itself, however, is not established by these data.

Summary. Let X_1 and X_2 be independent, normally distributed random variables. Their expected values are μ_1 and μ_2, and their variances are σ_1^2 and σ_2^2. A hypothesis is $\mu_1 - \mu_2 = \mu_0$, where μ_0 is a known number. Two random samples of sizes n_1 and n_2 are taken. If the variances are known, a level α test of the hypothesis is

reject if $$\bar{x}_1 - \bar{x}_2 \leq \mu_0 - z\left(\frac{\alpha}{2}\right)\sqrt{\frac{\sigma_1^2}{n_1} + \frac{\sigma_2^2}{n_2}}$$

or $$\mu_0 + z\left(\frac{\alpha}{2}\right)\sqrt{\frac{\sigma_1^2}{n_1} + \frac{\sigma_2^2}{n_2}} \leq \bar{x}_1 - \bar{x}_2.$$

If σ_1^2 and σ_2^2 are unknown but n_1 and n_2 are large, replace σ_1^2 by s_1^2 and σ_2^2 by s_2^2. For one-sided tests, use only one of the inequalities and replace $\frac{\alpha}{2}$ by α.

EXERCISES

25. X_1 and X_2 are independent, normally distributed random variables with $\sigma_1 = 2$ and $\sigma_2 = 3$. Using one observation of each variable ($n_1 = 1$ and $n_2 = 1$), construct a significance test for each of the following situations. Use $\alpha = .05$.

   a) hypothesis: $\mu_1 - \mu_2 = 0$.
   b) hypothesis: $\mu_1 - \mu_2 \geq 5$.
   c) hypothesis: $\mu_1 \leq 3\mu_2$.
   d) hypothesis: $4\mu_1 + 3\mu_2 = 50$.

26. X_1 and X_2 are normally distributed random variables with $\sigma_1^2 = 10$ and $\sigma_2^2 = 15$. Construct a test for the hypothesis $\mu_1 = \mu_2$ at the .01 level. Take $n_1 = 5$ and $n_2 = 3$.

27. The length of time that a coat of house paint remains on a board is a random variable. Suppose the distribution is normal. There are two brands, and the manufacturer of the expensive brand would like to claim that his paint will outlast the cheap one by more than 12 months. Let X_1 and X_2 be the variables for the expensive and cheap paints, respectively. To establish the claim, he tries to disprove the hypothesis $\mu_1 - \mu_2 \leq 12$. Each brand is independently tested with the following results:

$$n_1 = 100 \qquad n_2 = 30$$
$$\bar{x}_1 = 44 \qquad \bar{x}_2 = 28$$
$$s_1 = 14 \qquad s_2 = 9$$

   At the .05 level, can the hypothesis be rejected?

28. On the basis of the experimental results in exercise 27, the manufacturer of the expensive brand publicly claims that his brand outlasts the other by at least 12 months. Now, consider this claim from the viewpoint of a civic agency which wants to expose false advertising. For a new experimental program, set up the hypothesis with the same symbols.

29. For the two varieties of wheat, variables Y_1 and Y_2 of this section, the hypothesis is $E(Y_1) - E(Y_2) = 0$. At $\alpha = .05$, do the following data prove a difference in expected yields?

$$n_1 = 9 \qquad n_2 = 9$$
$$\bar{y}_1 = 82.3 \qquad \bar{y}_2 = 91.0$$

$\sigma_1 = \sigma_2 = 15$ is assumed known.

2
Decision Procedures

A *decision procedure* is a rule for choosing one of two statistical hypotheses about a random experiment. One of them is true, and the other is false. The decision maker, who does not know which is true, must accept one hypothesis as true, thereby rejecting the other as false. Accepting the first hypothesis leads to one plan for action, while accepting the second leads to a completely different plan for action. Often, the decision maker is not especially interested in proving either hypothesis to some wide audience, such as the scientific world. He is more interested in choosing from the two plans of action, when he is uncertain about the true hypothesis. To help himself make the decision, he performs the experiment several times. The decision rule associates one set of outcomes with accepting the first hypothesis; it associates the remaining outcomes with accepting the second hypothesis.

There are four possible combinations for this decision situation. Let H_1 and H_2 be the two hypotheses. One of them is true. There are two decisions: accept H_1 or accept H_2. The following chart shows the four combinations.

		Reality	
		H_1 is true	H_2 is true
Decision	accept H_1	correct	error II
	accept H_2	error I	correct

Accepting H_1 when it is true is a correct decision; accepting H_2 when it is true is also a correct decision. Accepting H_2 when H_1 is true is an error, called a *type I error*. That is, the decision maker follows the plan of action for H_2 when the other plan is appropriate. Presumably, he suffers some loss by the error. Accepting H_1 when H_2 is true is an error, called a *type II error*. In most situations the losses from these errors are very different.

The proper decision procedure for a particular H_1 and H_2 balances the losses from the two errors. A procedure with no chance of making either error is usually unobtainable. It is either impossible, or it is too expensive. The decision maker must decide with what chance he is willing to accept H_2, when H_1 is actually true; he must also decide with what chance he is willing to accept H_1, when H_2 is actually true. These chances are expressed as probabilities. A proper decision procedure does not exceed these probabilities.

Bakery Example. This example is one of quality control, where clearly defined decision situations exist. A commercial bakery produces cheese cakes for which a principal ingredient is baker's cheese. Suppose the baker's cheese is purchased in large shipments from various suppliers. A shipment from a supplier consists of many separate packages. Each has a per cent moisture content which varies from package to package. To make good cheese cakes the average moisture content of all the packages in a shipment is not to exceed 75 per cent. Consider the experiment of selecting a package at random from a particular shipment and measuring the per cent of moisture. Let M be the random variable, and let M have a normal distribution with unknown expected value $E(M)$ and known standard deviation $D(M) = 3$. Two hypotheses are:

first hypothesis: shipment satisfactory   or $E(M) \leq 75$,
second hypothesis: shipment unsatisfactory or $E(M) > 75$.

If the first hypothesis is true, the bakery wants to receive the shipment and pay for it. If the second hypothesis is true, the bakery wants to return the shipment to the supplier. These are the two plans of action. Accepting the second hypothesis when the first is true is an error. In this example, it is the error of returning a satisfactory shipment. If the bakery does this too often, the supplier will probably raise his price for the baker's cheese. Accepting the first hypothesis when the second is true is the other error. In this example, it is the error of receiving an unsatisfactory shipment. The bakery must bear the cost of correcting this in production.

After considering the costs of these errors, the bakery decides that it is willing to tolerate a 5 per cent chance of returning the shipment when $E(M) = 75$. Also, it is willing to tolerate a 20 per cent chance of receiving the shipment when $E(M) = 77$. The problem is to design a decision procedure that meets these limitations. The procedure is to be based on the outcomes of several moisture measurements.

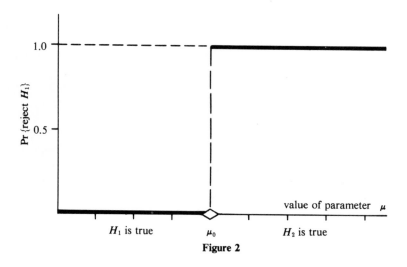

Figure 2

Every decision procedure has its own graph which is useful for evaluating the procedure. Competing decision procedures are conveniently compared by their graphs. For a particular procedure, consider the probability of rejecting H_1, Pr{reject H_1}. For those values of the unknown parameter that make H_1 true, Pr{reject H_1} is the probability of a type I error. For those values of the unknown parameter that make H_2 true, rejecting H_1 is a correct decision; therefore, Pr{reject H_1} is one minus the probability of a type II error. At one extreme, Figure 2 might be the graph of a perfect decision procedure. The possible values of the parameter are along the horizontal axis. In this case, small values of the parameter happen to correspond to a true H_1, and large values correspond to a true H_2. Pr{reject H_1} is on the vertical axis. For this perfect procedure, Pr{reject H_1} is zero, when H_1 is true; Pr{reject H_1} is one, when H_2 is true.

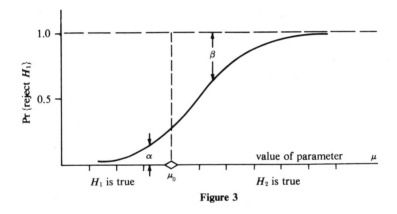

Figure 3

Figure 3 is more representative of practical decision procedures. When H_1 is true, Pr{reject H_1} is low, but not zero. The letter α is used for the probability of a type I error. A typical α is shown on the graph. When H_2 is true, Pr{reject H_1} is high, but not one. The letter β is used for the probability of a type II error. A typical β is shown on the graph.

The relation between the actual value of the parameter and the probability of rejecting H_1, Pr{reject H_1}, is the *power function* for the particular decision procedure. That is, Figure 3 is the graph of a power function. The power function and its graph completely characterize a decision procedure. Two or more procedures are compared by their power functions.

Using the bakery example we can graph the power functions for several different decision procedures. Recall that the per cent moisture M in a package has a normal distribution with $E(M) = ?$ and $D(M) = 3$. The hypotheses are

first hypothesis: $E(M) \leq 75$,

second hypothesis: $E(M) > 75$.

Initially, take a sample of only one package. Since $E(M)$ is a typical value for M, a decision procedure might be of the form

accept H_1 if $m < c$,

accept H_2 (reject H_1) if $c \leq m$.

For each value of c, the power function is

$$\Pr\{\text{reject } H_1\} = \Pr\{c \leq M\} = \Pr\left\{\frac{c - E(M)}{3} \leq Z\right\}.$$

Figure 4 shows the power functions for $c = 72, 75, 78, 81,$ and 84.

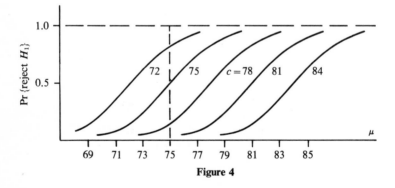

Figure 4

In order to discuss the curves in Figure 4, take two possible values of the expected value: $E(M) = 75$, which makes H_1 true, and $E(M) = 77$, which makes H_2 true. For the cut-off point $c = 78$, the power is

$$\Pr\{\text{reject } H_1\} = .16 = \alpha \text{ at } E(M) = 75,$$

$$\Pr\{\text{reject } H_1\} = .37 = 1 - \beta \text{ at } E(M) = 77.$$

Thus, this decision procedure has only a .16 probability of returning a shipment with 75 per cent moisture, but it has a .63 probability of accepting a shipment with 77 per cent moisture. Whether this is a good procedure or not depends on the consequences of these errors. With another c, the probability of one type of error may be lowered; however, this raises the probability of the other type of error. Figure 4 makes this point. The way to lower both α and β is to take a bigger sample.

The power function also depends on the sample size. To illustrate for the bakery, suppose $\alpha = .16$ at $E(M) = 75$ is satisfactory. If the bakery now samples five packages, a decision procedure might be

$$\text{accept } H_1 \text{ if } \bar{m} < c,$$

$$\text{accept } H_2 \text{ (reject } H_1\text{) if } c \leq \bar{m}.$$

To keep the same α at $E(M) = 75$, the cut-off point comes from

$$\alpha = .16 = \text{Pr}\{c \leq \bar{M}\} = \text{Pr}\left\{\frac{c - 75}{3/\sqrt{5}} \leq Z\right\},$$

and

$$\frac{c - 75}{3/\sqrt{5}} = z(.16) = 1.00 \quad \text{or} \quad c = 75 + \frac{3}{\sqrt{5}} = 76.34.$$

At $E(M) = 77$, the power of this procedure is

$$\text{Pr}\{\text{reject } H_1\} = \text{Pr}\{76.34 \leq \bar{M}\} = \text{Pr}\left\{\frac{76.34 - 77}{3/\sqrt{5}} \leq Z\right\}$$

$$= \text{Pr}\{-.49 \leq Z\} = .69.$$

Therefore, $\beta = 1 - \text{power} = 1 - .69 = .31$. If ten packages are sampled, the cut-off point comes from

$$\alpha = .16 = \{\text{Pr } c \leq \bar{M}\} = \text{Pr}\left\{\frac{c - 75}{3/\sqrt{10}} \leq Z\right\}$$

and

$$\frac{c - 75}{3/\sqrt{10}} = z(.16) = 1.00 \quad \text{or} \quad c = 75 + \frac{3}{\sqrt{10}} = 75.95.$$

At $E(M) = 77$, the power of this procedure is

$$\text{Pr}\{\text{reject } H_1\} = \text{Pr}\{75.95 \leq \bar{M}\} = \text{Pr}\left\{\frac{75.95 - 77}{3/\sqrt{10}} \leq Z\right\}$$

$$= \text{Pr}\{-1.11 \leq Z\} = .87.$$

Therefore, $\beta = 1 - \text{power} = 1 - .87 = .13$. Figure 5 shows the complete power functions for these three decision procedures:

$$c = 78.00 \quad \text{with} \quad n = 1,$$

$$c = 76.34 \quad \text{with} \quad n = 5,$$

$$c = 75.95 \quad \text{with} \quad n = 10.$$

The scales on the horizontal axes of Figures 4 and 5 are different; the curves for $c = 78$ and $n = 1$ are actually the same. Note in Figure 5 that the power function approaches that of a perfect power function as the sample size n increases. This is reasonable, because with complete inspection of the packages, the bakery knows the average moisture $E(M)$ without any uncertainty.

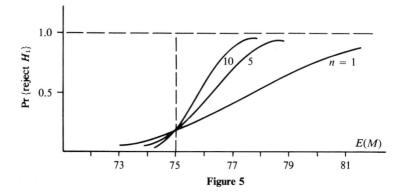

Figure 5

To get a satisfactory decision procedure directly, the decision maker frequently starts by specifying tolerable error probabilities, α and β, for two particular values of the parameters. The problem is then to find the appropriate sample size n and cut-off point c. For the bakery, $\alpha = .05$ at $E(M) = 75$ and $\beta = .20$ at $E(M) = 77$ are tolerable probabilities. Finding n and c leads to two simple equations in these two unknowns:

$$\alpha = .05 = \Pr\{c \le \bar{M}\} = \Pr\left\{\frac{c - 75}{3/\sqrt{n}} \le z\right\}$$

or

$$c = 75 + (1.65)\frac{3}{\sqrt{n}};$$

$$1 - \beta = .80 = \Pr\{c \le \bar{M}\} = \Pr\left\{\frac{c - 77}{3/\sqrt{n}} \le Z\right\}$$

or

$$c = 77 - (0.84)\frac{3}{\sqrt{n}}.$$

The solution is $n = 14$ and $c = 76.32$. That is, the bakery should sample 14 packages. If the mean moisture is less than 76.32 per cent, the shipment should be received; if the mean moisture is more than 76.32 per cent, the shipment should be returned to the supplier. With this procedure there is a .05 probability for making the error of returning a shipment with 75 per cent moisture; there is a .20 probability for making the error of receiving a shipment with 77 per cent moisture.

This illustration may be criticized, because assuming a knowledge of the variance is often unrealistic. The decision maker, however, can usually make a conservative (high) guess about the variance. The resulting decision procedure is at least as good as necessary.

Decision procedures are extensions of significance tests, not contradictions of them. There is a decision procedure corresponding to every significance test discussed in section 1 of this chapter. In symbols, let H be a hypothesis for a parameter of a random experiment. A significance test of level α is a rule for rejecting H as false. The power function associates a probability of rejection $\Pr\{\text{reject } H\}$ with every possible value of the parameter. When H is true, the probability $\Pr\{\text{reject } H\}$ is less than or equal to the significance level α. When H is false, the probability of rejection $\Pr\{\text{reject } H\}$ should be as large as possible.

Summary. In a decision situation, there are two hypotheses, H_1 and H_2, for an unknown parameter. A decision procedure is a rule that associates some outcomes of a random sample with accepting H_1 and the remaining outcomes with accepting H_2 (rejecting H_1). The power function characterizes a decision procedure. It associates the probability of rejecting H_1, $\Pr\{\text{reject } H_1\}$, with every possible value of the parameter. When H_1 is true, accepting H_2 is a type I error; the probability of this is α, where $\alpha = \Pr\{\text{reject } H_1\}$. When H_2 is true, accepting H_1 is a type II error; the probability of this is β, where $\beta = 1 - \Pr\{\text{reject } H_1\}$.

EXERCISES

30. In Shakespeare's *Hamlet*, read Hamlet's first soliloquy in scene 1 of act 3:

> *To be, or not to be: that is the question:*
> *Whether 'tis nobler in the mind to suffer*
> *The slings and arrows . . .*

Although this soliloquy is not concerned with a random experiment, consider the following decision situation:

> first hypothesis: There is a hereafter.
> second hypothesis: There is not a hereafter.

a) Interpret the four cases in the decision chart for Hamlet.
b) By his actions, Hamlet accepts which hypothesis?
c) Why does he make this decision?

31. The machine operator of exercise 14 (page 74) must choose between two hypotheses about the amount of cereal in a box W:

> first hypothesis: $E(W) = 12$.
> second hypothesis: $E(W) \neq 12$.

If $E(W) = 12$, he wants to let the machine run. If $E(W) \neq 12$, he wants to stop the machine and adjust it.
a) Interpret the four cases in the decision chart for this situation.
b) Sketch the power function for the perfect decision procedure.
c) From a sample of size 4, a decision procedure is
accept the first hypothesis, if $11.48 < \bar{w} < 12.52$,
accept the second hypothesis, if $\bar{w} \leq 11.48$ or $12.52 \leq \bar{w}$.
What is the power at $E(W) = 12.4$, if $D(W) = 0.4$?

32. In the test of exercise 2 a) (page 69), what is the power at $\mu = 6$, 8, 10, 12, and 14?

33. In the test of exercise 2 b), what is the power at $\mu = 6, 8, 10, 12$, and 14?

34. Suppose X is a continuous random variable with a uniform distribution:

$$f(x) = \frac{1}{\theta} \quad \text{for} \quad 0 \leq x \leq \theta \quad \text{and} \quad 0 < \theta.$$

A hypothesis for θ is $\theta = 2$. For one observation of X, a test is

reject if $x \leq .8$ or $2 \leq x$.

Recall from exercise 3 (page 69) that α is .40 for this test. What is the power of this test at $\theta = .5$, 1.0, and 3.0?

35. For the situation in exercise 34, suppose the test is

reject if $x \leq .4$ or $1.6 \leq x$.

a) What is the significance level of this test? Compare to exercise 34.

b) What is the power at $\theta = .5$, 1.0, and 3.0?

c) How does this test compare to the test in exercise 34?

36. Suppose the roulette player of subsection 1.2 in this chapter is actually in a decision situation.

first hypothesis: $E(R) = .50$.

second hypothesis: $E(R) \neq .50$.

R is the number of red outcomes on one spin of the wheel. Accepting the first hypothesis leads to going home without playing roulette; accepting the second hypothesis leads to playing roulette. A decision procedure for $n = 89$ is

accept the first hypothesis if $.36 < \bar{r} < .64$,

accept the second hypothesis if $\bar{r} \leq .36$ or $.64 \leq \bar{r}$.

a) What is the probability of his playing when he should go home?

b) What is the power at $E(R) = .60$?

c) What is the probability of his going home when red outcomes actually appear 60 per cent of the time?

37. In each of the four significance tests of exercise 25, what is the power for $\mu_1 = 8$ and $\mu_2 = 2$?

38. Weintraub, a real-estate developer, plans to plant many small trees in the next few years. Let θ be the proportion that will die in the first year under the proposed planting program. If θ is not more than about .10, he will be satisfied. If θ is as high as .20, he will be very dissatisfied with the proposed program. Weintraub wants to assume constant weather and to test his proposed planting program this year by planting n trees. His decision procedure is

continue program if $\bar{x} < c$,

use another program if $c \leq \bar{x}$,

where $\bar{x}$ is the proportion of trees that die. Find n and c so that .15 is the probability of changing to another program when $\theta = .10$, and .01 is the probability of continuing the present program, when $\theta = .20$.

39. For the two varieties of wheat, variables Y_1 and Y_2 in section 1.4 of this chapter, a decision situation is

first hypothesis: $E(Y_1) - E(Y_2) \geq 0$,

second hypothesis: $E(Y_1) - E(Y_2) < 0$.

If the first hypothesis is true, the old variety should be planted in the future; if the second is true, the new variety should be planted in the future. From two independent samples with $n_1 = n_2 = n$, a decision procedure is

accept the first hypothesis if $c < \bar{y}_1 - \bar{y}_2$,

accept the second hypothesis if $\bar{y}_1 - \bar{y}_2 \leq c$.

If the old variety is better by 3, the experimenter wants only a .05 probability of recommending the new variety. If the new variety is better by 7, he wants only a .05 probability of recommending the old variety. For purposes of experimental design, assume $\sigma_1 = \sigma_2 = 15$. Find n and c.

3

Minimax Procedures

A minimax procedure, which is a special type of decision procedure, uses the losses from a wrong decision to select the appropriate hypothesis. The possible losses are usually measured in monetary units. To use a minimax procedure, the decision maker must know these losses at the time of his decision.

As in the previous section, the problem is to choose from two hypotheses, H_1 and H_2, for a random experiment. One of them is true. A particular action follows the decision to accept H_1; a different action follows the decision to accept H_2. Accepting H_1 when H_1 is true is a correct decision with no resulting loss. Accepting H_2 when H_2 is true is also a correct decision with no resulting loss. Accepting H_2 when H_1 is true is a type I error. Let ℓ_1 be the loss from this error. Accepting H_1 when H_2 is true is a type II error. Let ℓ_2 be the loss from this error. The chart of losses for these four combinations is

		Reality	
		H_1 is true	H_2 is true
Decision	accept H_1	0	ℓ_2
	accept H_2	ℓ_1	0

For this simplified discussion, H_1 and H_2 must be statements that the parameter has one particular value. For an example with the normal distribution, $\mu = \mu_1$ and $\mu = \mu_2$ are two possible hypotheses, but hypotheses like $\mu \leq \mu_0$ and $\mu > \mu_0$ are not being discussed here.

Bakery Example, Modified. The bakery purchases baker's cheese in large shipments. Each shipment contains many separate packages. The per cent moisture M varies from package to package. Two hypotheses are

first hypothesis: $E(M) = 75$,
second hypothesis: $E(M) = 77$.

If the first hypothesis is true, the bakery wants to receive the shipment and pay for it. If the second hypothesis is true, the bakery wants to return the shipment to the supplier. Returning the shipment when $E(M) = 75$ is an error with a loss of $300. Receiving the shipment when $E(M) = 77$ is an error with a loss of $600.

Recall that a decision procedure is a rule that associates accepting H_1 with some of the outcomes of a random sample. Accepting H_2 is associated with the remaining outcomes. For a particular decision procedure, α is the probability of a type I error, and β is the probability of a type II error. The chart of probabilities is

		Reality	
		H_1 is true	H_2 is true
Decision	accept H_1	$1 - \alpha$	β
	accept H_2	α	$1 - \beta$

To each decision procedure, the decision maker can now calculate the maximum possible loss which he can expect with the procedure. This expected loss indicates the worst consequence from using the procedure. In this sense, the maximum expected loss measures the decision procedure. From the charts of losses and probabilities, the expected loss when H_1 is true is

$$0(1 - \alpha) + \ell_1 \alpha = \ell_1 \alpha.$$

The expected loss when H_2 is true is

$$\ell_2 \beta + 0(1 - \beta) = \ell_2 \beta.$$

The maximum expected loss is the larger of $\ell_1 \alpha$ and $\ell_2 \beta$.

The *minimax procedure* is the decision procedure which minimizes the maximum expected loss. With the minimax procedure, the maximum of $\ell_1 \alpha$ and $\ell_2 \beta$ is as small as possible. That is, the decision maker minimizes the worst possible consequence when he uses the minimax decision procedure.

For a numerical illustration with the modified bakery example, let the sample size be 4 and $D(M) = 3$. The general form of a decision procedure based on the sample mean is

$$\text{accept the hypothesis } E(M) = 75 \text{ if } \bar{m} < c,$$

$$\text{accept the hypothesis } E(M) = 77 \text{ if } c \le \bar{m}.$$

Each value of c determines a particular decision procedure.

If $E(M) = 75$, the expected loss is

$$\ell_1\alpha = \ell_1 \Pr\{c \le \bar{M}\} = 300\Pr\left\{\frac{c - 75}{1.5} \le Z\right\}.$$

If $E(M) = 77$, the expected loss is

$$\ell_2\beta = \ell_2 \Pr\{\bar{M} < c\} = 600\Pr\left\{Z < \frac{c - 77}{1.5}\right\}.$$

Figure 6 shows these two expected losses as two functions of c. For each decision procedure, value of c, the higher curve indicates the maximum expected loss. When $\ell_1\alpha = \ell_2\beta = 102$, the maximum expected loss is minimized. This occurs at approximately $c = 75.6$. The corresponding error probabilities are $\alpha = .34$ and $\beta = .17$.

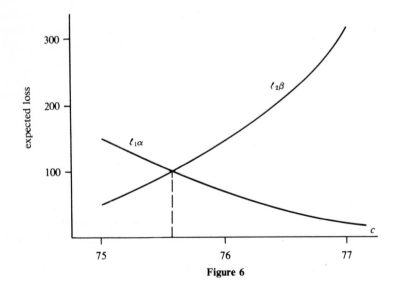

Figure 6

In summary, the bakery accepts the shipment of baker's cheese, if the mean moisture is less than 75.6 in a random sample of four packages. If the mean is greater than 75.6, the shipment is returned to the supplier. This minimax procedure has a .34 probability of returning a good shipment and a .17 probability of receiving a bad shipment. The average loss for each shipment is $102.

EXERCISES

40. X is a continuous random variable with a uniform distribution

$$f(x) = \frac{1}{\theta} \quad \text{for} \quad 0 \le x \le \theta \quad \text{and} \quad 0 < \theta.$$

Consider the decision situation

first hypothesis: $\theta = 2$,

second hypothesis: $\theta = 3$,

where $\ell_1 = 2$ and $\ell_2 = 5$. A sample of size 1 is taken. A decision procedure is

accept first hypothesis if $x < c$,

accept second hypothesis if $c \le x$.

a) Find c for the minimax procedure.
b) What are the corresponding α and β?
c) What is the expected loss for this minimax procedure?

41. In exercise 38 of section 2 (page 93), suppose the loss is $20,000 for wrongly continuing the proposed program; suppose the loss is $3000 for unnecessarily changing to another program. Let $n = 100$ in

continue program if $\bar{x} < c$,

use another program if $c \le \bar{x}$.

a) Find c for the minimax procedure.
b) What are the corresponding α and β?
c) What is the expected loss for this minimax procedure?

42. Ferguson and his partner frequently play golf together. They are evenly matched, and each player's score varies from game to game according to a normal distribution with $\mu = 100$ and $\sigma = 4$. Assume independence between players. For his lessons, costing fifty dollars, the club pro claims to lower a player's average score

by exactly 5 strokes (σ remains 4). Ferguson's partner takes the lessons. On the first four rounds after the lessons, his partner scores 96, 101, 98, and 94. Should Ferguson take the lessons? Failure to take the lessons, if they are really effective, will mean a $200 loss to Ferguson's pride.

4

Bayes Procedures

A Bayes procedure, which is a special type of decision procedure, uses the decision maker's subjective feelings about the truth or falsity of each hypothesis. These feelings must be expressed as probabilities. The losses for wrong decisions can be used also.

All the conditions for a minimax procedure exist. The problem is to choose from two hypotheses, H_1 and H_2, for a random experiment. One of them is true. A particular action follows the decision to accept H_1; a different action follows the decision to accept H_2. Accepting H_1 when H_1 is true is a correct decision with no resulting loss. Accepting H_2 when H_2 is true is also a correct decision with no resulting loss. Accepting H_2 when H_1 is true is a type I error with a loss ℓ_1. Accepting H_1 when H_2 is true is a type II error with a loss ℓ_2. The chart of losses for these four combinations is

		Reality	
		H_1 is true	H_2 is true
Decision	accept H_1	0	ℓ_2
	accept H_2	ℓ_1	0

For this simplified discussion, H_1 and H_2 again must be statements that the parameter has one particular value.

The decision maker has prior feelings about H_1 and H_2 that he wants to use in the decision procedure. These feelings may be very subjective and may even be unreasonable to someone else. Nevertheless, he wants to use them along with available experimental results. The Bayes procedure is a quantitative method for combining these two sources of information about a random experiment.

The decision maker must express his subjective feelings as probabilities. In our simplified situation, this means he must give the probability that H_1

is true and the probability that H_2 is true. Each of these probabilities must be a non-negative number, and their sum must be one. That is, he must specify a probability distribution for two events: $\{H_1\}$ and $\{H_2\}$, where $\Pr\{H_1\}$ is the decision maker's subjective probability that H_1 is true. This probability distribution is the *prior distribution*. For example, $\Pr\{H_1\} = .80$ and $\Pr\{H_2\} = .20$ mean that he is 80 per cent sure H_1 is true and 20 per cent sure that H_2 is true. Or in other words, he is willing to bet on H_2 at odds of 4 to 1.

Bakery Example, Modified. The bakery purchases baker's cheese in large shipments. Each shipment contains many separate packages. The per cent moisture M varies from package to package. Two hypotheses are

first hypothesis: $E(M) = 75$,

second hypothesis: $E(M) = 77$.

If the first hypothesis is true, the bakery wants to receive the shipment and pay for it. If the second hypothesis is true, the bakery wants to return the shipment to the supplier. Returning the shipment when $E(M) = 75$ is an error with a loss of $300. Receiving the shipment when $E(M) = 77$ is an error with a loss of $600. The inspector at the bakery is 80 per cent sure that $E(M) = 75$, and he is 20 per cent sure that $E(M) = 77$. Perhaps he bases this prior distribution on a personal inspection of the supplier's methods.

Recall that a decision procedure is a rule that associates accepting H_1 with some of the outcomes of a random sample. Accepting H_2 is associated with the remaining outcomes. For a particular decision procedure, α is the probability of a type I error, and β is the probability of a type II error.

The decision maker now can associate an overall expected loss to each particular decision procedure. That is, the worth of a decision procedure can be measured by one number, its overall expected loss. When H_1 is true, the expected loss is

$$0(1 - \alpha) + \ell_1\alpha = \ell_1\alpha.$$

When H_2 is true, the expected loss is

$$\ell_2\beta + 0(1 - \beta) = \ell_2\beta.$$

The expected value of these expected losses is

$$\text{expected expected loss} = \ell_1\alpha\Pr\{H_1\} + \ell_2\beta\Pr\{H_2\}.$$

This is the overall measure of worth of the decision procedure.

The *Bayes procedure* is the decision procedure that minimizes expected expected loss. That is, the decision maker minimizes the overall anticipated loss, $\ell_1\alpha\Pr\{H_1\} + \ell_2\beta\Pr\{H_2\}$, in using the Bayes decision procedure.

For a numerical illustration with the modified bakery example, let the sample size be 4 and $D(M) = 3$ again. The general form of a decision procedure based on the sample mean is

accept the hypothesis $E(M) = 75$ if $\bar{m} < c$,

accept the hypothesis $E(M) = 77$ if $c \le \bar{m}$.

Each value of c determines a particular decision procedure. If $E(M) = 75$, the expected loss is

$$\ell_1\alpha = \ell_1 \Pr\{c \le \bar{M}\} = 300\Pr\left\{\frac{c - 75}{1.5} \le Z\right\}.$$

If $E(M) = 77$, the expected loss is

$$\ell_2\beta = \ell_2 \Pr\{\bar{M} < c\} = 600\Pr\left\{Z < \frac{c - 77}{1.5}\right\}.$$

The expected expected loss is

$$\ell_1\alpha\Pr\{H_1\} + \ell_2\beta\Pr\{H_2\} = 240\Pr\left\{\frac{c - 75}{1.5} \le Z\right\}$$

$$+ 120\Pr\left\{Z < \frac{c - 77}{1.5}\right\}.$$

Figure 7 shows this function of c. The minimum occurs at $c = 76.8$. The corresponding α is .12; the β is .44; and the minimum expected expected loss is $81.

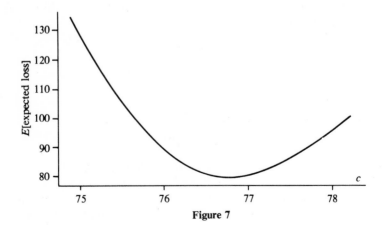

Figure 7

EXERCISES

43. As in exercise 40, X has a uniform distribution with

$$f(x) = \frac{1}{\theta} \quad \text{for} \quad 0 \le x \le \theta \quad \text{and} \quad 0 < \theta.$$

The decision situation is

first hypothesis: $\theta = 2$,

second hypothesis: $\theta = 3$,

where $\ell_1 = 2$ and $\ell_2 = 5$. A prior distribution is $\Pr\{\theta = 2\} = .60$ and $\Pr\{\theta = 3\} = .40$. From one observation of X, a decision procedure is

accept first hypothesis if $x < c$,

accept second hypothesis if $c \le x$,

where $0 \le c \le 2$.
a) What is c for the Bayes procedure?
b) What are the corresponding α and β?
c) What is the minimum expected expected loss?

* 44. Suppose X has a normal distribution with unknown expected value μ and known variance σ^2. A decision situation is

first hypothesis: $\mu = \mu_1$.

second hypothesis: $\mu = \mu_2$,

where $\mu_1 < \mu_2$. Let ℓ_1 and ℓ_2 be the two losses for wrong decisions. Let $\pi_1 = \Pr\{\mu = \mu_1\}$ be the prior probability for the first hypothesis, and let $\pi_2 = \Pr\{\mu = \mu_2\}$ be the prior probability for the second hypothesis. A decision procedure for a sample of size n is

accept first hypothesis if $\bar{x} < c$,

accept second hypothesis if $c \le \bar{x}$.

Prove that the cut-off point c for the Bayes procedure is

$$c = \frac{\mu_1 + \mu_2}{2} + \frac{1}{\mu_2 - \mu_1} \frac{\sigma^2}{n} \log_e \frac{\pi_1 \ell_1}{\pi_2 \ell_2}.$$

Hint: To minimize $\ell_1 \alpha \pi_1 + \ell_2 \beta \pi_2$, differentiate with respect to c. Note that

$$\alpha = 1 - F\left(\frac{c - \mu_1}{\sigma / \sqrt{n}}\right) \quad \text{and} \quad \beta = F\left(\frac{c - \mu_2}{\sigma / \sqrt{n}}\right),$$

where F is the distribution function for the unit normal.

45. Prior to his partner's taking lessons, Ferguson was 90 per cent sure the pro was a fraud. With the losses and the partner's scores of exercise 42, should Ferguson take the lessons?
Hint: Use the formula of exercise 44.

ADDITIONAL READINGS

Brownlee, K., *Statistical Theory and Methodology in Science and Engineering.* 2nd ed. New York: John Wiley & Sons, Inc., 1965.

Brunk, H., *An Introduction to Mathematical Statistics.* 2nd ed. New York: Blaisdell Publishing Co., 1965.

Fisher, R., *Statistical Methods and Scientific Inference.* 2nd ed. New York: Hafner Publishing Co., 1959.

———, *Statistical Methods for Research Workers.* 12th ed. New York: Hafner Publishing Company, 1954.

Grant, E., *Statistical Quality Control.* 3rd edition. New York: McGraw-Hill Book Company, 1964.

Hogg, R., and A. Craig, *Introduction to Mathematical Statistics.* 2nd ed. New York: The Macmillan Company, 1965.

Mood, A., and F. Graybill, *Introduction to the Theory of Statistics.* 2nd ed. New York: McGraw-Hill Book Company, 1963.

Savage, L., *The Foundations of Statistics.* New York: John Wiley & Sons, Inc., 1954.

Schlaifer, R., *Probability and Statistics for Business Decisions.* New York: McGraw-Hill Book Company, 1959.

Wallis, W., and H. Roberts, *Statistics: A New Approach.* New York: The Free Press, 1956.

Problems

1. A large manufacturing company has dealers throughout the nation. The advertising department claims:
   1) the expected useful life of the product is at least 1000 hours;
   2) exactly 50 per cent of the dealers own their stores;
   3) their dealers make more net profit than the rival company's dealers.

In a random sample of 100 of the company's dealers, 62 owned their stores; the mean profit was $14,500 last year; and the sample standard deviation was $5000. In an independent random sample of 40 of the rival's dealers, 32 owned their stores; the average profit was $15,000 last year; and the sample standard deviation was $2000. In a third sample of size 10, the mean useful life of the product was 960 hours; the sample standard deviation was 100 hours. With significance tests at the .05 level, attempt to disprove the three claims of the advertising department.

2. In a community it is known that 70 per cent of the families are home-owners, and 30 per cent are renters. The chamber of commerce claims that the average family spends $1400 for housing in one year. In a sample of 40 renters, the mean expense was $1200, and the sample standard deviation was $150. In a sample of 40 homeowners, the mean expense was $1700, and the sample standard deviation was $300. At the .01 level, do these data disprove the claim?

3. There are two candidates for chairman of the school board—Ladd and his rival. In a sample of 36 voters, how many supporters does Ladd need to feel victorious for the coming election? Use $\alpha = .05$.

4. If 60 per cent or more of the homes in a new community do not have color TV, Brand X wants to enter the market with a dealership. If less than 60 per cent are without a set, Brand X wants to stay out of the market. A survey of size n of the community is to be planned. Let $\bar{x}$ be the sample proportion without color TV. The decision procedure is

$$\text{enter the market if } c < \bar{x},$$

$$\text{don't enter the market if } \bar{x} \le c.$$

Brand X wants no more than a .20 chance of passing up a good market. On the other hand, if only 50 per cent actually are without a color TV, Brand X wants no more than a .05 chance of entering this market. Find n and c.

5. The Chief and his large family make a type of pottery bowl for the tourists. There is no danger of too uniform a product, but the Chief is worried about too much variation. He wants 95 per cent of the bowls to have volumes within .2 quart of the average volume for all the bowls. In a sample of 5 bowls, he finds the following volumes in quarts: 2.1, 2.5, 2.0, 2.3, and 2.1. At the .05 level, should he conclude there is too much variation?

6. It is claimed that two brands of tires have equal life. In a random sample of 9 of the first brand, the average life is 20,000 miles; in a random sample of 3 of the second brand, the average life is 21,000 miles. If $\sigma = 1000$ for both brands, at what significance level could you reject the claim?

7. A company claims to have at least 30 per cent of a market. In a sample of 84 customers, there are 21 who favor the company's product. Is this difference significant at the .05 level?

8. X has a normal distribution with unknown μ and $\sigma = 1$. A decision situation is

$$\text{first hypothesis: } \mu \leq 0,$$

$$\text{second hypothesis: } \mu > 0.$$

In a random sample of size 2, let

$$y_1 = .5x_1 + .5x_2 = \bar{x},$$

$$y_2 = .8x_1 + .2x_2.$$

One decision procedure is

$$\text{accept first hypothesis if} \quad y_1 < .707,$$

$$\text{accept second hypothesis if } .707 \leq y_1.$$

A second decision procedure is

$$\text{accept first hypothesis if} \quad y_2 < .825,$$

$$\text{accept second hypothesis if } .825 \leq y_2.$$

a) Plot the power functions of the two decision procedures.
b) Which is the better procedure?

* 9. In the context of the previous problem, let
$$y_3 = a_1x_1 + a_2x_2,$$

where a_1 and a_2 are constants.
a) Using y_3 find the decision procedure that has the same power at $\mu = 0$ as those of problem 8.
b) Prove that this decision procedure cannot be more powerful than that based on $y_1 = \bar{x}$, when the second hypothesis is true.

10. X has a normal distribution with $E(X) = \mu = ?$ and $D(X) = \sigma = 10$. A hypothesis for μ is $60 \leq \mu \leq 70$. From a random sample of

size 4, a significance test is

$$\text{reject if } \bar{x} \leq c_1 \quad \text{or} \quad c_2 \leq \bar{x}.$$

Find the "symmetric" c_1 and c_2 such that the probability of rejecting a true hypothesis is at most .05.

11. Kornegay is responsible for the maintenance of a fleet of cars. He is considering two brands of wax, A and B, for the exteriors of the cars. On a randomly chosen car, let X_A be the length of protection for wax A; define X_B similarly. Suppose X_A and X_B are normal with

$$E(X_A) = \mu_A, \quad E(X_B) = \mu_B, \quad D(X_A) = D(X_B) = \sigma.$$

To select the wax, Kornegay wants to test n cars with A and another n cars with B. His decision procedure is

$$\text{adopt A if } \bar{x}_A - \bar{x}_B \geq c,$$

$$\text{adopt B if } \bar{x}_A - \bar{x}_B < c.$$

From costs and other considerations, he wants no more than a 10 per cent chance of adopting wax A if $\mu_A - \mu_B = 0$. If $\mu_A - \mu_B = \dfrac{\sigma}{2}$ he wants a 70 per cent chance of adopting A. Find n.

Estimation | *IV*

A random experiment may be performed many times for the simple purpose of estimating the unknown value of some parameter. There are usually several reasonable ways to use the outcomes of such trials to estimate the unknown parameter. The theory of estimation examines these methods and attempts to find optimal methods.

The estimation situation differs from a testing situation in one essential way. There is no hypothesis about the unknown parameter. Hence, there is no question of accepting or rejecting. The experimenter's only purpose is to use the outcomes of the random sample to find the unknown value of the parameter.

There are two general methods of estimation. In *point estimation*, the experimenter uses the outcomes of the random sample to produce a single number which is his estimate of the unknown parameter. In *interval estimation*, the experimenter uses the random sample to produce an interval in which he estimates that the unknown parameter lies.

We shall discuss point estimation and interval estimation in general, and we shall illustrate with four particular cases: the expected value for the normal distribution, the proportion for the Bernoulli distribution, the variance for the normal distribution, and the expected values for two normal distributions.

1
Point Estimation

In this simpler method, the experimenter gives one number, based on a random sample, which estimates the unknown value of the parameter. Let X be the random variable with unknown parameter θ. A random sample $x_1, x_2, \ldots, x_n$, of size n is observed for X. From these outcomes, the experimenter wants one number y as an estimator of θ. That is, he seeks a function g which determines the point estimator $y = g(x_1, x_2, \ldots, x_n)$ of θ.

There are numerous possible functions in any particular case. The central problem of point estimation is to find general criteria for a good estimator and to apply them to the particular cases of interest.

Suppose a particular function g is proposed, and its worth is to be determined. If the calculated y is actually near the unknown θ, this is a good estimate; if y is not near the unknown θ, this is not a good estimate. Of course, the experimenter does not know the value of the parameter θ; he cannot evaluate g quite as simply. However, he can imagine repetitions of the random sample and evaluate the average quality of this estimator. In this context, Y is a random variable $Y = g(X_1, X_2, \ldots, X_n)$ with its own parameters. In particular, Y has an expected value $E(Y)$. If this is near the unknown parameter, the experimenter knows that the function g gives a good estimator on the average.

If the expected value of the estimator Y equals the unknown parameter, $E(Y) = \theta$, then the estimator is *unbiased*. If the expected value of the estimator does not equal the unknown parameter, $E(Y) \neq \theta$, then the estimator is *biased*. One cannot prove that estimators should be unbiased, but one may accept the criterion as reasonable and apply it to particular cases.

For a simple example, suppose X has a normal distribution with unknown expected value μ. If the random sample consists of only one observation of X, there is only one unbiased estimator of μ: $y = g(x) = x$. If $x = 82$ is observed, then 82 is also the experimenter's unbiased estimate of μ. Next, suppose the random sample consists of two observations of X, x_1, and x_2. There are many unbiased estimators of μ. Two of them are $y_1 = .5x_1 + .5x_2 = \bar{x}$ and $y_2 = .8x_1 + .2x_2$. They are unbiased because $E(Y_1) = .5\mu + .5\mu = \mu$ and $E(Y_2) = .8\mu + .2\mu = \mu$. If $x_1 = 82$ and $x_2 = 90$ are actually observed, the two unbiased estimates are $y_1 = 86$ and $y_2 = 83.6$.

Accepting the criterion of unbiasedness does not solve the problem of point estimation. For a random sample of size n, there are usually any number of unbiased estimators of the unknown parameter. A further criterion must be developed in order to compare the various unbiased estimators. For an estimator $y = g(x_1, x_2, \ldots, x_n)$ and a parameter θ, unbiasedness, $E(Y) = \theta$, only guarantees that the distribution of Y is centered in the right place. It still may be very probable that the error $Y - \theta$ is large in absolute value. The point is that the experimenter would prefer that Y have a small variation about θ. The usual measure of variation about $E(Y)$ is the variance of Y, $V(Y) = E[Y - E(Y)]^2 = E(Y - \theta)^2$. It therefore seems desirable to look in the class of unbiased estimators for the one with the smallest variance. Accepting this second criterion completes our description of a good point estimator—the unbiased estimator with minimum variance.

In the simple example with the normal distribution given above, the variances for the two unbiased estimators are

$$V(Y_1) = (.5)^2\sigma^2 + (.5)\sigma^2 = .50\sigma^2,$$
$$V(Y_2) = (.8)^2\sigma^2 + (.2)^2\sigma^2 = .68\sigma^2.$$

Therefore, y_1 is the better point estimator of μ.

Table 1

Distribution	Parameter	Unbiased estimator
Normal	Expected value μ	$\bar{x}$
	Variance σ^2	s^2
Two Normals	Difference of expected values $\mu_1 - \mu_2$	$\bar{x}_1 - \bar{x}_2$
Bernoulli	Proportion θ	$\bar{x}$

Table 1 gives the minimum-variance unbiased estimators for four important particular cases. In every case, the estimators are the statistics for the corresponding significance tests in Chapter III. The unbiasedness of $\bar{X}$ and $\bar{X}_1 - \bar{X}_2$ in the relevant cases was indicated in Chapter II. The proof for the unbiased estimator s^2 is

$$E(S^2) = E\left[\frac{\sum(X_i - \bar{X})^2}{n-1}\right] = \frac{1}{n-1}E[\sum(X_i - \bar{X})^2]$$

$$= \frac{1}{n-1}E(\sum X_i^2 - n\bar{X}^2) = \frac{1}{n-1}[\sum E(X_i^2) - nE(\bar{X}^2)]$$

$$= \frac{n}{n-1}[E(X^2) - E(\bar{X}^2)].$$

The indicated expectations are

$$E(X^2) = V(X) - E^2(X) \text{ and } E(\bar{X}^2) = V(\bar{X}) - E^2(\bar{X}) = \frac{V(X)}{n} - E^2(X).$$

When these are inserted above, $E(S^2) = V(X)$, and the proof is complete. This explains the use of $n - 1$ in the denominator of the definition of s^2. It is interesting to observe that the usual estimator of $\sigma = D(X)$ is the sample standard deviation s. It is a biased estimator. The proofs of minimum variance for the four estimators in Table 1 will not be given; they are beyond the level of this book.

Summary. The random variable X has an unknown parameter θ. From a random sample $x_1, x_2, \ldots, x_n$ for X, let $y = g(x_1, x_2, \ldots, x_n)$ be a point estimator for θ. If $E(Y) = E[g(X_1, X_2, \ldots, X_n)] = \theta$, this estimator is unbiased. From the class of all unbiased estimators for θ, it is desirable to use the one with minimum variance $V(Y) = E(Y - \theta)^2$.

EXERCISES

1. Let X be a random variable with unknown expected value $E(X)$. For a random sample of size 2, consider the class of linear estimators of $E(X)$: $y = a_1x_1 + a_2x_2$, where a_1 and a_2 are constants.
   a) If y is unbiased, prove $a_1 + a_2 = 1$.
   b) If y is of minimum variance, prove $a_1 = a_2 = 1/2$.
   c) Why doesn't this prove that $\bar{x}$ is *the* minimum-variance unbiased estimator of $E(X)$?

* 2. Generalize the results in exercise 2 to a random sample of size n. Hint: Use a Lagrange multiplier.

3. Let X be a continuous random variable with a uniform distribution:

$$f(x) = \frac{1}{\theta} \quad \text{for} \quad 0 \leq x \leq \theta \quad \text{and} \quad 0 < \theta.$$

Recall that $E(X) = \theta/2$ and $V(X) = \theta^2/12$. For a random sample of size 2, consider $y_1 = x_1 + x_2$.
   a) Prove y_1 is an unbiased estimator of θ.
   b) Show that the variance of Y_1 is $\theta^2/6$.

4. In the context of exercise 3, let u be the maximum of x_1 and x_2:
$$u = \max(x_1, x_2).$$
The continuous random variable U has the density function of problem 8 in Chapter II:

$$f(u) = \frac{2u}{\theta^2} \quad \text{for} \quad 0 \leq u \leq \theta \quad \text{and} \quad 0 < \theta.$$

That problem was to show that $E(U) = \dfrac{2\theta}{3}$ and $V(U) = \dfrac{\theta^2}{18}$.

Let $y_2 = au$ be an unbiased estimator of θ.
   a) Find a.
   b) Find $V(Y_2)$.
   c) How does y_2 compare to y_1 of exercise 3?

5. Let y_1 and y_2 be unbiased estimators of θ_1 and θ_2, respectively. If k_1 and k_2 are known constants, show that $k_1y_1 + k_2y_2$ is an unbiased estimator of $k_1\theta_1 + k_2\theta_2$. Show that it is the only unbiased estimator of $k_1\theta_1 + k_2\theta_2$ of the linear form $a_1y_1 + a_2y_2$.

6. Thirty per cent of the Christians in a city are Catholics. In a sample of 60 Catholics, 50 went to church last Sunday; in a sample of 70 Protestants, 40 went to church last Sunday.

    a) Estimate the proportion of Catholics in the city who went to church.

    b) Estimate the proportion of Protestants in the city who went to church.

    c) Estimate the proportion of Christians in the city who went to church.

7. Thirty per cent of a city's employees are professional; fifty per cent are factory workers; and twenty per cent are in other vocations. In a sample of 30 professionals, the mean salary is $15,000, and the sample standard deviation is $5000. For 30 factory workers, the mean is $7000, and the standard deviation is $3000. For 30 of the others, the mean is $9000, and the standard deviation is $4000.

    a) Estimate the expected income for the entire city.

    b) Estimate the variance of the estimator in part a).

2

Interval Estimation

The point estimators discussed in the previous section are not completely satisfactory solutions to the estimation problem. Usually, the experimenter wants to give some indication of the uncertainty in the point estimator. He can accomplish this by giving an interval in which he believes the unknown parameter lies. Statistical theory contains several types of intervals for this general situation; only confidence intervals are discussed here.

In interval estimation, the experimenter gives two numbers between which he thinks the unknown parameter lies. The two numbers are based only on the outcomes of a random sample. The interval between them is a *confidence interval* for the parameter. Let X be the random variable, θ be the unknown parameter, and $x_1, x_2, \ldots, x_n$ be a random sample for X. Let d_1 be the lower end of the interval and d_2 be the upper end of the interval. If d_1 and d_2 depend only on the random sample, there must be two corresponding functions, say h_1 and h_2, where $d_1 = h_1(x_1, x_2, \ldots, x_n)$ and $d_2 = h_2(x_1, x_2, \ldots, x_n)$. The experimenter estimates the parameter by the statement $d_1 < \theta < d_2$.

The unknown parameter either lies in the confidence interval, or it does not. The experimenter usually wants to indicate the level of certainty with which he makes the statement $d_1 < \theta < d_2$. The central problem of this section is to develop a measure of this level of certainty and to apply it to the particular cases of interest.

Suppose a particular confidence interval, $d_1 = h_1(x_1, x_2, \ldots, x_n)$ and $d_2 = h_2(x_1, x_2, \ldots, x_n)$, is proposed; the level of certainty for the interval is to be determined. Imagine repetitions of the random sample. In this context, the endpoints of the interval become random variables: $D_1 = h_1(X_1, X_2, \ldots, X_n)$ and $D_2 = h_2(X_1, X_2, \ldots, X_n)$. The interval itself is random, and it is meaningful to consider the probability that the interval covers the unknown parameter, $\Pr\{D_1 < \theta < D_2\}$. Either this probability depends on θ, or it does not. Suppose it does not. Then $\Pr\{D_1 < \theta < D_2\}$ is a constant between 0 and 1, which measures the experimenter's certainty that the statement $d_1 < \theta < d_2$ is true. If this constant is .95, for example, the experimenter knows that in many repetitions of the random sample 95 per cent of the intervals constructed in this manner would cover the unknown parameter θ. Or in other words, the statements $d_1 < \theta < d_2$ would be true 95 per cent of the time.

When the probability $\Pr\{D_1 < \theta < D_2\}$ that the interval covers the unknown parameter does not depend on θ, this probability is the *confidence coefficient* for the confidence interval $d_1 < \theta < d_2$. The usual symbol for this constant is $1 - \alpha$.

$$1 - \alpha = \Pr\{D_1 < \Theta < D_2\} \text{ for all } \theta.$$

When the probability that the interval covers the unknown parameter does depend on θ, we shall not define a measure of the certainty for the interval.

For a simple example, let X have a normal distribution with unknown expected value μ and standard deviation 2. Suppose the sample size is 1 and the confidence interval for μ is defined by $d_1 = h_1(x) = x - 1$ and $d_2 = h_2(x) = x + 1$, where x is the observed value of X. If the observed value is 10, the confidence interval is $9 < \mu < 11$. To find the confidence coefficient, consider $\Pr\{D_1 < \mu < D_2\} = \Pr\{X - 1 < \mu < X + 1\}$. Within the braces, $X - 1 < \mu$ if and only if $X < \mu + 1$; and $\mu < X + 1$ if and only if $\mu - 1 < X$. This and Table III in the appendix give

$$1 - \alpha = \Pr\{D_1 < \mu < D_2\} = \Pr\{\mu - 1 < X < \mu + 1\}$$

$$= \Pr\left\{\frac{\mu - 1 - \mu}{\sigma} < Z < \frac{\mu + 1 - \mu}{\sigma}\right\} = \Pr\left\{-\frac{1}{2} < Z < \frac{1}{2}\right\} = .38.$$

Therefore, .38 is the confidence coefficient for the interval $9 < \mu < 11$.

Extend this example somewhat, and suppose the random sample is of size 4. Let the endpoints be $d_1 = \bar{x} - 1$ and $d_2 = \bar{x} + 1$. If the observations are 8, 11, 8, and 13, $\bar{x}$ is 10 and the interval is again $9 < \mu < 11$. What is the confidence coefficient? Consider

$$\begin{aligned} \Pr\{D_1 < \mu < D_2\} &= \Pr\{\bar{X} - 1 < \mu < \bar{X} + 1\} \\ &= \Pr\{\mu - 1 < \bar{X} < \mu + 1\} \\ &= \Pr\left\{\frac{\mu - 1 - \mu}{D(\bar{X})} < \frac{\bar{X} - \mu}{D(\bar{X})} < \frac{\mu + 1 - \mu}{D(\bar{X})}\right\}. \end{aligned}$$

Since $D(\bar{X}) = \sigma/\sqrt{n} = 1$, this reduces to

$$\Pr\{D_1 < \mu < D_2\} = \Pr\{-1.00 < Z < 1.00\} = .68.$$

This probability does not depend on the unknown μ, and .68 is the confidence coefficient for the interval $9 < \mu < 11$. It is *not* correct to say that .68 is the probability that μ is between 9 and 11. The parameter μ is an unknown constant, not a random variable. It is correct to say that the interval, 9 to 11, was obtained by a procedure which would include the unknown μ 68 per cent of the time in many repetitions of the random sample.

Summary. Let X be a random variable with unknown parameter θ. Two functions, $d_1 = h_1(x_1, x_2, \ldots, x_n)$ and $d_2 = h_2(x_1, x_2, \ldots, x_n)$, of a random sample define the endpoints of a confidence interval for θ: $d_1 < \theta < d_2$. The confidence coefficient is $1 - \alpha = \Pr\{D_1 < \theta < D_2\}$, where this probability does not depend on θ.

EXERCISES

8. X has a normal distribution with unknown μ and $\sigma = 2$. For one observation of X, let the confidence interval be

$$\begin{aligned} d_1 &= h_1(x) = x - 2 \\ d_2 &= h_2(x) = x + 2 \end{aligned} \quad \text{or} \quad x - 2 < \mu < x + 2$$

Find the confidence coefficient.

9. For the situation of exercise 8, let the interval be

$$\begin{aligned} d_1 &= h_1(x) = x - 1 \\ d_2 &= h_2(x) = x + 3 \end{aligned} \quad \text{or} \quad x - 1 < \mu < x + 3$$

Find the confidence coefficient.

10. For the situation of exercise 8, try to find a confidence coefficient for

$$d_1 = h_1(x) = \frac{1}{2}x$$
$$\text{or} \quad \frac{1}{2}x < \mu < 2x$$
$$d_2 = h_2(x) = 2x$$

where X is known to be positive.

11. The continuous random variable X has a uniform distribution with

$$f(x) = \frac{1}{\theta} \quad \text{for} \quad 0 \leq x \leq \theta \quad \text{and} \quad 0 < \theta.$$

For one observation of X, a confidence interval for θ is $x < \theta < 3x$. Find the confidence coefficient.

12. For the situation of exercise 11, try to find a confidence coefficient for $x - 1 < \theta < x + 1$.

13. X has a normal distribution with unknown μ and $\sigma = 2$. For a random sample of size 2, let the confidence interval be

$$d_1 = h_1(x_1, x_2) = .5x_1 + .5x_2 - 2 = \bar{x} - 2,$$
$$d_2 = h_2(x_1, x_2) = .5x_1 + .5x_2 + 2 = \bar{x} + 2.$$

Find the confidence coefficient.

14. For the situation in exercise 13, let the confidence interval be

$$d_1 = h_1(x_1, x_2) = .8x_1 + .2x_2 - 2,$$
$$d_2 = h_2(x_1, x_2) = .8x_1 + .2x_2 + 2.$$

Find the confidence coefficient.

15. X has the uniform distribution of exercise 11. For a random sample of size 2, let $U = \max(X_1, X_2)$. Then, U has the density function $f(u) = 2u/\theta^2$ for $0 \leq u \leq \theta$ and $0 < \theta$. Let the confidence interval be $u < \theta < 3u$. Find the confidence coefficient.

16. X_1 has a normal distribution with unknown μ_1 and $\sigma_1 = 3$. X_2 has a normal distribution with unknown μ_2 and $\sigma_2 = 4$. In random samples of sizes $n_1 = 9$ and $n_2 = 8$, the sample means are $\bar{x}_1$ and $\bar{x}_2$. Find the confidence coefficient for $\bar{x}_1 - \bar{x}_2 - 2 < \mu_1 - \mu_2 < \bar{x}_1 - \bar{x}_2 + 2$.

17. In exercise 7 of this chapter, the estimate of the city's expected income μ is $9800, and the estimate of the variance of this is

$171,333. Adding and subtracting $800 to $9800 give a confidence interval for the city's expected income: $9000 < \mu < 10,600$. Find the confidence coefficient.

2.1 *EXPECTED VALUE FOR THE NORMAL DISTRIBUTION*

In this subsection, the random experiment has a normal probability distribution with unknown expected value. A confidence interval for the expected value is to be constructed from the outcomes of several trials of the experiment. The desired confidence coefficient is specified first; the problem is to find a corresponding interval. This is an inversion of the order in the introductory discussion.

Let X be the normally distributed random variable with unknown expected value μ. Initially, assume the variance σ^2 is known. The specified confidence coefficient is $1 - \alpha$. The random sample is $x_1, x_2, \ldots, x_n$. To construct a confidence interval, the problem is to find two functions, h_1 and h_2, of the random sample which determine the endpoints, d_1 and d_2, of the interval: $d_1 = h_1(x_1, x_2, \ldots, x_n)$ and $d_2 = h_2(x_1, x_2, \ldots, x_n)$. The functions must be such that the probability of the interval including the unknown μ is $1 - \alpha$. That is, $\Pr\{D_1 < \mu < D_2\} = 1 - \alpha$ for all μ.

One general procedure for finding the functions h_1 and h_2 considers the corresponding two-sided significance test of level α. In this case, the hypothesis is $\mu = \mu_0$. Recall that the test is

reject if $\qquad \bar{x} \leq \mu_0 - z\left(\dfrac{\alpha}{2}\right)\dfrac{\sigma}{\sqrt{n}}$ or $\mu_0 + z\left(\dfrac{\alpha}{2}\right)\dfrac{\sigma}{\sqrt{n}} \leq \bar{x}.$

This comes from the following probabilistic statement:

$$\Pr\left\{\mu - z\left(\frac{\alpha}{2}\right)\frac{\sigma}{\sqrt{n}} < \bar{X} < \mu + z\left(\frac{\alpha}{2}\right)\frac{\sigma}{\sqrt{n}}\right\} = 1 - \alpha,$$

where $E(X) = \mu$. The subscript on μ is dropped, because the statement applies for the true value of μ. Within the braces, $\bar{X} < \mu + z\left(\dfrac{\alpha}{2}\right)\dfrac{\sigma}{\sqrt{n}}$ may be solved for μ to give $\bar{X} - z\left(\dfrac{\alpha}{2}\right)\dfrac{\sigma}{\sqrt{n}} < \mu$. Similarly, the other inequality yields $\mu < \bar{X} + z\left(\dfrac{\alpha}{2}\right)\dfrac{\sigma}{\sqrt{n}}$. Therefore, a value of $\bar{X}$ which satisfies the expression in the braces also satisfies $\bar{X} - z\left(\dfrac{\alpha}{2}\right)\dfrac{\sigma}{\sqrt{n}} < \mu < \bar{X} +$

$z\left(\dfrac{\alpha}{2}\right)\dfrac{\sigma}{\sqrt{n}}$. Since these steps are reversible, the converse is also true; and the following holds for the actual value of μ:

$$\Pr\left\{\bar{X} - z\left(\frac{\alpha}{2}\right)\frac{\sigma}{\sqrt{n}} < \mu < \bar{X} + z\left(\frac{\alpha}{2}\right)\frac{\sigma}{\sqrt{n}}\right\} = 1 - \alpha.$$

This is precisely the type of statement required for a confidence interval. The desired functions, h_1 and h_2, are

$$d_1 = h_1(x_1, x_2, \ldots, x_n) = \bar{x} - z\left(\frac{\alpha}{2}\right)\frac{\sigma}{\sqrt{n}} = \bar{x} - z\left(\frac{\alpha}{2}\right)D(\bar{X}),$$

$$d_2 = h_2(x_1, x_2, \ldots, x_n) = \bar{x} + z\left(\frac{\alpha}{2}\right)\frac{\sigma}{\sqrt{n}} = \bar{x} + z\left(\frac{\alpha}{2}\right)D(\bar{X}).$$

The $1 - \alpha$ confidence interval is

$$\bar{x} - z\left(\frac{\alpha}{2}\right)\frac{\sigma}{\sqrt{n}} < \mu < \bar{x} + z\left(\frac{\alpha}{2}\right)\frac{\sigma}{\sqrt{n}}.$$

The length of the interval, $2z\left(\dfrac{\alpha}{2}\right)\dfrac{\sigma}{\sqrt{n}}$, depends on three variables.

As the confidence coefficient $1 - \alpha$ increases, so does $z\left(\dfrac{\alpha}{2}\right)$ and the length of the interval. As the sample size n increases, the length of the interval decreases. As the underlying variance σ^2 increases, so does the length of the interval. For fixed values of these three variables, the experimenter wants the shortest possible interval, because short intervals are stronger statements than long intervals. This confidence interval is the shortest possible.

If the variance σ^2 is unknown, the confidence interval is a simple modification of this interval. Recall that the significance test of level α for the hypothesis $\mu = \mu_0$ is

reject if $\bar{x} \le \mu_0 - t\left(\dfrac{\alpha}{2}, n-1\right)\dfrac{s}{\sqrt{n}}$ or $\mu_0 + t\left(\dfrac{\alpha}{2}, n-1\right)\dfrac{s}{\sqrt{n}} \le \bar{x}$.

This comes from the statement

$$\Pr\left\{\mu - t\left(\frac{\alpha}{2}, n-1\right)\frac{S}{\sqrt{n}} < \bar{X} < \mu + t\left(\frac{\alpha}{2}, n-1\right)\frac{S}{\sqrt{n}}\right\} = 1 - \alpha.$$

After the pivotal step of solving the two inequalities, the statement becomes

$$\Pr\left\{ \bar{X} - t\left(\frac{\alpha}{2}, n - 1\right)\frac{S}{\sqrt{n}} < \mu < \bar{X} + t\left(\frac{\alpha}{2}, n - 1\right)\frac{S}{\sqrt{n}} \right\} = 1 - \alpha.$$

The $1 - \alpha$ confidence interval is

$$\bar{x} - t\left(\frac{\alpha}{2}, n - 1\right)\frac{s}{\sqrt{n}} < \mu < \bar{x} + t\left(\frac{\alpha}{2}, n - 1\right)\frac{s}{\sqrt{n}}.$$

Recall from the corresponding discussion of significance tests that $t\left(\frac{\alpha}{2}, n - 1\right)$ approaches $z\left(\frac{\alpha}{2}\right)$ as n becomes large.

For a numerical example, suppose a variety of wheat is planted in five randomly chosen fields. If the yields are 82, 90, 110, 78, and 85, then the sample mean is 89 and the sample standard deviation is 12.5. A .95 confidence interval for the expected yield $E(Y)$ in the region is

$$89 - (2.776)\frac{12.5}{\sqrt{5}} < E(Y) < 89 + (2.776)\frac{12.5}{\sqrt{5}},$$

$$73.5 < E(Y) < 104.5.$$

Summary. Let X be a normally distributed random variable with unknown expected value μ. If the variance σ^2 is unknown, a $1 - \alpha$ confidence interval for μ is

$$\bar{x} - t\left(\frac{\alpha}{2}, n - 1\right)\frac{s}{\sqrt{n}} < \mu < \bar{x} + t\left(\frac{\alpha}{2}, n - 1\right)\frac{s}{\sqrt{n}}.$$

If σ^2 is known, replace $t\left(\frac{\alpha}{2}, n - 1\right)$ by $z\left(\frac{\alpha}{2}\right)$ and s by σ.

EXERCISES

18. A mail-order company would like to know the distribution of yearly maintenance expenditures by home owners. For a particular city, suppose this distribution is normal. The company hires Race and Associates to survey the city and to estimate the expected expenditure μ. A random sample of 15 homes yields a sample mean of $600 and a sample standard deviation of $200.
    a) What is a .99 confidence interval for μ?
    b) What is a .90 confidence interval for μ?
    c) For the same mean and standard deviation and for $n = 60$, what is a .90 confidence interval?

19. As in exercise 18, Race is retained to survey another city to obtain a .95 confidence interval. Let X be the random variable, and suppose Race is instructed to come back with an interval of the following form: $\bar{x} - 25 < \mu < \bar{x} + 25$. How large a sample should Race take? Assume $\sigma = 200$.

20. X has a normal distribution. A random sample of 3 observations gives 8, 10, and 12. Construct a .90 confidence interval for μ.

21. The random variable X has a normal distribution. A random sample for X is observed. Consider the two-sided (level α) significance test for the hypothesis $\mu = 0$. Show that the data reject the hypothesis if and only if the corresponding $1 - \alpha$ confidence interval does not include zero.

22. In a sample of 50 employees, the mean sick time was 30.2 hours for the last year. The sample standard deviation was 5.1 hours. Find a .95 confidence interval for the expected sick time for the entire company.

2.2 PROPORTION FOR THE BERNOULLI DISTRIBUTION

A random experiment with a Bernoulli distribution of probability essentially has only one parameter, the proportion. This parameter is the probability of the event $\{1\}$, and it is also the expected value for the random experiment. A confidence interval for the proportion is to be constructed from the outcomes of several trials of the experiment.

Let the random variable X have a Bernoulli distribution with unknown proportion θ, where $\Pr\{X = 1\} = E(X) = \theta$. The desired confidence coefficient is $1 - \alpha$. The random sample of size n is $x_1, x_2, \ldots, x_n$. To construct the interval, $d_1 < \theta < d_2$, we need two functions for the endpoints: $d_1 = h_1(x_1, x_2, \ldots, x_n)$ and $d_2 = h_2(x_1, x_2, \ldots, x_n)$. To have the desired confidence coefficient, $\Pr\{D_1 < \theta < D_2\}$ must be $1 - \alpha$ for all θ.

Our general procedure for generating the functions is to consider the related two-sided significance test. For this case, the hypothesis is $\theta = \theta_0$. According to the Central Limit Theorem, $\bar{X}$ has a normal distribution (approximately) with $E(\bar{X}) = \theta$ and $V(\bar{X}) = V(X)/n = \theta(1 - \theta)/n$. The significance test of level α uses these facts about $\bar{X}$ to give

reject if $\quad \bar{x} \leq \theta_0 - z\left(\dfrac{\alpha}{2}\right)\sqrt{\dfrac{\theta_0(1 - \theta_0)}{n}}$

$$\text{or} \quad \theta_0 + z\left(\dfrac{\alpha}{2}\right)\sqrt{\dfrac{\theta_0(1 - \theta_0)}{n}} \leq \bar{x}.$$

This comes from the probabilistic statement

$$\Pr\left\{\theta - z\left(\frac{\alpha}{2}\right)\sqrt{\frac{\theta(1-\theta)}{n}} < \bar{X} < \theta + z\left(\frac{\alpha}{2}\right)\sqrt{\frac{\theta(1-\theta)}{n}}\right\} = 1 - \alpha.$$

One method used to perform the pivotal step is to solve the two inequalities within the braces. This is equivalent to solving two quadratic equations, and the development is omitted. The usual method makes a further approximation. The quantity $\sqrt{\theta(1-\theta)}$ does not vary greatly unless θ is near zero or one. This suggests an approximation that is satisfactory except in extreme cases. Since $E(\bar{X}) = \theta$, replace $\sqrt{\theta(1-\theta)}$ by $\sqrt{\bar{X}(1-\bar{X})}$ and solve the two inequalities to get

$$\Pr\left\{\bar{X} - z\left(\frac{\alpha}{2}\right)\sqrt{\frac{\bar{X}(1-\bar{X})}{n}} < \theta < \bar{X} + z\left(\frac{\alpha}{2}\right)\sqrt{\frac{\bar{X}(1-\bar{X})}{n}}\right\} = 1 - \alpha.$$

From this, the desired functions are

$$d_1 = h_1(x_1, x_2, \ldots, x_n) = \bar{x} - z\left(\frac{\alpha}{2}\right)\sqrt{\frac{\bar{x}(1-\bar{x})}{n}},$$

$$d_2 = h_2(x_1, x_2, \ldots, x_n) = \bar{x} + z\left(\frac{\alpha}{2}\right)\sqrt{\frac{\bar{x}(1-\bar{x})}{n}}.$$

The $1 - \alpha$ confidence interval is

$$\bar{x} - z\left(\frac{\alpha}{2}\right)\sqrt{\frac{\bar{x}(1-\bar{x})}{n}} < \theta < \bar{x} + z\left(\frac{\alpha}{2}\right)\sqrt{\frac{\bar{x}(1-\bar{x})}{n}}.$$

Examples of this situation are very common. Suppose a poll is conducted to determine the proportion of an electorate which favors a certain candidate. In a sample of 100, there are 40 who favor him. Then $\bar{x}$ is .40, and the .99 confidence interval is

$$.40 - 2.58\sqrt{\frac{.4(1-.4)}{100}} < \theta < .40 + 2.58\sqrt{\frac{.4(1-.4)}{100}},$$

$$.27 < \theta < .53.$$

Since several approximations preceded this result, a word of caution is necessary. When n is less than 30 or when $\bar{x}$ is not between .15 and .85, this method may not be satisfactory.

There is one very common variation of this situation. It is related to point estimation. Suppose the experimenter wants to choose the sample size n so that the point estimator has a specified accuracy. He does this by specifying the probability $1 - \alpha$ that the point estimator $\bar{X}$ does not miss the parameter θ by more than a specified amount ϵ. The probabilistic statement of this is

$$1 - \alpha = \Pr\{|\bar{X} - \theta| < \epsilon\} = \Pr\{-\epsilon < \bar{X} - \theta < \epsilon\}$$
$$= \Pr\{\bar{X} - \epsilon < \theta < \bar{X} + \epsilon\}.$$

This is also the form of the probabilistic statement for the $1 - \alpha$ confidence interval, where

$$\epsilon = z\left(\frac{\alpha}{2}\right)\sqrt{\frac{\theta(1 - \theta)}{n}}.$$

This equation must be solved for n. Since θ is also unknown, it cannot be solved immediately. The three common practical solutions are:

1. Guess θ from some supplementary information.
2. When $\theta = .5$, the resulting n is as large as possible. Hence, this solution gives the required accuracy or something more accurate.
3. Conduct a small, pilot sample to get a rough idea of θ. Use it to calculate n for the large sample.

In any case, the experimenter uses the actual results, not his guesses, to compute the estimate and its accuracy.

For the example of the political poll, suppose the pollster wants a point estimator $\bar{x}$ of the candidate's proportion θ of the electorate. He wants to be at least 95 $(1 - \alpha)$ per cent sure that the estimator is not off by more than .02 (ϵ) in absolute per cent. To illustrate the first case, assume recent polls have shown that the candidate has about 20 per cent of the electorate. The sample size n is the solution of

$$.02 = 1.96\sqrt{\frac{.2(1 - .2)}{n}},$$

$$n = 1537.$$

To illustrate the second case, assume no information about the unknown proportion θ. The sample size n is the solution of

$$.02 = 1.96\sqrt{\frac{.5(1 - .5)}{n}},$$

$$n = 2401.$$

The third case is more complicated, and no illustration is given here.

Summary. Let X have a Bernoulli distribution with unknown parameter θ. For a random sample of size n (large) the approximate $1 - \alpha$ confidence interval is

$$\bar{x} - z\left(\frac{\alpha}{2}\right)\sqrt{\frac{\bar{x}(1 - \bar{x})}{n}} < \theta < x + z\left(\frac{\alpha}{2}\right)\sqrt{\frac{\bar{x}(1 - \bar{x})}{n}}.$$

EXERCISES

23. The state police stop 35 trucks and find 8 overloaded. Estimate with a .90 confidence interval the proportion of overloaded trucks in the population of trucks on the road in the area.

24. A power company wants to estimate the proportion θ of its customers who own air conditioners. The company wants to be 95 per cent sure that the point estimate is not off by more than .05. What sample size is sufficient, if
   a) nothing is known about θ?
   b) θ is thought to be about .15?

25. In the city of exercise 6, thirty per cent of the Christians are Catholics. In a sample of 60 Catholics, 50 went to church last Sunday; in a sample of 70 Protestants, 40 went to church last Sunday. Construct a .95 confidence interval for
   a) the proportion of Catholics who went to church last Sunday.
   b) the proportion of Protestants who went to church last Sunday.

26. If X has a Bernoulli distribution, then $V(X) = \theta(1 - \theta)$ for $0 \leq \theta \leq 1$. Prove $V(X)$ is maximized at $\theta = .5$. How does this relate to one of the methods for finding the proper sample size for a point estimator?

27. X has a Bernoulli distribution, and the sample size is large.

   a) Prove that $s^2 = \dfrac{\sum(x_i - \bar{x})}{n - 1} = \dfrac{n\bar{x}(1 - \bar{x})}{n - 1} \doteq \bar{x}(1 - \bar{x}).$

   b) The Central Limit Theorem and subsection 2.1 of this chapter also give an approximate $1 - \alpha$ confidence interval for $\theta = E(X)$:

$$\bar{x} - z\left(\frac{\alpha}{2}\right)\frac{s}{\sqrt{n}} < \theta < \bar{x} + z\left(\frac{\alpha}{2}\right)\frac{s}{\sqrt{n}}.$$

   Relate this interval to the interval discussed in this subsection by using the result in a).

2.3 VARIANCE FOR THE NORMAL DISTRIBUTION

In this subsection as in subsection 2.1, the random experiment has a normal probability distribution with unknown expected value and unknown variance. A confidence interval for the variance is to be constructed from the outcomes of several trials of the experiment. Finding an interval for the variance is equivalent to finding an interval for the standard deviation.

Let X be the normally distributed random variable with variance σ^2. The confidence coefficient is $1 - \alpha$. The random sample is $x_1, x_2, \ldots, x_n$. The problem is to find two functions, h_1 and h_2, of the random sample which determine the endpoints, d_1 and d_2, of the confidence interval: $d_1 = h_1(x_1, x_2, \ldots, x_n)$ and $d_2 = h_2(x_1, x_2, \ldots, x_n)$. The functions must be such that $\Pr\{D_1 < \sigma^2 < D_2\} = 1 - \alpha$ for all σ^2.

Our general procedure for generating the functions is to consider the related two-sided significance test. For this situation, the hypothesis is $\sigma^2 = \sigma_0^2$. The significance test of level α is

$$\text{reject if } s^2 \leq \frac{\chi^2\left(1 - \frac{\alpha}{2}, n - 1\right)\sigma_0^2}{n - 1} \quad \text{or} \quad \frac{\chi^2\left(\frac{\alpha}{2}, n - 1\right)\sigma_0^2}{n - 1} \leq s^2.$$

This test comes from the probabilistic statement

$$\Pr\left\{\frac{\chi^2\left(1 - \frac{\alpha}{2}, n - 1\right)\sigma^2}{n - 1} \leq S^2 \leq \frac{\chi^2\left(\frac{\alpha}{2}, n - 1\right)\sigma^2}{n - 1}\right\} = 1 - \alpha.$$

Solving the two inequalities within the braces for σ^2 gives

$$d_1 = h_1(x_1, x_2, \ldots, x_n) = \frac{(n - 1)s^2}{\chi^2\left(\frac{\alpha}{2}, n - 1\right)},$$

$$d_2 = h_2(x_1, x_2, \ldots, x_n) = \frac{(n - 1)s^2}{\chi^2\left(1 - \frac{\alpha}{2}, n - 1\right)}.$$

The $1 - \alpha$ confidence interval for σ^2 is

$$\frac{(n - 1)s^2}{\chi^2\left(\frac{\alpha}{2}, n - 1\right)} < \sigma^2 < \frac{(n - 1)s^2}{\chi^2\left(1 - \frac{\alpha}{2}, n - 1\right)}.$$

In the numerical example of subsection 2.1, a variety of wheat gives five yields: 82, 90, 110, 78, and 85. The sample variance s^2 is 157. The .95 confidence intervals for σ^2 and σ are

$$\frac{(5-1)(157)}{11.1} < \sigma^2 < \frac{(5-1)(157)}{.484},$$

$$56.6 < \sigma^2 < 1297.5,$$

$$7.5 < \sigma < 36.0.$$

Summary. Let X be a normally distributed random variable with unknown expected value and unknown variance. A $1 - \alpha$ confidence for the variance of σ^2 is

$$\frac{(n-1)s^2}{\chi^2\left(\frac{\alpha}{2}, n-1\right)} < \sigma^2 < \frac{(n-1)s^2}{\chi^2\left(1 - \frac{\alpha}{2}, n-1\right)},$$

where n is the sample size and s^2 is the sample variance.

EXERCISES

28. Verify that the length of the confidence interval for σ^2
    a) increases with increasing confidence coefficient;
    b) decreases with increasing sample size;
    c) increases with increasing variance.

29. If X has a normal distribution and $n = 6$, what is the confidence coefficient for the interval $.45s^2 < \sigma^2 < 4.4s^2$?

30. As in exercise 20 of this chapter, let three observations of normally distributed random variable be 8, 10, and 12. Construct a .95 confidence interval
    a) for σ^2;
    b) for σ.

2.4 EXPECTED VALUES FOR TWO NORMAL DISTRIBUTIONS

Two different random experiments may require a confidence interval for some linear function of their unknown expected values. In the most common situation, the linear function is the difference of the expected values. Each random experiment has a normal distribution of probability. The confidence interval is to be constructed from two sets of experimental outcomes, one for each random experiment.

Let X_1 and X_2 be two independent, normally distributed random variables with unknown expected values, μ_1 and μ_2, and variances, σ_1^2 and σ_2^2. Initially, consider the problem of constructing a $1 - \alpha$ confidence interval for $\mu_1 - \mu_2$. A random sample of size n_1 for X_1 is $x_{11}, x_{12}, \ldots, x_{1n_1}$; a random sample of size n_2 for X_2 is $x_{21}, x_{22}, \ldots, x_{2n_2}$. We seek two functions, h_1 and h_2, that determine the endpoints of the confidence interval $d_1 < \mu_1 - \mu_2 < d_2$:

$$d_1 = h_1(x_{11}, x_{12}, \ldots, x_{1n_1}, x_{21}, x_{22}, \ldots, x_{2n_2}),$$
$$d_2 = h_2(x_{11}, x_{12}, \ldots, x_{1n_1}, x_{21}, x_{22}, \ldots, x_{2n_2}).$$

To have the specified confidence coefficient, $\Pr\{D_1 < \mu_1 - \mu_2 < D_2\}$ must equal $1 - \alpha$ for all $\mu_1 - \mu_2$.

It is possible to generate these functions by referring back to the related significance test, but there is a simpler and more useful method which reduces the problem to one previously discussed. Consider the random variable $\bar{X}_1 - \bar{X}_2$, which is normally distributed with $E(\bar{X}_1 - \bar{X}_2) = \mu_1 - \mu_2$ and $V(\bar{X}_1 - \bar{X}_2) = \sigma_1^2/n_1 + \sigma_2^2/n_2$ The next step depends on the experimenter's knowledge of the variances and on the sample sizes. Three cases are discussed in this book.

CASE 1. The variances, σ_1^2 and σ_2^2, are both known. The situation is now reduced to that of subsection 2.1 for finding a confidence interval for the expected value of one normally distributed random variable. In that discussion the variable was X, and the endpoints of the $1 - \alpha$ confidence interval for $E(X)$ were $\bar{x} \pm z\left(\dfrac{\alpha}{2}\right)D(\bar{X})$. Therefore, the endpoints of a $1 - \alpha$ interval for $E(X_1 - X_2) = \mu_1 - \mu_2$ are

$$(\bar{x}_1 - \bar{x}_2) \pm z\left(\frac{\alpha}{2}\right)D(\bar{X}_1 - \bar{X}_2).$$

The confidence interval itself is

$$(\bar{x}_1 - \bar{x}_2) - z\left(\frac{\alpha}{2}\right)\sqrt{\frac{\sigma_1^2}{n_1} + \frac{\sigma_2^2}{n_2}} < \mu_1 - \mu_2$$
$$< (\bar{x}_1 - \bar{x}_2) + z\left(\frac{\alpha}{2}\right)\sqrt{\frac{\sigma_1^2}{n_1} + \frac{\sigma_2^2}{n_2}}.$$

CASE 2. The variances, σ_1^2 and σ_2^2, are unknown, but n_1 and n_2 are both large, each about 30 or more. In this case, the two sample variances, s_1^2 and s_2^2, are adequate approximations to σ_1^2 and σ_2^2. The interval is as in Case 1 with σ_1^2 replaced by s_1^2 and σ_2^2 replaced by s_2^2.

CASE 3. The variances, σ_1^2 and σ_2^2, are unknown, but they are equal. Also, n_1 and n_2 are equal. (See Chapter VII.)

For an illustration, suppose the army is considering two types of rifles for infantry. A group of 60 soldiers is picked at random, trained on the first type of rifle, and run through a firing exercise that simulates combat. Each soldier makes a score between 0 and 100 on the exercise. A second group of 100 soldiers is trained similarly for the second type of rifle. The results are:

$$n_1 = 60 \qquad n_2 = 100$$
$$\bar{x}_1 = 75 \qquad \bar{x}_2 = 65$$
$$s_1^2 = 120 \qquad s_2^2 = 100$$

The .95 confidence interval for the difference of the expected values is

$$(75 - 65) \pm (1.96)\sqrt{\frac{120}{60} + \frac{100}{100}},$$

$$6.6 < \mu_1 - \mu_2 < 13.4.$$

This method is easily modified to construct a $1 - \alpha$ confidence interval for a linear combination $a_1\mu_1 + a_2\mu_2$ of the two expected values. The constants, a_1 and a_2, are known. Consider the normally distributed random variable $a_1\bar{X}_1 + a_2\bar{X}_2$. The parameters are

$$E(a_1\bar{X}_1 + a_2\bar{X}_2) = a_1\mu_1 + a_2\mu_2,$$

$$V(a_1\bar{X}_1 + a_2\bar{X}_2) = \frac{a_1^2\sigma_1^2}{n_1} + \frac{a_2^2\sigma_2^2}{n_2}.$$

If the variances, σ_1^2 and σ_2^2, are known, the endpoints of the $1 - \alpha$ confidence interval are

$$(a_1\bar{x}_1 + a_2\bar{x}_2) \pm z\left(\frac{\alpha}{2}\right)D(a_1\bar{X}_1 + a_2\bar{X}_2).$$

If σ_1^2 and σ_2^2 are unknown but n_1 and n_2 are each large, s_1^2 and s_2^2 are sufficiently good estimators to replace σ_1^2 and σ_2^2. Some of the exercises provide illustrations.

Summary. Let X_1 and X_2 be independent, normally distributed random variables with parameters $E(X_1) = \mu_1$, $V(X_1) = \sigma_1^2$, $E(X_2) = \mu_2$, and $V(X_2) = \sigma_2^2$. If random samples of sizes n_1 and n_2 are taken and if σ_1^2 and σ_2^2 are known, then the $1 - \alpha$ confidence interval for $\mu_1 - \mu_2$ is

$$(\bar{x}_1 - \bar{x}_2) - z\left(\frac{\alpha}{2}\right)\sqrt{\frac{\sigma_1^2}{n_1} + \frac{\sigma_2^2}{n_2}} < \mu_1 - \mu_2$$

$$< (x_1 - \bar{x}_2) + z\left(\frac{\alpha}{2}\right)\sqrt{\frac{\sigma_1^2}{n_1} + \frac{\sigma_2^2}{n_2}}.$$

If σ_1^2 and σ_2^2 are unknown but n_1 and n_2 are about 30 or more, replace σ_1^2 by s_1^2 and σ_2^2 by s_2^2.

EXERCISES

31. There are two ways, one expensive and one cheap, to manufacture an electronic component. For the expensive component, a sample of 30 showed an average useful life of 520 hours and a sample standard deviation of 130 hours. For the cheap component a sample of 60 showed an average useful life of 400 hours and a sample standard deviation of 120 hours. Give a .95 confidence interval for the difference of the corresponding expected values.

32. Prior to the experiment of exercise 31, suppose the experimenter assumes $\sigma_1 = \sigma_2 = 120$ for the purpose of designing the experiment. He wants a .95 confidence interval $(\bar{x}_1 - \bar{x}_2) \pm \epsilon$, where $\epsilon = 20$ hours. If $n_1 = n_2 = n$, what is n?

33. X_1 and X_2 are independent, normally distributed random variables. Large samples of each are taken. Consider the hypothesis $\mu_1 - \mu_2 = 0$. Show that the data reject the hypothesis, if and only if the corresponding $1 - \alpha$ confidence interval does not include zero.

34. A reducing diet is given to 100 obese people—40 men and 60 women. After 10 weeks, the weight losses, X_1 for the men and X_2 for the women, are measured. The results are:

$$\bar{x}_1 = 15.1 \qquad\qquad \bar{x}_2 = 10.3$$
$$s_1 = 6.2 \qquad\qquad s_2 = 4.1$$

a) Construct a .90 confidence interval for the difference $\mu_1 - \mu_2$ in the populations represented by these people.

b) At the .10 level, would these data reject the hypothesis $\mu_1 - \mu_2 = 0$?

35. A reducing diet is given to 100 obese people—40 men and 60 women. After 10 weeks, 60 per cent of the men and 50 per cent of the women lose at least 10 pounds. Construct a .90 confidence interval for the difference of the corresponding proportions in the populations represented by these people.

36. Three normally distributed random variables X_1, X_2, and X_3 have unknown expectations and known variances $\sigma_1^2 = 4$, $\sigma_2^2 = 6$, $\sigma_3^2 = 8$. Independent random samples are taken according to $n_1 = 2$, $n_2 = 1$, $n_3 = 4$. Construct a .99 confidence interval for $\mu_1 + 2\mu_2 - 3\mu_3$ from $\bar{x}_1 = 10$, $\bar{x}_2 = 17$, $\bar{x}_3 = 12$.

37. Prior to an advertising campaign, a sample of 100 consumers showed 16 favoring a particular brand. After the campaign, a sample of 200 showed 50 favoring the brand. If any change in the market is due to the campaign, construct a .95 confidence interval for the effect of the campaign.

38. In the city of exercise 6, thirty per cent of the Christians are Catholics. In a sample of 60 Catholics, 50 went to church last Sunday; in a sample of 70 Protestants, 40 went to church last Sunday. Construct a .95 confidence interval for the proportion of Christians in the city who went to church last Sunday.

ADDITIONAL READINGS

Brownlee, K., *Statistical Theory and Methodology in Science and Engineering.* 2nd ed. New York: John Wiley & Sons, Inc., 1965.

Brunk, H., *An Introduction to Mathematical Statistics.* 2nd ed. New York: Blaisdell Publishing Company, 1965.

Hogg, R., and A. Craig, *Introduction to Mathematical Statistics.* 2nd ed. New York: The Macmillan Company, 1965.

Mood, A., and F. Graybill, *Introduction to the Theory of Statistics.* 2nd ed. New York: McGraw-Hill Book Company, 1963.

Wallis, W., and H. Roberts, *Statistics: A New Approach.* New York: The Free Press, 1956.

Problems

A large corporation wants personal information about its employees' opinions. Sixty per cent of the employees are in the production department; thirty per cent are in sales; and ten per cent are in research and development. Beebe, a psychological consultant, is hired to conduct and evaluate a survey. From the company's records, 60 persons in production are randomly selected, 40 persons from sales, and 30 persons from research. After a confidential interview in depth, Beebe rates each person's general opinion of the company. The rating is on a scale from 1 for a very unfavorable opinion to 10 for a very favorable opinion. Beebe also indicates whether he thinks the person will remain with the company until retirement. The results are:

	Production	Sales	Research
sample size	60	40	30
general opinion			
mean	5.1	4.3	5.7
std. dev.	2.3	1.9	1.4
number planning to remain to retirement	36	10	11

When required in the following problems, use a .95 confidence interval or a .05 significance level test. Treat each problem individually. There is some loss from constructing numerous intervals or tests from the same data, but ignore this problem.

1. Give a point estimator for the overall expected opinion in the corporation.
2. Give a confidence interval for the overall expected opinion.
3. Test the hypothesis that the opinions in production and research have the same expected value. Prior to the sample, there was no idea that one was higher than the other. Use a two-sided test.
4. Test the hypothesis that the proportions of personnel who plan to remain to retirement are the same for production and research. Use a two-sided test.
5. Estimate the overall proportion planning to remain to retirement.
6. Give a confidence interval for the overall proportion planning to remain to retirement.
7. Give a confidence interval for the expected opinion in sales.
8. Give a confidence interval for the proportion planning to remain to retirement in production.
9. Prior to the sample, there was a belief that opinion was lower in sales than in the other departments. If μ_2 is the expected value in sales, attempt to prove the belief by disproving the hypothesis

$$\mu_2 \geq \frac{\mu_1 + \mu_3}{2},$$

where μ_1 and μ_3 refer to production and research.

Probability and Correlation | V

1
Multi-Dimensional Experiments

A numerical-valued random experiment is multi-dimensional if more than one real number is required to describe an outcome. If two numbers are required, the experiment is two-dimensional; if n numbers are required, the experiment is n-dimensional.

Corresponding to each multi-dimensional random experiment there is a multi-dimensional random variable. A general two-dimensional random variable, for example, might be (X, Y). An outcome or observation for this variable is (x, y), where x and y are the two numbers which describe the outcome. Most of the important topics can be illustrated with two-dimensional random variables.

Stock-Market Example. The closing market price of a particular stock Y varies from day to day. In this simplified example, the price can drop only a dollar from the previous day, remain unchanged, or rise a dollar. A second stock X also varies from day to day. Stock X also drops a dollar, remains unchanged, or rises a dollar. In the two-dimensional random experiment, a day of trading on the market is randomly selected. X is the change in stock X on that day; Y is the change in stock Y on the *next* day of trading. The random variable is (X, Y). The outcome $(1, 0)$, for example, indicates a rise of one dollar for stock X on the chosen day and no change in stock Y on the next day of trading.

The definitions of space, event, and probability are almost unchanged. The space for a multi-dimensional random variable or random experiment is the set of all n-dimensional outcomes. An event is a subset of the space. The probability of an event is the long-term relative frequency of the event in many trials of the experiment.

In the example of the stock market, the space consists of nine two-dimensional outcomes: $\{(-1, -1), (-1, 0), (-1, 1), (0, -1), (0, 0), (0, 1), (1, -1), (1, 0), (1, 1)\}$. The event of an increase in stock Y is $\{(-1, 1), (0, 1), (1, 1)\}$. Two other notations for this event are $\{-1 \leq X \leq 1$ and $Y = 1\}$ and $\{Y = 1\}$. If stock Y increases on 30 per cent of the days, the probability of this event is .30, or $\Pr\{(-1, 1), (0, 1), (1, 1)\} = .30$.

An n-dimensional random variable or random experiment is discrete, if there is a finite number of outcomes in the space. The random variable is continuous, if the space is an n-dimensional interval. The example of the stock market is discrete, because there are nine outcomes in the space.

EXERCISES

1. A realtor has a house to sell. A prospective buyer views the house, and he may buy after seeing the house. If he does not buy, he may disappear, or he may want to see the house again. Suppose no one buys without viewing, and no one views more than four times. To the realtor, the prospective buyer is a random experiment. Let the random variable be (X, Y), where X is the total number of visits by the buyer and Y is the number of purchases (0 or 1) by the buyer.
   a) What is the space for this random experiment?
   b) What is the event of selling the house to the prospective buyer?
   c) What is the event of selling after three or four visits?
   d) Describe the single-outcome event $\{(3, 0)\}$.
   e) Describe the event $\{1 \leq X \leq 3, \ Y = 0\}$.

2

Two-Dimensional Distributions

Whether the two-dimensional random variable (X, Y) is discrete or continuous, we need methods for finding probabilities of events. We also need parameters to characterize the distribution of probability. Separate discussions are necessary for the two cases, discrete and continuous. Many of the ideas are simple generalizations of those in Chapter II, but some ideas are new.

2.1 DISCRETE RANDOM VARIABLES

The *joint probability function* for a discrete random variable (X, Y) associates a probability $\Pr\{(x, y)\}$ with every two-dimensional outcome (x, y) in the space. That is, the joint probability function gives the probability of every single-outcome event $\{(x, y)\}$. Mathematically, there are only two restrictions on the joint probability function:

1) $\Pr\{(x, y)\} \geq 0$ for every outcome (x, y);
2) $\Pr \text{Space} = \sum_{\text{space}} \Pr\{(x, y)\} = 1.$

The probabilities of all events are determined by the joint probability function. Consider first an event with two outcomes $\{(x, y), (x', y')\}$. The relative-frequency interpretation of probability suggests

$$\Pr\{(x, y), (x', y')\} = \Pr\{(x, y)\} + \Pr\{(x', y')\}.$$

Consider next any event G. The probability of G is calculated from the joint probability function by

$$\Pr G = \sum_{(x,y) \in G} \Pr\{(x, y)\},$$

where the right-hand side is the sum of all the values of the probability function for the outcomes in G.

Table 1

case A

$\Pr\{(x, y)\}$

1	.02	.15	.13
$y =$ 0	.05	.30	.05
-1	.13	.15	.02
	-1	0	1
		x	

case B

$\Pr\{(x, y)\}$

1	.13	.15	.02
$y =$ 0	.05	.30	.05
-1	.02	.15	.13
	-1	0	1
		x	

case C

$\Pr\{(x, y)\}$

1	.06	.18	.06
$y =$ 0	.08	.24	.08
-1	.06	.18	.06
	-1	0	1
		x	

case D

$\Pr\{(x, y)\}$

1	.00	.30	.00
$y =$ 0	.05	.30	.05
-1	.15	.00	.15
	-1	0	1
		x	

To illustrate the joint probability function and other concepts, take the four distributions of probability in Table 1. Each is a possible description of the experiment involving the changes in the prices of the two stocks. Of course, there are many other possibilities. Figure 1 is a sketch of $\Pr\{(x, y)\}$ for case A. There is a similar sketch for each of the others. To illustrate the calculations, take the event that X goes up a dollar, but Y does not, $\{X = 1 \text{ and } -1 \leq Y \leq 0\}$ or $\{(1, -1), (1, 0)\}$.

$$\Pr\{(1, -1), (1, 0)\} = \Pr\{(1, -1)\} + \Pr\{(1, 0)\}$$

$$= .02 + .05 = .07 \text{ for case A}$$

$$= .13 + .05 = .18 \text{ for case B}$$

$$= .06 + .08 = .14 \text{ for case C}$$

$$= .15 + .05 = .20 \text{ for case D}$$

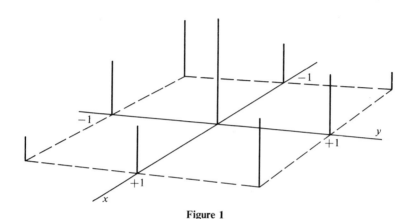

Figure 1

Expected Value

A parameter for the variable (X, Y) is the expected value of some function $g(X, Y)$ of the two component variables, X and Y. In symbols, the definition of the expected value of $g(X, Y)$ is

$$E[g(X, Y)] = \sum_x \sum_y g(x, y)\Pr\{(x, y)\}.$$

That is, each value $g(x, y)$ is weighted by its probability $\Pr\{(x, y)\}$ in the sum. When $g(x, y) = x$, we obtain the definition for $E(X)$ in this two-dimensional context.

$$E(X) = \sum_x \sum_y x\Pr\{(x, y)\}.$$

When $g(x, y) = y$, we obtain the definition for $E(Y)$.

$$E(Y) = \sum_x \sum_y y\Pr\{(x, y)\}.$$

When $g(x, y) = x + y$, we have the frequently used

$$E(X + Y) = \sum_x \sum_y (x + y) \Pr\{(x, y)\}$$

$$= \sum_x \sum_y x \Pr\{(x, y)\} + \sum_x \sum_y y \Pr\{(x, y)\}$$

$$= E(X) + E(Y).$$

In words, the expected value of a sum of random variables is the sum of the expected values. This fact was used many times in the first four chapters. When $g(x, y) = [x - E(X)]^2$, we obtain the definition for $V(X)$.

$$V(X) = E[X - E(X)]^2 = \sum_x \sum_y [x - E(X)]^2 \Pr\{(x, y)\}.$$

When $g(x, y) = [(x + y) - E(X + Y)]^2$, we have the definition of $V(X + Y)$.

$$V(X + Y) = E[(X + Y) - E(X + Y)]^2.$$

For a numerical illustration, take $E(X + Y)$ for case A of Table 1.

$$E(X + Y) = \sum_x \sum_y (x + y) \Pr\{(x, y)\} = (-2)(.13) + (-1)(.05 + .15)$$

$$+ (0)(.02 + .30 + .02) + (1)(.15 + .05) + (2)(.13) = 0.$$

Next, take $V(X + Y)$ for the same case.

$$V(X + Y) = E[(X + Y) - 0]^2 = (-2)^2(.13) + (-1)^2(.20)$$

$$+ (0)^2(.34) + (1)^2(.20) + (2)^2(.13) = 1.44.$$

Marginal Probability Functions

Although the experimenter may have the joint probability function for (X, Y), he frequently needs only the probability function for one of the component variables, say for X. That is, he needs to know the probability of every single-outcome event $\{x\}$. This event occurs, if and only if a corresponding two-dimensional event occurs,

$$\{X = x \text{ and } -\infty < Y < +\infty\}.$$

Therefore, the probability function for X is

$$\Pr\{x\} = \Pr\{X = x \text{ and } -\infty < Y < +\infty\} = \sum_y \Pr\{(x, y)\},$$

where the summation is over all the single-outcome events for (X, Y)

with x fixed. In this context, the resulting function of x is the *marginal probability function for X*. *The marginal probability function for Y is*

$$\Pr\{y\} = \sum_{x}\Pr\{(x, y)\},$$

where the summation is over all the single-outcome events for (X, Y) with y fixed.

These marginal probability functions are used in the same way as the probability functions discussed in Chapter II. In particular, the expected value of $h(X)$ can be calculated from

$$E[h(X)] = \sum_{x}h(x)\Pr\{x\},$$

where $h(X)$ is some given function. Since $E[g(X, Y)]$ has already been defined for (X, Y) and since $h(X)$ may be considered a special case of $g(X, Y)$, the two definitions should be checked for consistency.

$$E[h(X)] = \sum_{x}h(x)\Pr\{x\} = \sum_{x}h(x)\sum_{y}\Pr\{(x, y)\}$$
$$= \sum_{x}\sum_{y}h(x)\Pr\{(x, y)\} = E[h(X)].$$

In particular, this means that $E(X)$, $E(Y)$, $V(X)$, and $V(Y)$ can be calculated from the appropriate marginal probability functions, rather than from the joint probability function.

In case A of Table 1, the marginal probability function for X is:

$$\Pr\{-1\} = \sum_{y}\Pr\{(-1, y)\} = .13 + .05 + .02 = .20,$$

$$\Pr\{0\} = \sum_{y}\Pr\{(0, y)\} \quad = .15 + .30 + .15 = .60,$$

$$\Pr\{1\} = \sum_{y}\Pr\{(1, y)\} \quad = .02 + .05 + .13 = .20.$$

The marginal probability function for Y in the same case is:

$$\Pr\{-1\} = \sum_{x}\Pr\{(x, -1)\} = .13 + .15 + .02 = .30,$$

$$\Pr\{0\} = \sum_{x}\Pr\{(x, 0)\} \quad = .05 + .30 + .05 = .40,$$

$$\Pr\{1\} = \sum_{x}\Pr\{(x, 1)\} \quad = .02 + .15 + .13 = .30.$$

The marginal probability functions in cases B, C, and D are exactly the same as those for case A. In all four illustrative cases of Table 1, the expected values and variances are $E(X) = 0$, $E(Y) = 0$, $V(X) = .40$, $V(Y) = .60$. Notice for case A that $1.44 = V(X + Y) \neq V(X) + V(Y) = 1.00$.

Conditional Probability Functions

For the two stocks X and Y, let case A of Table 1 be the joint probability function for their price changes. Not knowing anything about X, an experimenter uses the marginal probability function for events involving only Y. For example, the probability that Y goes up a dollar is $\Pr\{Y = 1\} = .30$. Suppose, however, the experimenter knows that stock X went up a dollar on the previous day. Now what is the probability that stock Y will go up a dollar? In this situation, Y is a one-dimensional random variable with space $\{-1, 0, 1\}$. The problem is to lay down a probability distribution over this space for Y. To motivate the definition of this probability, imagine a large number N of observations of the two-dimensional random variable (X, Y). Stock X goes up a dollar approximately $.20N$ times. Both X and Y go up a dollar approximately $.13N$ times. Of the $.20N$ times that X goes up, Y also goes up $.13N$ times. This suggests the following ratio for the desired probability of $\{Y = 1\}$:

$$\frac{.13N}{.20N} = \frac{.13}{.20} = .65 = \frac{\Pr\{X = 1 \text{ and } Y = 1\}}{\Pr\{X = 1\}}.$$

As indicated by this calculation, the suggested probability is the ratio of the joint probability function to the marginal probability function. Similarly, the suggested probability of no change in Y, when X goes up, is

$$\frac{.05N}{.20N} = \frac{.05}{.20} = .25 = \frac{\Pr\{X = 1 \text{ and } Y = 0\}}{\Pr\{X = 1\}}.$$

Finally, the suggested probability of a drop in Y, when X goes up, is

$$\frac{.02N}{.20N} = \frac{.02}{.20} = .10 = \frac{\Pr\{X = 1 \text{ and } Y = -1\}}{\Pr\{X = 1\}}.$$

The three ratios are non-negative numbers which add to one.

In the general situation, (X, Y) is a discrete random variable with a joint density function $\Pr\{(x, y)\}$. If $X = x$ is observed, the *conditional probability function for Y* is

$$\Pr\{y|x\} = \Pr\{Y = y \,|\, X = x\} = \frac{\Pr\{(x, y)\}}{\Pr\{x\}}.$$

For every possible x, there is a conditional probability function for Y. Generally, these functions all can be different. If $Y = y$ is observed, the *conditional probability function for X* is

$$\Pr\{x|y\} = \Pr\{X = x \,|\, Y = y\} = \frac{\Pr\{(x, y)\}}{\Pr\{x\}}.$$

For every possible y, there is also a conditional probability function for X. These conditional distributions of probability are very important for the topics of this chapter.

In case A of Table 1, the three conditional probability functions for Y are given in the following columns:

$$\Pr\{y\,|\,x\}$$

	1	.10	.25	.65
y	0	.25	.50	.25
	-1	.65	.25	.10
		-1	0	1
			x	

In terms of the stocks, if X goes up a dollar, .65 is the probability that Y will go up a dollar; if X does not change, .25 is the probability that Y will go up a dollar; if X drops a dollar, .10 is the probability that Y will go up a dollar. Recall that .30 is the unconditional probability that Y will go up a dollar.

Independence

The two component variables of a two-dimensional random variable can be completely unrelated. This important case needs a special discussion. Let (X, Y) be the discrete random variable with known joint probability function $\Pr\{(x, y)\}$. The two marginal probability functions and the many conditional probability functions can be derived from $\Pr\{(x, y)\}$. If the experimenter is interested in an event G for Y and if X is unobserved, he calculates the probability from the marginal $\Pr\{x\}$. If he is interested in the event G for Y and if X is observed, he uses the appropriate conditional $\Pr\{y\,|\,x\}$. Suppose the marginal and the appropriate conditional are identical. In fact, suppose the marginal for Y and the conditional for Y are identical for all observed values of X. In this case, the conditional and the unconditional probabilities of G are identical, and the observed value of X is irrelevant for events involving Y. When this is true, Y is *independent* of X. That is, Y is independent of X if

$$\Pr\{y\,|\,x\} = \Pr\{y\} \text{ for all } x.$$

If Y is independent of X, then X is independent of Y. The proof is

$$\Pr\{x\,|\,y\} = \frac{\Pr\{(x, y)\}}{\Pr\{y\}} = \frac{\Pr\{(x, y)\}}{\Pr\{y\,|\,x\}} = \frac{\Pr\{(x, y)\}}{\Pr\{(x, y)\}/\Pr\{x\}} = \Pr\{x\}.$$

It is common to refer to X and Y simply as "independent." Variables that are not independent are *dependent*. There is a small, but important relation to observe when X and Y are independent.

$$\Pr\{y\} = \Pr\{y|x\} = \frac{\Pr\{(x, y)\}}{\Pr\{x\}}$$

leads to

$$\Pr\{(x, y)\} = \Pr\{x\} \cdot \Pr\{y\}.$$

In words, the joint probability function is the product of the marginal probability functions, when X and Y are independent. In summary, the following four statements are equivalent:

1. X and Y are independent,
2. $\Pr\{y|x\} = \Pr\{y\}$,
3. $\Pr\{x|y\} = \Pr\{x\}$,
4. $\Pr\{(x, y)\} = \Pr\{x\} \cdot \Pr\{y\}$.

Previous calculations with case A of Table 1 showed that the conditionals for Y are not identical to the marginal for Y. Hence X and Y are dependent in case A. In case C, however, X and Y are independent. The quickest way to verify this is to check

$$\Pr\{(x, y)\} = \Pr\{x\} \cdot \Pr\{y\}$$

by looking at the nine cases.

$$.06 = \Pr\{(-1, -1)\} = \Pr\{-1\} \cdot \Pr\{-1\} = (.2)(.3) = .06,$$

and so on.

In most statistical situations the experimenter is not interested in verifying independence from a given joint distribution of probability. Instead, he takes his observations in such a way that he can assume independence. He then uses the independence and the marginal distributions to obtain the joint distribution of probability.

Another by-product of independence is the additivity of variances.

$$V(X + Y) = V(X) + V(Y).$$

This is now easily proved.

$$
\begin{aligned}
V(X + Y) &= E[(X + Y) - E(X + Y)]^2 \\
&= E\{[X - E(X)] + E[Y - E(Y)]\}^2 \\
&= E[X - E(X)]^2 + 2E\{[X - E(X)][Y - E(Y)]\} \\
&\qquad\qquad\qquad\qquad\qquad\qquad + E[Y - E(Y)]^2 \\
&= V(X) + V(Y).
\end{aligned}
$$

The middle term is zero, because

$$E\{[X - E(X)][Y - E(Y)]\}$$

$$= \sum_x \sum_y [x - E(X)][y - E(Y)] \cdot \Pr\{x\} \cdot \Pr\{y\}$$

$$= \sum_x [x - E(X)] \cdot \Pr\{x\} \sum_y [y - E(Y)] \Pr\{y\}$$

$$= \sum_x [x - E(X)] \Pr\{x\} \cdot 0$$

$$= 0.$$

The independence is used in the first line. Since X and Y are independent in numerical example C of Table 1, the variances add. $V(X + Y) = V(X) + V(Y) = .4 + .6 = 1.0$.

Correlation Coefficient

When two component random variables are not independent, we often want to measure the degree of dependence between them. That is, we want another parameter for the two-dimensional random variable. The old parameters, expected values and variances, do not indicate the strength of the relationship between the two component random variables. If (X, Y) is the random variable, we seek a function $g(x, y)$ such that $E[g(X, Y)]$ measures the degree of dependence between X and Y. Ideally, this measure $E[g(X, Y)]$ might be one value when X and Y are independent; it might be another value when X and Y are very dependent. Intermediate values for $E[g(X, Y)]$ might even indicate the degree of dependence.

There is no perfect function $g(x, y)$ for this parameter, but something comes close to perfection. Consider $g(x, y) = [x - E(X)][y - E(Y)]$. When X and Y are independent, the expected value of $g(X, Y)$ is zero. This was proved in the previous discussion about the additivity of variances. What happens to $E[g(X, Y)]$ when X and Y are very dependent? For one possibility, suppose all the probability lies on a straight line. That is, $Y = aX + b$ for every outcome (X, Y) with positive probability. Then $V(Y)$ is $a^2 V(X)$, and the expected value is

$$E[g(X, Y)] = E\{[X - E(X)][(aX + b) - E(aX + b)]\}$$

$$= aV(X) = \frac{1}{a}V(Y) = \frac{1}{a}D(Y)D(Y).$$

If a is positive, $D(Y) = aD(X)$ and $E[g(X, Y)] = D(X)D(Y)$. If a is negative, $D(Y) = -aD(X)$ and $E[g(X, Y)] = -D(X)D(Y)$. Although we do not prove it, these two cases give the upper and lower bounds for the expected value of $g(X, Y)$. That is, the expected value is limited according to

$$- D(X)D(Y) \le E\{[X - E(X)][Y - E(Y)]\} \le D(X)D(Y),$$

or

$$-1 \le \frac{E\{[X - E(X)][Y - E(Y)]\}}{D(X)D(Y)} \le 1.$$

The quantity in the middle is the desired parameter. It is the *correlation coefficient* for X and Y,

$$\mathrm{Cor}(X,\ Y) = \frac{E\{[X - E(X)][Y - E(Y)]\}}{D(X)D(Y)}.$$

As a practical matter, the numerator is usually computed from the equivalent form $E(XY) - E(X)E(Y)$. When X and Y are independent, the correlation coefficient is zero. When X and Y are nearly positively related, as in $Y = aX + b$ with $a > 0$, the correlation coefficient is near positive one. When X and Y are nearly negatively related, as in $Y = aX + b$ with $a < 0$, the correlation coefficient is near negative one.

The correlation coefficients for the four cases in Table 1 are

	$\mathrm{Cor}(X,\ Y)$
case A	.45
case B	$-.45$
case C	.00
case D	.00

The positive value in case A suggests some tendency for the probability to lie near a line with positive slope. One should verify this by looking at the joint probability function. The negative value in case B suggests an equal tendency to lie near a line with negative slope. Indeed, the joint distribution in B is the mirror image of that in A. The zero in case C reflects the independence of X and Y. Case D illustrates the danger: the correlation coefficient is zero, but X and Y are definitely not independent. This more complicated form of dependence will be considered later in this chapter.

Summary. The discrete random variable $(X,\ Y)$ has three types of probability distribution associated with it.

1) The joint probability function $\mathrm{Pr}\{(x,\ y)\}$ is used for calculating the probability of any event in the two-dimensional space.

2) The marginal probability function $\Pr\{x\} = \sum_y \Pr\{(x, y)\}$ is used for calculating the probability of any event involving only one of the variables.

3) The conditional probability function $\Pr\{y|x\} = \dfrac{\Pr\{(x, y)\}}{\Pr\{x\}}$ is used for calculating the probability of an event involving one of the variables when the value of the other is known.

When all the conditionals for Y are the same as the marginal for Y, X and Y are independent. In this case, the joint probability function is the product of the marginals $\Pr\{(x, y)\} = \Pr\{x\}\Pr\{y\}$. A parameter that measures the degree of dependence between X and Y is the correlation coefficient.

$$\text{Cor}(X, Y) = \frac{E\{[X - E(X)][Y - E(Y)]\}}{D(X)D(Y)} = \frac{E(XY) - E(X)E(Y)}{D(X)D(Y)}.$$

When X and Y are independent, $\text{Cor}(X, Y) = 0$.

EXERCISES

2. The parts of this exercise refer to the probability distributions in Table 1.
   a) For each of the four cases, find $\Pr\{X + Y = 1\}$.
   b) Verify that all the marginals for X are the same.
   c) Verify that all the marginals for Y are the same.
   d) Verify that $E(X) = E(Y) = 0$, $V(X) = .40$, and $V(Y) = .60$.
   e) From the definition verify that $V(X + Y) = E[(X + Y)^2 - 0]^2 = 1.00$ for case C.
   f) Calculate $E(XY)$ for all four cases.
   g) Calculate $\Pr\{X = 0 | Y = 1\}$ for all four cases.
   h) Verify the results for $\text{Cor}(X, Y)$ in all four cases.

3. For the two-dimensional experiment of exercise 1 (page 133), let the joint probability function be

	1	.06	.06	.05	.07
y					
	0	.54	.14	.05	.03
		1	2	3	4
			x		

Recall that X is the number of visits by a prospective buyer, and Y is the number of purchases.

a) Find the probabilities for the events of parts b) through e) of exercise 1.

b) Find the marginal probability function for X.

c) Find the marginal probability function for Y.

d) Compute $E(X)$, $E(Y)$, $V(X)$, and $V(Y)$.

e) Find the two conditional probability functions for X.

f) Find the four conditional probability functions for Y.

g) The prospective buyer takes the house. What is the probability that he made at least 3 visits?

h) The prospective buyer made a total of 2 visits. What is the probability he took the house?

i) Compute $E(XY)$ and $Cor(X, Y)$.

j) Each visit by the buyer costs the realtor $30. If he sells the house, the realtor's commission is $900. Interpret the new random variable $W = -30X + 900Y$.

k) Compute $E(W)$ and interpret it.

l) Construct a different probability function $Pr\{(x, y)\}$ that has the marginal probability functions of b) and c), but make X and Y independent.

4. With the probability function of exercise 3, let $U = 0$ if the buyer visits less than three times; let $U = 1$ if the buyer visits three or more times.

a) Find the joint probability function for (U, Y).

b) Find the conditional probability of $\{Y = 1\}$, if $U = 1$ is observed. Interpret this probability for the realtor who now sees the prospective buyer for the third time.

5. M and N are independent random variables with the same space $\{1, 2, 3\}$. Their marginal probability functions are:

m, n	$Pr\{m\}$	$Pr\{n\}$
1	.7	.3
2	.2	.3
3	.1	.4

Find:

a) $Pr\{M + N \leq 4\}$

b) $Pr\{MN \leq 4\}$

c) $Pr\{M = 3 \mid N = 2\}$

d) $E(M)$

e) $E(N)$

f) Calculate $E(MN)$ from the definition, and verify that $E(MN) = E(M)E(N)$.

6. For a discrete random variable (X, Y) prove directly from the definition of expected value that

$$E(aX + bY + c) = aE(X) + bE(Y) + c,$$

where a, b, and c are constants.

7. If X and Y are independent, prove $V(aX + bY + c) = a^2V(X) + b^2V(Y)$.

8. For a discrete random variable (X, Y), prove that the conditional probabilities add to one.

$$\sum_y \Pr\{y|x\} = 1.$$

9. Prove the most general formula for the variance of a sum of random variables. $V(X + Y) = V(X) + V(Y) + 2D(X)D(Y)\text{Cor}(X, Y)$.

10. If (X, Y) is a two-dimensional random variable, then (aX, bY) is also a two-dimensional random variable, where a and b are positive constants. Show $\text{Cor}(aX, bY) = \text{Cor}(X, Y)$.

11. Use exercises 9 and 10 to prove

$$V(aX + bY + c)$$
$$= a^2V(X) + b^2V(Y) + 2ab\,D(X)D(Y)\text{Cor}(X, Y).$$

* 2.2 *CONTINUOUS RANDOM VARIABLES*

A two-dimensional random variable or random experiment is continuous, if the space is a two-dimensional interval of numbers. That is, each of the two component variables is continuous and takes values in an interval. This subsection discusses the same topics for the continuous case as the previous subsection did for the discrete case: joint distribution, probability, marginal and conditional distributions, independence, and the correlation coefficient.

Motorist Example. A motorist takes his car through a two-stage testing lane. Let X be the waiting time at the first stage, and let Y be the waiting time at the second stage. Neither wait is more than one minute. The space is the two-dimensional interval $\{0 \le X \le 1 \text{ and } 0 \le Y \le 1\}$. The outcome, $(.5, .7)$ for example, corresponds to a wait of .5 minute at the first stage and .7 minute at the second.

Let (X, Y) be a general continuous random variable. An event for (X, Y) is a subset of the space. Just as in the one-dimensional case, there is a density function $f(x, y)$ for finding the probability of an event. In this case it is called the *joint density function*. The probability of an event G is the integral of $f(x, y)$ over G. $\text{Pr } G = \iint_G f(x, y)\,dx\,dy$. Mathematically, the joint density function must satisfy these familiar conditions:

1) $f(x, y) \geq 0$,
2) $\iint f(x, y)\,dx\,dy = 1$,

where the last integral is over the entire space.

If $g(x, y)$ is a function of x and y, then $g(X, Y)$ is a random variable. Its expectation is

$$E[g(X, Y)] = \iint g(x, y)f(x, y)\,dx\,dy,$$

where the integral is over the entire space. The parameters $E(X)$, $E(Y)$, $V(X)$, and $V(Y)$ are defined by appropriate choices of $g(x, y)$. For example, $g(x, y) = x$ generates

$$E(X) = \iint xf(x, y)\,dx\,dy,$$

and $g(x, y) = [x - E(X)]^2$ generates

$$V(X) = \iint [x - E(X)]^2 f(x, y)\,dx\,dy.$$

The marginal density function $f(x)$ for X is obtained by integrating the joint density function with respect to y: $f(x) = \int f(x, y)\,dy$. Similarly, the marginal density function $f(y)$ for Y is obtained by integrating the joint density function with respect to x: $f(y) = \int f(x, y)\,dx$. The expected values and variances for X and Y can be calculated directly from the marginal density functions, just as in Chapter II.

A conditional density function is the ratio of the joint density function to the appropriate marginal density function,

$$f(y\,|\,x) = \frac{f(x, y)}{f(x)} \quad \text{or} \quad f(x\,|\,y) = \frac{f(x, y)}{f(y)}.$$

When all the conditionals for Y are the same as the marginal for Y, then X and Y are independent. The four following statements are equivalent:

1) X and Y are independent;
2) $f(y\,|\,x) = f(y)$ for all x;
3) $f(x\,|\,y) = f(x)$ for all y;
4) $f(x, y) = f(x)f(y)$.

The correlation coefficient for X and Y is

$$\text{Cor}(X, Y) = \frac{E\{[X - E(X)][Y - E(Y)]\}}{D(X)D(Y)} = \frac{E(XY) - E(X)E(Y)}{D(X)D(Y)}.$$

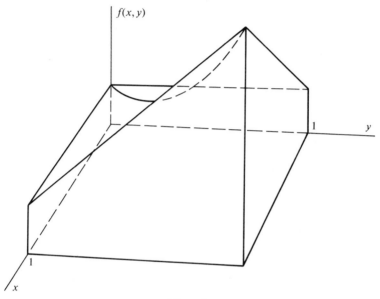

Figure 2

For the example of the motorist in the two-stage testing lane, let the joint density function be $f(x, y) = \frac{1}{2}(1 + 4xy)$. Figure 2 is a picture of this function. Probably this density function is not very realistic, but the realistic ones are much harder to integrate. Consider the event A that the wait at each stage is less than .5 minute. $A = \{0 \le X, Y \le .5\}$. The probability is

$$\text{Pr } A = \int_0^{.5} \int_0^{.5} \frac{1}{2}(1 + 4xy)\,dx\,dy = \frac{5}{32} = .156.$$

In geometric terms, this is the volume under the surface $f(x, y)$ and over the square determined by A. The expected value of $g(X, Y) = XY$ is

$$E(XY) = \int_0^1 \int_0^1 xy\,f(x, y)\,dx\,dy = \frac{25}{72}.$$

The marginal density function for X is

$$f(x) = \int_0^1 \frac{1}{2}(1 + 4xy)\,dy = \frac{1}{2}(1 + 2x) \quad \text{for} \quad 0 \le x \le 1.$$

The marginal density function for Y is

$$f(y) = \int_0^1 \frac{1}{2}(1 + 4xy)\,dx = \frac{1}{2}(1 + 2y) \quad \text{for} \quad 0 \le y \le 1.$$

Some parameters are

$$E(X) = \int_0^1 x\frac{1}{2}(1 + 2x)\,dx = \frac{7}{12},$$

$$E(Y) = \frac{7}{12},$$

$$E(X^2) = \int_0^1 x^2 \frac{1}{2}(1 + 2x)\,dx = \frac{5}{12},$$

$$V(X) = \frac{5}{12} - \left(\frac{7}{12}\right)^2 = \frac{11}{144},$$

$$V(Y) = \frac{11}{144}.$$

The probability of waiting less than .5 minute at the second stage is

$$\int_0^{.5} \frac{1}{2}(1 + 2y)\,dy = \frac{3}{8} = .375.$$

The conditional density functions for this example are

$$f(y|x) = \frac{\frac{1}{2}(1 + 4xy)}{\frac{1}{2}(1 + 2x)} = \frac{1 + 4xy}{1 + 2x} \quad \text{for} \quad 0 \le y \le 1;$$

$$f(x|y) = \frac{1 + 4xy}{1 + 2y} \quad \text{for} \quad 0 \le x \le 1.$$

Since the marginals are not identical to the conditionals, the waiting times are not independent. If $X = .1$ is observed, the conditional probability of waiting less than .5 minutes at the second stage is

$$\int_0^{.5} \frac{1 + .4y}{1 + .2}\,dy = .46.$$

The correlation coefficient is

$$\operatorname{Cor}(X, Y) = \frac{E(XY) - E(X)E(Y)}{D(X)D(Y)} = \frac{\frac{25}{72} - \frac{7}{12}\frac{7}{12}}{\sqrt{\frac{11}{144}}\sqrt{\frac{11}{144}}} = \frac{1}{11} = .09.$$

EXERCISES

12. Scores on a general intelligence test may be adjusted to have a uniform distribution over the interval from zero to one. For example, a score of .65 means that 65 per cent of the entire population would do worse, and 35 per cent would do better. Let X be the continuous random variable for the experiment of randomly selecting a person and testing him. The density function is $f(x) = 1$ for $0 \le x \le 1$. Two persons are independently selected and tested. Let the random variable be (X, Y).
    a) What are the space and joint density function for (X, Y)?
    b) Find $\Pr\{Y \le .40\}$.
    c) Find $\Pr\{X \text{ and } Y \le .40\}$.
    d) Find $\Pr\{X + Y \le .40\}$.

13. A person is selected and given the test described in exercise 12. Let X be his score. He then names his best friend, who is also given the test. Let Y be his score.
    a) Would you expect X and Y to be independent? Suppose the joint density function for (X, Y) is

    $$f(x, y) = 2(1 - x - y + 2xy) \text{ for } 0 \le x, y \le 1.$$

    b) Find $\Pr\{X \text{ and } Y \le .40\}$.
    c) Find $\Pr\{Y \le X\}$.
    d) Find the marginal density function for X.
    e) Find the marginal density function for Y.
    f) Compute $E(X)$, $E(Y)$, $V(X)$, and $V(Y)$.
    g) Find $\Pr\{Y \le .40\}$.
    h) Find the conditional density function for Y.
    i) Suppose the first person scores .10. What is the probability that his friend scores less than .40?
    j) Compute $E(XY)$ and $\operatorname{Cor}(X, Y)$.

14. For a continuous random variable (X, Y), prove from the definition

of $E[g(X, Y)]$ that $E(aX + bY + c) = aE(X) + bE(Y) + c$, where a, b, and c are constants.

15. Re-prove the result in exercise 9 for the continuous case. $V(X + Y) = V(X) + V(Y) + 2D(X)D(Y)\text{Cor}(X, Y)$.

16. Re-prove the result in exercise 10 for the continuous case. $\text{Cor}(aX, bY) = \text{Cor}(X, Y)$, where a and b are positive constants.

17. Re-prove the result in exercise 11 for the continuous case. $V(aX + bY + c) = a^2V(X) + b^2V(Y) + 2abD(X)D(Y)\text{Cor}(X, Y)$.

2.3 THE NORMAL DISTRIBUTION

The normal distribution of probability is the most important type for a two-dimensional random variable. The variable must be continuous, and its space must be the entire plane, at least in theory. For a variable (X, Y), this means the bounds are $-\infty < x < +\infty$ and $-\infty < y < +\infty$. Even with the aid of calculus, it is not always easy to answer all the probabilistic questions about the two-dimensional normal distribution. For example, even finding the probability of an event may be very difficult. Fortunately, statistical topics usually involve only the marginal or conditional probability distributions. Since these are one-dimensional distributions, the methods of Chapter II are usually sufficient. This subsection illustrates the applications of these methods. The proofs are beyond the level of this book.

*   The joint density function is

$$f(x, y) = \frac{1}{2\pi\sigma_X\sigma_Y\sqrt{1 - \rho^2}} e^{Q(x,y)},$$

where

$$Q(x, y) = -\frac{1}{2(1 - \rho^2)}\left[\left(\frac{x - \mu_X}{\sigma_X}\right)^2 - 2\rho\left(\frac{x - \mu_X}{\sigma_X}\right)\left(\frac{y - \mu_Y}{\sigma_Y}\right) + \left(\frac{y - \mu_Y}{\sigma_Y}\right)^2\right].$$

There are five parameters in this function. Topographically, this function looks like a worn mountain with concentric, elliptical contours.

When the variable (X, Y) has a normal distribution, the special symbols for the familiar parameters are $E(X) = \mu_X$, $E(Y) = \mu_Y$, $V(X) = \sigma_X^2$, $V(Y) = \sigma_Y^2$, and $\text{Cor}(X, Y) = \rho$. These five parameters uniquely determine a two-dimensional normal distribution. When the experimenter knows these five parameters, he has a complete description of the corresponding random experiment.

When the component variables are independent, the correlation coefficient is zero. This is true for any random variable—discrete or continuous. For the normal distribution, the converse is also true. That is, the component variables are independent when the correlation coefficient is zero.

If the random variable (X, Y) has a normal distribution, then the marginal distributions are also normal. The component variable X has a normal distribution with expected value μ_X and variance σ_X^2. The component variable Y has a normal distribution with expected value μ_Y and variance σ_Y^2.

All the conditional distributions are also normal. If $X = x$ is observed, then the conditional distribution of Y is normal with

$$\text{expected value} = \mu_Y + \rho \frac{\sigma_Y}{\sigma_X}(x - \mu_X),$$

$$\text{variance} = (1 - \rho^2)\sigma_Y^2.$$

For future reference, notice that the expected value is a linear function of x and that the variance does not depend on x. If $Y = y$ is observed, the conditional distribution of X is normal with

$$\text{expected value} = \mu_X + \rho \frac{\sigma_X}{\sigma_Y}(y - \mu_Y),$$

$$\text{variance} = (1 - \rho^2)\sigma_X^2.$$

For an illustration of these methods, suppose the value of the home X and the yearly income Y for a randomly chosen family in some community have a joint normal distribution. Let the parameters be $\mu_X = 20{,}000$, $\mu_Y = 9{,}000$, $\sigma_X = 4{,}000$, $\sigma_Y = 2{,}000$, and $\rho = .80$. These five parameters completely describe the random experiment. The event of the family's having a home valued between \$20,000 and \$25,000 and having an income of more than \$10,000 is $\{20{,}000 \le X \le 25{,}000 \text{ and } 10{,}000 \le Y\}$. This event is a two-dimensional interval, but it is not easy to find the probability of this simple event. Consider next the event that a family's income is at least \$12,000. Since this involves only one variable Y, the marginal distribution may be used as follows:

$$\Pr\{12000 \le Y\} = \Pr\left\{\frac{12000 - 9000}{2000} \le Z\right\} = \Pr\{1.50 \le Z\} = .07.$$

Finally, consider the probability that a family in a \$25,000 home has an income of at least \$12,000. This too can be solved with a one-dimensional method of Chapter II. Provided that $X = 25{,}000$ is observed, Y has a conditional normal distribution with

$$\text{expected value} = 9000 + (.8)\frac{2000}{4000}(25000 - 20000) = 11000,$$

$$\text{variance} = (1 - .64)(2000)^2 = 1{,}440{,}000,$$

$$\text{standard deviation} = 1200.$$

The desired conditional probability is

$$\Pr\{12000 \leq Y \mid X = 25000\} = \Pr\left\{\frac{12000 - 11000}{1200} \leq Z\right\}$$

$$= \Pr\{0.83 \leq Z\} = .20.$$

Notice that the conditional probability .20 is greater than the unconditional probability .07. This is reasonable because family income and home value are positively correlated, and a \$25,000 home is above average for the community.

Summary. A continuous random variable (X, Y) with a two-dimensional normal distribution is completely described by five parameters: the two expected values μ_X and μ_Y, the two variances σ_X^2 and σ_Y^2, and the correlation coefficient ρ. X and Y are independent, if and only if $\rho = 0$. Each of the two marginal distributions is a one-dimensional normal distribution. Each conditional distribution is a one-dimensional normal distribution. If $X = x$ is observed, the parameters for Y are

$$\text{expected value} = \mu_Y + \rho\frac{\sigma_Y}{\sigma_X}(x - \mu_X),$$

$$\text{variance} = (1 - \rho^2)\,\sigma_Y^2.$$

EXERCISES

18. (X, Y) has a normal distribution with $\mu_X = 10$, $\mu_Y = 15$, $\sigma_X = 3$, $\sigma_Y = 4$, and $\rho = 0$. Find
    a) $\Pr\{X \leq 12\}$.
    b) $\Pr\{10 \leq Y \leq 16\}$.
    c) $\Pr\{X + Y \leq 30\}$.
  * d) $\Pr\{X \text{ and } Y \leq 14\}$.
    e) $\Pr\{10 \leq Y \leq 16 \mid X = 7\}$.
    f) $\Pr\{X \leq 12 \mid Y = 16\}$.

19. (X, Y) has a normal distribution with

$$\mu_X = 10 \qquad\qquad \mu_Y = 15$$

$$\sigma_X = 3 \qquad\qquad \sigma_Y = 4$$

$$\rho = .60$$

Find:

a) $\Pr\{10 \le Y \le 16 \,|\, X = 7\}$.

b) $\Pr\{X + Y \le 30\}$. Use exercise 11 (actually, exercise 17).

c) the value of c such that $\Pr\{c \le Y \,|\, X = 7\} = .10$.

20. Answer the questions in exercise 19 for $\rho = -.60$.

21. X is the score on an aptitude test for an entering freshman, and Y is the grade-point average after the freshman year. At a particular college, suppose (X, Y) has a normal distribution with

$$\mu_X = 600 \qquad\qquad \mu_Y = 2.20$$

$$\sigma_X = 80 \qquad\qquad \sigma_Y = .50$$

$$\rho = .40$$

a) What per cent of those who score 680 on the aptitude test will have a grade-point average of at least 2.00?

b) Without knowing his test score, what is the probability of at least 2.00 for a freshman?

22. Two entering freshmen take the test mentioned in exercise 21. Not knowing any more, one would say the first has a .50 probability of doing better than the second. Now, suppose the first scores 710 (x_1), and the second scores 550 (x_2) on the aptitude test. Assuming independent performances during the year, find the probability that the first (Y_1) will get a higher grade-point average than the second (Y_2).

Hint: Find $\Pr\{Y_1 - Y_2 \ge 0\}$.

23. Olson Auto Products makes seat covers for cars and sells them through a large number of dealers. By personal inspection Olson identifies a group of effective dealers. Within this group, yearly gross sales Y and auto population X in the dealer's area have a joint normal distribution. For an observed $X = x$, the parameters for Y are expected value $= 0.1x$, standard deviation $= 10,000$. One of the other dealers sells 25,000 cars with a population of 500,000 cars in his area. Should Olson consider him an effective dealer?

3

Prediction for the
Two-Dimensional Case

The central problem of this chapter is to find a method to predict the outcome of a trial of a particular random experiment. The probability distribution for the random experiment is known to the experimenter. The predictor must be a number. In terms of a random variable, let Y be associated with the random experiment, and let p be the predictor. Prior to observing the outcome y, the experimenter must choose a value for p. The error is the difference $y - p$ between the actual outcome and the predictor. The basic problem is to use the probability distribution for Y to select the best predictor p.

In order to find the best predictor for a random variable Y, the experimenter needs a criterion for measuring each particular predictor p. Presumably, a small error $y - p$ is good, and a large error $y - p$ is bad. Consider the squared error $(y - p)^2$. This non-negative number is near zero for a small error, and it is large for a large error. Of course, the experimenter does not know the outcome y at the time of the prediction. Since he knows the probability distribution for Y, however, he can calculate the expected squared error $E(Y - p)^2$ for each particular predictor p. The smaller this is, the better the predictor p is. The best predictor minimizes the expected squared error.

To find the best predictor according to this criterion, rewrite the expected squared error as

$$E(Y - p)^2 = E[Y - E(Y) + E(Y) - p]^2$$
$$= E[Y - E(Y)]^2 + E\{2[Y - E(Y)][E(Y) - p]\}$$
$$+ E[E(Y) - p]^2.$$

The first term is the variance of Y. The middle term is zero, because

$$E\{2[Y - E(Y)][E(Y) - p]\} = 2[E(Y) - p]E[Y - E(Y)]$$
$$= 2[E(Y) - p](0) = 0.$$

The last term is the expected value of a constant. Therefore, the expected squared error reduces to

$$E(Y - p)^2 = V(Y) + [E(Y) - p]^2.$$

Since $V(Y)$ does not depend on p, the expected squared error $E(Y - p)^2$ is minimized when $p = E(Y)$. That is, the best predictor for Y is its expected value $E(Y)$. Any other predictor p' is worse, because the expected squared error $E(Y - p')^2$ is larger. For the best predictor, $p = E(Y)$, the variance of Y is a numerical measure of the worth of the predictor.

This method of predicting Y with $E(Y)$ is *method I*. The variance of Y, which measures the worth of method I, is the *total variation* in this context.

* There is an alternate method, using calculus, to derive method I. The problem is to find the value of p that minimizes $E(Y - p)^2$. Differentiating with respect to p and equating to zero gives

$$0 = \frac{d}{dp}E(Y - p)^2 = E\left[\frac{d}{dp}(Y - p)^2\right]$$

$$= E[(-2)(Y - p)] = -2E(Y) + 2p.$$

Therefore, $p = E(Y)$ is the solution again. This derivation assumes that it is all right to change the order of taking the derivative and the expected value.

We shall use the four cases of Table 1, involving stocks X and Y, to illustrate the methods of prediction. In all four cases, the marginal distributions for Y are identical. The predictor for Y by method I is $E(Y) = 0$, and the total variation is $V(Y) = .60$.

3.1 REGRESSION OF Y ON X

In this subsection, the random variable Y to be predicted is one of the components of a two-dimensional random variable (X, Y). At the time of prediction, the experimenter observes the outcome x of the other component variable X. He also knows the joint probability distribution of the two-dimensional random variable (X, Y). The predictor can be a function $p(x)$ of the observed value x of the other component variable. The problem is to find the best predictor function $p(x)$. Expected squared error measures the worth of a predictor again.

Stock Market Example. X is the change in price of stock X on a day of trading on the market, and Y is the change in price of stock Y on the next day of trading. To predict the change in stock Y, the experimenter observes the change x in stock X. Except for its extreme simplicity, this situation is similar to that of a market analyst who wants to use the market's past performance to predict its future performance.

For an observed value x of the component variable X, the conditional probability distribution $\Pr\{y \mid x\}$ or $f(y \mid x)$ completely describes the random aspects of the experimenter's position. The best predictor $p(x)$ comes from a study of this conditional distribution. The problem is to find the predictor that minimizes the expected squared error $E[Y - p(x)]^2$, where the expectation is with respect to the conditional distribution for Y. For this observed outcome x there are a conditional expected value $E(Y|x)$ and a conditional variance $V(Y|x)$ for the random variable Y:

$$E(Y|x) = \begin{cases} \sum_y y\Pr\{y|x\} \\ \int yf(y|x)\,dy \end{cases}$$

$$V(Y|x) = \begin{cases} \sum_y [y - E(Y|x)]^2\Pr\{y|x\} \\ \int [y - E(Y|x)]^2f(y|x)\,dy \end{cases}$$

With expected values replaced by conditional expected values and variances replaced by conditional variances, the previous discussion of a best predictor now applies. That is, the best predictor $p(x)$ with this outcome x is the conditional expected value $E(Y|x)$. For the outcome x, the measure of this predictor's worth is the conditional variance $V(Y|x)$. Any other predictor $p'(x)$ is inferior, because the conditional expected squared error is larger.

The function that associates the conditional expected value $E(Y|x)$ with each outcome x is the *regression of Y on X*, or the *regression function*. *Method II* uses the regression function to predict the component variable Y from an outcome x of the component variable X.

To evaluate method II, we need an overall measure of its worth. The conditional variance $V(Y|x)$ measures the worth for each outcome x. To obtain the overall measure, we find the average conditional variance. That is, take the expected conditional variance $E[V(Y|X)]$, where the expectation is with respect to the marginal distribution of the component variable X. The result is a single number which depends only on the joint probability distribution of the two-dimensional random variable (X, Y). This number indicates the average squared error in predicting Y with method II. The number $E[V(Y|X)]$ is called the *error variation*.

Method II is at least as good as method I for predicting Y from an outcome x. On the average, the experimenter does not lose accuracy by observing the component variable X. The improvement of method II over method I is the *regression variation:*

regression variation = total variation − error variation,

regression variation = $V(Y) - E[V(Y|X)]$.

If the regression function is perfect for predicting Y, then the error variation is zero, and the regression and total variations are equal. If the regression function is worthless for predicting Y, then the total variation and the error variation are equal, and the regression variation is zero. In this sense, the regression variation measures the improvement of method II, which uses the outcome of X, over method I, which ignores the outcome of X.

It is useful for the next subsection to indicate that the error variation is actually an expected squared error.

$$E[V(Y|X)] = \sum_x V(Y|x)\Pr\{x\} = \sum_x \sum_y [y - E(Y|x)]^2 \Pr\{y|x\}\Pr\{x\}$$
$$= \sum_x \sum_y [y - E(Y|x)]^2 \Pr\{(x, y)\} = E[Y - E(Y|X)]^2,$$

where the last expectation is with respect to the joint distribution. The proof for the continuous case requires an obvious change to integrals and density functions.

* As an alternate derivation, one can start with the problem of choosing a function $p(x)$ to minimize $E[Y - p(X)]^2$, where the expectation is with respect to the joint distribution of (X, Y). The goal is to prove that $p(x) = E(Y|x)$ is the choice, and $E[V(Y|X)]$ is the minimum.

The four cases in Table 1 illustrate some of the possibilities. In every case, method I yielded the same result:

$$\text{predictor} = E(Y) = 0,$$
$$\text{total variation} = V(Y) = .60.$$

To apply method II, we need the conditional distributions. For case A of Table 1, they are

$$\Pr\{y|x\}$$

	1	.10	.25	.65
y	0	.25	.50	.25
	-1	.65	.25	.10
		-1	0	1
			x	

The conditional expected values are

$$E(Y|-1) = (-1)(.65) + (0)(.25) + (1)(.10) = -.55,$$
$$E(Y|0) = .0,$$
$$E(Y|1) = .55.$$

This is the regression of Y on X. Predicting .55 for variable Y, which can take only values of -1, 0, and 1, may seem ridiculous. Perhaps it is, but then so is the numerical example. In most applications of the method the space for Y is more dense, and this strange situation doesn't occur. The conditional expected values of Y^2 are

$$E(Y^2|-1) = (-1)^2(.65) + (0)^2(.75) + (1)^2(.10) = .75,$$
$$E(Y^2|0) = .50,$$
$$E(Y^2|1) = .75.$$

The conditional variances are

$$V(Y|-1) = E(Y^2|-1) - E^2(Y|-1) = .75 - (-.55)^2 = .4475,$$
$$V(Y|0) = .5000,$$
$$V(Y|1) = .4475.$$

The error variation is

$$E[V(Y|X)] = \sum_x V(Y|x)\Pr\{x\}$$
$$= (.4474)(.20) + (.50)(.60) + (.4475)(.20)$$
$$= .4790.$$

The regression variation is

$$\text{regression variation} = \text{total variation} - \text{error variation}$$
$$= .6000 - .4790 = .1210.$$

This measures the improvement of method II over method I. That is, without using the outcome of X, there is a variation of .60 for the method of predicting Y. When the outcome of X is used, there is a variation of .4790 for the method of predicting Y—an improvement of .1210.

Table 2

		$x =$ $\Pr\{x\} =$	-1 .20	0 .60	1 .20	error variation	regression variation
Case A	$E(Y\|x)$ $V(Y\|x)$		$-.55$ .4475	.00 .5000	.55 .4475	.4790	.1210
Case B	$E(Y\|x)$ $V(Y\|x)$		.55 .4475	.00 .5000	$-.55$ .4475	.4790	.1210
Case C	$E(Y\|x)$ $V(Y\|x)$		.00 .6000	.00 .6000	.00 .6000	.6000	.0000
Case D	$E(Y\|x)$ $V(Y\|x)$		$-.75$ .1875	.50 .2500	$-.75$ .1875	.2250	.3750

Table 2 summarizes the results for all four cases. In cases A and B, which are mirror images, the improvement for method II over method I is the same. In case C, X and Y are independent. There is no improvement, and the outcome of X is worthless for predicting Y. In case D, the correlation coefficient is zero, but X and Y are not independent. There is a great improvement in method II over method I. This interesting case will be discussed further in section 4 of this chapter.

Summary. If (X, Y) is a two-dimensional random variable, there are two methods to predict the outcome y of the component variable Y. Method I does not use the outcome x; method II uses the outcome x. The characteristics of these methods are

Method	Predictor	Measure of Worth
I	$E(Y)$	$E[Y - E(Y)]^2 = V(Y) =$ total variation
II	$E(Y \mid x)$	$E[V(Y \mid X)] = E[Y - E(Y \mid X)]^2 =$ error variation

The improvement of method II over method I is
$$\text{regression variation} = \text{total variation} - \text{error variation.}$$

EXERCISES

24. For the joint probability function of exercise 3, find the
    a) total variation in Y,
    b) regression of Y on X,
    c) conditional variance of Y for each x,
    d) error variation,
    e) regression variation.

25. For the joint probability function of exercise 3, find the
    a) total variation in X,
    b) regression of X on Y,
    c) conditional variance of X for each y,
    d) error variation,
    e) regression variation.

26. If X and Y are independent, prove that the
    a) regression of Y on X is $E(Y)$,
    b) conditional variance of Y for each x is $V(Y)$,
    c) error variation is $V(Y)$,
    d) regression variation is zero.

* 27. For the joint density function in exercise 13, find the
     a) total variation in Y,
     b) regression of Y on X,
     c) conditional variance of Y for each x,
     d) error variation,
     e) regression variation.

28. Mrs. Katz has studied carburetor icing in her car. The temperature
    X and the number of stalls Y in the morning are the components
    of the two-dimensional random variable (X, Y). In a simplified
    form with only four possible temperatures, the conditional proba-
    bility functions for Y are

$$\Pr\{y\,|\,x\}$$

	2	.1	.3	.3	.1
y	1	.1	.5	.5	.1
	0	.8	.2	.2	.8
		20	30	40	50

$$x$$

The marginal distribution for X is

$x =$	20	30	40	50,
$\Pr\{x\} =$	.1	.2	.3	.4.

Find the
a) total variation in Y,
b) regression of Y on X,
c) conditional variance of Y for each x,
d) error variation,
e) regression variation.

29. In exercise 28 suppose that Mrs. Katz stalls her car 2 times.
    What is the probability that the temperature is 40 degrees?

30. The following joint probability function is related to case A of
    Table 1. Find k so that $V(Y\,|\,x)$ is the same for each x.

	1	k	.15	$.20 - k$
y	0	.05	.30	.05
	-1	$.20 - k$	.15	k
		-1	0	1

$$x$$

31. On the space of the cases in Table 1, construct a joint probability function such that $\text{Cor}(X, Y)$ is zero and the error variation in Y is zero.

32. The marginal probability functions for Table 1 are given in the margins of the chart below. Fill in the joint probability function to maximize the regression variation without changing the marginals.

		.2	.6	.2	
	1				.3
y	0				.4
	-1				.3
		-1	0	1	
			x		

3.2 LINEAR REGRESSION

In an important special case, the regression of Y on X is a linear function of the outcome x. That is, $E(Y|x) = \beta_0 + \beta_1 x$. This function defines two new parameters β_0 and β_1. At least seven other parameters have been defined previously—$E(X)$, $E(Y)$, $V(X)$, $V(Y)$ or total variation, $\text{Cor}(X, Y)$, error variation, and regression variation. β_0 and β_1 are related to these seven parameters. When the regression of Y on X is linear, some of these seven parameters also have a special relation among themselves.

To find the relations of β_0 and β_1 to the other seven parameters, recall that the regression function minimizes the expected squared error $E[Y - p(X)]^2$, where the expectation is taken with respect to the joint distribution of (X, Y). Therefore, β_0 and β_1 must be such that $E[Y - \beta_0 - \beta_1 X]^2$ is minimized. To the reader with calculus, this is an easy problem of finding the minimum of a function of two variables, β_0 and β_1. The next paragraph contains the derivation.

* The necessary conditions for a minimum require the partial derivatives to be zero.

$$\frac{\partial}{\partial \beta_0} E[Y - \beta_0 - \beta_1 X]^2 = E\left\{\frac{\partial}{\partial \beta_0}[Y - \beta_0 - \beta_1 x]^2\right\}$$

$$= -2E[Y - \beta_0 - \beta_1 X]$$

$$= -2[E(Y) - \beta_0 - \beta_1 E(X)] = 0.$$

$$\frac{\partial}{\partial \beta_1} E[Y - \beta_0 - \beta_1 X]^2 = E\left\{\frac{\partial}{\partial \beta_1}[Y - \beta_0 - \beta_1 X]^2\right\}$$

$$= -2E[XY - \beta_0 X - \beta_1 X^2]$$

$$= -2[E(XY) - \beta_0 E(X) - \beta_1 E(X^2)] = 0.$$

These simplify to the equations below.

The desired β_0 and β_1 satisfy the following two linear equations.

$$E(Y) \quad = \beta_0 \quad\quad + \beta_1 E(X),$$

$$E(XY) = \beta_0 E(X) + \beta_1 E(X^2).$$

The solution is

$$\beta_0 = E(Y) - \beta_1 E(X),$$

$$\beta_1 = \frac{E(XY) - E(X)E(Y)}{E(X^2) - E^2(X)} = \mathrm{Cor}(X,\, Y)\frac{D(Y)}{D(X)}.$$

These are the relations between the β's and the other parameters. This regression function is sometimes written as

$$E(Y \,|\, x) = \beta_0 + \beta_1 x = E(Y) + \mathrm{Cor}(X,\, Y)\frac{D(Y)}{D(X)}[x - E(X)].$$

Under the linear regression function, the error and regression variations are simply related to the total variation as follows:

$$\begin{aligned}\text{error}\atop\text{variation}\end{aligned} = E[V(Y \,|\, X)] = E[Y - E(Y \,|\, X)]^2$$

$$= E\left\{[Y - E(Y)] - \mathrm{Cor}(X,\, Y)\frac{D(Y)}{D(X)}[X - E(X)]\right\}^2$$

$$= E[Y - E(Y)]^2$$

$$- 2\mathrm{Cor}(X,\, Y)\frac{D(Y)}{D(X)}E\{[Y - E(Y)][X - E(X)]\}$$

$$+ \mathrm{Cor}^2(X,\, Y)\frac{V(Y)}{V(X)}E[X - E(X)]^2$$

$$= V(Y) - \mathrm{Cor}^2(X,\, Y)V(Y)$$

$$= [1 - \mathrm{Cor}^2(X,\, Y)]V(Y)$$

$$= [1 - \mathrm{Cor}^2(X,\, Y)][\text{total variation}].$$

$\dfrac{\text{regression}}{\text{variation}}$ = total variation − error variation

$$= V(Y) - [1 - \text{Cor}^2(X, Y)]V(Y)$$
$$= \text{Cor}^2(X, Y)V(Y)$$
$$= \text{Cor}^2(X, Y)[\text{total variation}].$$

This last equation gives an interesting interpretation of the correlation coefficient: the square of the correlation coefficient is the per cent reduction of the total variation that can be attributed to observing X. If $\text{Cor}(X, Y) = 0$, there is no reduction; if $\text{Cor}(X, Y) = .50$, there is a 25 per cent reduction; if $\text{Cor}(X, Y) = 1.00$, there is a 100 per cent reduction.

We have previously discussed two specific cases with linear regression functions. At one extreme, suppose X and Y are independent. The conditional distribution for Y is then the same as the marginal distribution for Y. The regression of Y on X is $E(Y|x) = E(Y)$. This is a linear regression function with $\beta_0 = E(Y)$ and $\beta_1 = 0$. Method I and method II are identical. Observing X yields no improvement in the accuracy of prediction. Since $\text{Cor}(X, Y) = 0$ for an independent X and Y, the regression variation is $\text{Cor}^2(X, Y)[\text{total variation}] = 0$. This says again that observing X yields no improvement in the accuracy of prediction.

In the second familiar case with a linear regression function, the variable (X, Y) has a two-dimensional normal distribution. Recall that the conditional expected value is

$$E(Y|x) = \mu_Y + \rho\frac{\sigma_Y}{\sigma_X}(x - \mu_X).$$

Except for the special notation, this is the same as the result obtained earlier in this subsection. The conditional variance of Y is $V(Y|x) = (1 - \rho^2)\sigma_Y^2$. Since this does not depend on x, it is also the

error variation $= E[V(Y|X)] = (1 - \rho^2)\sigma_Y^2 = (1 - \rho^2)$ [total variation].

Table 2, which gives the regression functions for the cases of Table 1, shows that case A has a linear regression function with $\beta_0 = 0$ and $\beta_1 = .55$. These values can also be obtained from the equations for β_0 and β_1.

$$\beta_0 = E(Y) - \beta_1 E(X) = 0 - (.55)(0) = 0,$$

$$\beta_1 = \text{Cor}(X, Y)\frac{D(Y)}{D(X)} = (.45)\frac{\sqrt{.60}}{\sqrt{.40}} = .55.$$

Case B is the same, except $\beta_1 = -.55$. In case C with X and Y independent, Table 2 shows that the function is linear with $\beta_0 = \beta_1 = 0$. In case **D**, the regression function is quadratic, not linear.

Summary. For a two-dimensional random variable (X, Y), the regression of Y on X is linear if $E(Y|x) = \beta_0 + \beta_1 x$. β_0 and β_1 are related to the other parameters for (X, Y) by

$$\beta_0 = E(Y) - \beta_1 E(X),$$

$$\beta_1 = \text{Cor}(X, Y)\frac{D(Y)}{D(X)}.$$

The error, regression, and total variations are related by

$$\text{error variation} = [1 - \text{Cor}^2(X, Y)][\text{total variation}],$$

$$\text{regression variation} = [\text{Cor}^2(X, Y)][\text{total variation}].$$

EXERCISES

33. For the distribution of exercise 3, the regression of Y on X is linear.
    a) Find β_0 and β_1 from the answer to exercise 24.
    b) Verify numerically that

$$\beta_0 = E(Y) - \beta_1 E(X),$$

$$\beta_1 = \text{Cor}(X, Y)\frac{D(Y)}{D(X)},$$

    regression variation $= \text{Cor}^2(X, Y)[\text{total variation}]$.

* 34. For the distribution of exercise 13, the regression of Y on X is linear.
    a) Find β_0 and β_1 from the answer to exercise 27.
    b) Verify numerically the formulas for β_0, β_1, and the regression variation.

35. For Mrs. Katz's carburetor of exercise 28, is the regression of Y on X a linear function? Would you expect the relation between the regression variation, $\text{Cor}(X, Y)$, and the total variation to hold?

36. If the component variable X in (X, Y) can take only two values, prove that

$$\text{regression variation} = \text{Cor}^2(X, Y)[\text{total variation}].$$

37. The regression of Y on X is linear; the conditional variance of Y is a constant and is one fourth of the unconditional variance of Y. What is the correlation coefficient?

38. In Case D of Tables 1 and 2 the regression function is of the form $E(Y|x) = \beta_0 + \beta_2 x^2$. Find β_0 and β_2.

* 39. The regression of Y on X is $E(Y|x) = \beta_0 + \beta_2 x^2$. Show that

$$\beta_0 = E(Y) - \beta_2 E(X^2),$$

$$\beta_2 = \frac{E(X^2 Y) - E(X^2)E(Y)}{E(X^4) - E^2(X^2)}.$$

40. For the two-dimensional variable (X, Y), the regression of Y on X is $E(Y|x) = 2 + 3x$. Also, $\text{Cor}(X, Y) = .60$, $E(X) = 1$, and $D(X) = 1$. Find the expected value and variance of Y.

3.3 STATISTICAL TOPICS

Up to this point, the discussions of this chapter have been probabilistic, not statistical. When the parameters are unknown and a random sample is observed, the usual statistical problems of testing and estimation arise. This subsection presents one test of a hypothesis and three point estimators. Some of the properties of the test and of the estimators are proved in this chapter; some are proved in Chapter VI; and some are not proved in this book.

There are three probabilistic assumptions about the random variable (X, Y) in this discussion.

1. The regression of Y on X is linear, $E(Y|x) = \beta_0 + \beta_1 x$.
2. The conditional variance of Y does not depend on X, $V(Y|x) = \sigma^2$.
3. The conditional distribution of Y is normal for each outcome of X.

The three parameters, β_0, β_1, and σ^2, are unknown. A random sample of size n of (X, Y) is observed:

$$(x_1, y_1), (x_2, y_2), \ldots, (x_j, y_j), \ldots, (x_n, y_n).$$

All the results of this subsection are strictly correct when the three assumptions about (X, Y) are correct. In particular, a joint normal distribution for (X, Y) satisfies these assumptions. In many practical cases the experimenter does not know whether these assumptions are true. Failure to satisfy the first assumption, a linear regression function, is usually serious. We shall say more about this problem in section 4 of this chapter. Failure to satisfy the second assumption, a constant variance, can often be corrected by a simple transformation of the data, such as log y_j. Failure to satisfy the third assumption about normality is not always serious for the significance test we are discussing here.

Usually, the first question in the experimenter's mind is, "Are X and Y related?" If $\beta_1 = 0$, they are not. Future observations of X will be useless for predicting Y. If $\beta_1 \neq 0$, then X and Y are related. Future observations of X will be useful for predicting Y. Therefore, the experimenter's first question suggests the statistical hypothesis $\beta_1 = 0$. Under the assumed linear regression function, β_1 is related to $\text{Cor}(X, Y)$ by

$$\beta_1 = \text{Cor}(X, Y)\frac{D(Y)}{D(X)}.$$

Hence, the hypothesis $\beta_1 = 0$ has the equivalent form $\text{Cor}(X, Y) = 0$. The experimenter wants to use the results of the random experiment to test this hypothesis. If the hypothesis is rejected, the importance of X for predicting Y is established.

If the hypothesis is rejected, the experimenter next might need a point estimator for each of the parameters—β_0, β_1, and σ^2.

Technically, it is easier to reverse the logical order and to derive the estimators of β_0 and β_1 first. Let these be b_0 and b_1, respectively. Each of them is some function of the observed values of (X, Y), the x_j's and the y_j's. We seek two such functions. For each x_j, $b_0 + b_1 x_j$ would have been the predicted value of Y; the actual corresponding value would have been y_j; and the error would have been $y_j - b_0 - b_1 x_j$. Under the squared-error criterion the best b_0 and b_1 would have minimized

$$\sum_j (y_j - b_0 - b_1 x_j)^2.$$

As in subsection 3.2, this is a calculus problem, which is left to an exercise. The result is that the best values for b_0 and b_1 would have satisfied the following *normal equations:*

$$\sum y_j - b_0 n \quad - b_1 \sum x_j = 0,$$
$$\sum x_j y_j - b_0 \sum x_j - b_1 \sum x_j^2 = 0.$$

The solution is

$$b_0 = \frac{\sum y_j}{n} - b_1 \frac{\sum x_j}{n} = y. - b_1 x.,$$

$$b_1 = \frac{n \sum x_j y_j - (\sum x_j)(\sum y_j)}{n \sum x_j^2 - (\sum x_j)^2},$$

where $y.$ and $x.$ are new symbols for the sample means $\bar{y}$ and $\bar{x}$. These are the *least-squares estimators* of β_0 and β_1. As shown in Chapter VI, they are unbiased.

$$E(B_0) = \beta_0 \quad \text{and} \quad E(B_1) = \beta_1.$$

We next seek an estimator of σ^2. Define the *total sum of squares* as the sum of the deviations of the y_j's from the sample mean.

$$\text{total sum of squares} = \sum (y_j - y.)^2.$$

(When divided by $n - 1$, this is the sample variance s_y^2 for Y.) The total sum of squares is the sample analog of the total variation; it also can be separated into two components.

$$\sum (y_j - y.)^2 = \sum [(y_j - b_0 - b_1 x_j) + (b_0 + b_1 x_j - y.)]^2$$
$$= \sum (y_j - b_0 - b_1 x_j)^2 + \sum (b_0 + b_1 x_j - y.)^2.$$

The middle term is zero, because an application of the normal equations yields

$$2\sum (y_j - b_0 - b_1 x_j)(b_0 + b_1 x_j - y.)$$
$$= 2(b_0 - y.)\sum (y_j - b_0 - b_1 x_j) + 2b_1 \sum (x_j)(y_j - b_0 - b_1 x_j)$$
$$= 2(b_0 - y.)(0) + 2b_1(0) = 0.$$

The first component, $\sum (y_j - b_0 - b_1 x_j)^2$, is the *error sum of squares*. It is a measure of the difference between the actual values y_j and the regression values $b_0 + b_1 x_j$. When divided by $n - 2$, it is an unbiased estimator of the unknown conditional variance σ^2. Let the symbol be

$$s^2 = \frac{\text{Error SS}}{n - 2}, \text{ where } E(S^2) = \sigma^2.$$

Proof of the unbiasedness is given in Chapter VI. The second component, $\sum (b_0 + b_1 x_j - y.)^2$, is the *regression sum of squares*.

The error and the regression sums of squares are the sample analogs of the error and the regression variations, respectively. Had the experimenter known and used the sample mean $y.$ to predict the y_j's, the total sum of squares would have measured his success. Had he used b_0 and b_1 from the normal equations, the error sum of squares would have measured his success. The regression sum of squares would have measured the improvement. Figure 3 shows this situation. P_j is the point for a typical outcome (x_j, y_j). The solid line is the estimated regression function $b_0 + b_1 x$. The three components for P_j are labeled on the figure. The estimated regression line must go through the point with coordinates $(x., y.)$.

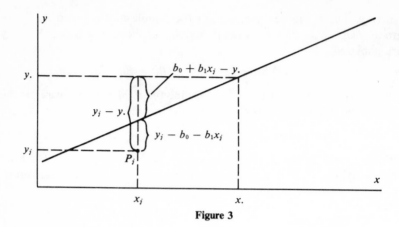

Figure 3

In computations the total sum of squares is most easily calculated from

$$\text{Total SS} = \sum(y_i - y.)^2 = \sum y_i^2 - \frac{(\sum y_i)^2}{n}.$$

A good computing formula for the regression sum of squares is

$$\begin{aligned}
\text{Regression SS} &= \sum(b_0 + b_1 x_i - y.)^2 \\
&= \sum(y. - b_1 x. + b_1 x_i - y.)^2 \\
&= b_1^2 \sum(x_i - x.)^2 = b_1^2 \left[\sum x_i^2 - \frac{(\sum x_i)^2}{n} \right].
\end{aligned}$$

The error sum of squares is the difference of these.

$$\text{Error SS} = \text{Total SS} - \text{Regression SS}.$$

The regression sum of squares measures that portion of the total sum of squares allocated to the estimated regression function. The analogous situation with the regression variation and the total variation suggests defining the *sample correlation coefficient r* by

$$r^2 = \frac{\text{Regression SS}}{\text{Total SS}}.$$

The algebraic sign of r is defined to be the same as that of b_1. Of course, r^2 lies in the interval from zero to one. If the estimated regression function goes through every data point (x_i, y_i), then the error sum of squares is zero; the regression sum of squares equals the total sum of squares; and r^2 is one. If the estimated regression function is no better estimator than $y.$, then the regression sum of squares is zero, and r^2 is zero. In this sense, r^2 measures the degree to which $b_0 + b_1 x$ fits the data. There is another expression for the sample correlation coefficient.

$$r^2 = \frac{\text{Regression SS}}{\text{Total SS}} = \frac{b_1^2 \sum (x_j - x.)^2}{\sum (y_j - y.)^2} = b_1^2 \frac{s_x^2}{s_y^2},$$

or

$$r = b_1 \frac{s_x}{s_y} \quad \text{and} \quad b_1 = r \frac{s_y}{s_x}.$$

This is the sample analog of

$$\beta_1 = \text{Cor}(X, Y) \frac{D(Y)}{D(X)}.$$

Before giving a numerical example, we discuss a test for the hypothesis

$$\beta_1 = 0 \quad \text{or} \quad \text{Cor}(X, Y) = 0.$$

The regression sum of squares may be considered as a random variable. The expected value will be derived in Chapter VI. Essentially, the result is

$$E(\text{Regression SS}) = \sigma^2 + (n - 1)\beta_1^2 V(X).$$

If the hypothesis is true, the regression sum of squares is an unbiased estimator of σ^2.

$$E(\text{Regression SS}) = \sigma^2.$$

If the hypothesis is false, $(n - 1)\beta_1^2 V(X)$ is a positive number, and the regression sum of squares tends to overestimate σ^2. When divided by $n - 2$, the error sum of squares is always an unbiased estimator of σ^2. Consider the ratio

$$\frac{\dfrac{\text{Regression SS}}{1}}{\dfrac{\text{Error SS}}{n - 2}}.$$

When the hypothesis is true, the numerator and the denominator are unbiased estimators of σ^2, and the ratio should be near one. When the hypothesis is false, the ratio tends to be larger than one. The test is of the form

$$\text{reject if } c \le \text{observed} \quad \frac{\dfrac{\text{Regression SS}}{1}}{\dfrac{\text{Error SS}}{n - 2}}.$$

To find c, it is necessary to introduce a new distribution.

Ratios of sums of squares appear often in the rest of this book. Under certain conditions, these ratios have an *F-distribution*. There are two parameters: ν_1 is the *degrees of freedom for the numerator*, and ν_2 is the *degrees of freedom for the denominator*. The graph looks somewhat like a chi-square graph. Some critical values appear in Table VI of the appendix. If F is the random variable, these values are indicated by $F(\alpha, \nu_1, \nu_2)$, where $\Pr\{F(\alpha, \nu_1, \nu_2) \leq F\} = \alpha$. For example, an F variable with 1 and 8 degrees of freedom has a .05 probability of exceeding 5.32.

$$F(.05, 1, 8) = 5.32 \quad \text{and} \quad \Pr\{5.32 \leq F\} = .05.$$

When the hypothesis, $\beta_1 = 0$ or $Cor(X, Y) = 0$, is true, the ratio

$$\frac{\dfrac{\text{Regression SS}}{1}}{\dfrac{\text{Error SS}}{n - 2}}$$

has an F-distribution with 1 and $n - 2$ degrees of freedom. (It is here that the assumed conditional normal distribution is used.) For a significance level of α, the test of the hypothesis is

$$\text{reject if } F(\alpha, 1, n - 2) \leq \text{observed} \quad \frac{\dfrac{\text{Regression SS}}{1}}{\dfrac{\text{Error SS}}{n - 2}}.$$

In the numerical example of subsection 2.3, X was the value of a randomly chosen family's home, and Y was the family's yearly income. Now suppose the parameters are unknown. It is assumed that the regression function is linear, $E(Y|x) = \beta_0 + \beta_1 x$, the conditional variance is constant, $V(Y|x) = \sigma^2$, and the conditional distribution of Y is normal. From a random sample of (X, Y), the problems are to test the hypothesis $\beta_1 = 0$ and to estimate the three parameters if the hypothesis is rejected.

Suppose a random sample of 10 families yields the following (in thousands of dollars):

x_j:	16.9	23.3	15.5	25.9	16.9	24.8	15.7	22.7	17.0	31.8
y_j:	9.8	11.5	7.3	12.6	6.2	11.8	7.8	10.7	7.2	12.0

The test and the estimators require the two sums, the two sums of squares, and the one sum of products:

$$\sum x_j = 210,500,$$
$$\sum y_j = 96,900,$$
$$\sum x_j^2 = 4,702,230,000,$$
$$\sum y_j^2 = 989,190,000,$$
$$\sum x_j y_j = 2,139,830,000.$$

The solution to the normal equations is

$$b_0 = \frac{\sum y_j}{n} - b_1 \frac{\sum x_j}{n} = 1922,$$

$$b_1 = \frac{n \sum x_j y_j - (\sum x_j)(\sum y_j)}{n \sum x_j^2 - (\sum x_j)^2} = .3690.$$

The sums of squares are

$$\text{Total SS} = \sum y_j^2 - \frac{(\sum y_j)^2}{n} = 50,229,000,$$

$$\text{Regression SS} = b_1^2 \left[\sum x_j^2 - \frac{(\sum x_j)^2}{n} \right] = 36,933,000,$$

$$\text{Error SS} = \text{Total SS} - \text{Regression SS} = 13,296,000.$$

The estimator of σ^2 is

$$\frac{\text{Error SS}}{n - 2} = 1,662,000.$$

The sample correlation coefficient is

$$r^2 = \frac{\text{Regression SS}}{\text{Total SS}} = .735,$$

$$r = .86.$$

The F-ratio is

$$F = \frac{\dfrac{\text{Regression SS}}{1}}{\dfrac{\text{Error SS}}{n - 2}} = 22.2.$$

At the .05 significance level, the cut-off point for the F-test is $F(.05, 1, 8) = 5.32$. Since the observed F-ratio exceeds this cut-off point, the hypothesis of no correlation between X and Y is rejected at the .05 level. Since $F(.01, 1, 8) = 11.3$, the hypothesis is also rejected at the .01 level of significance.

To continue the numerical example, suppose another family is selected. Its home is worth $17,000. The experimenter's predictor of the family's income is

$$E(Y|x) = 1922 + (.3690)(17000) = 8195.$$

The experimenter can use the conditional normal distribution to calculate some prediction limits. As a first approximation the conditional distribution of Y is normal with the above expectation and with

$$V(Y|x) = 1,662,000,$$

$$D(Y|x) = \quad 1,289.$$

Suppose he wants limits, c_1 and c_2, such that

$$.95 = \Pr\{c_1 < Y < c_2\} = \Pr\left\{\frac{c_1 - 8195}{1289} < Z < \frac{c_2 - 8195}{1289}\right\}.$$

Therefore, c_1 and c_2 are

$$c_1 = 8195 + (-1.96)(1289) = \quad 5669,$$

$$c_2 = 8195 + \quad (1.96)(1289) = 10721.$$

These should not be confused with confidence limits for an unknown parameter; they are prediction limits for a random variable Y. They are only approximations, since 8195 is only an estimator of $E(Y|x)$ and 1289 is only an estimator of $D(Y|x)$.

Although the mistake is not too likely in this example, there is often a tendency to use the regression function in an improper manner. For an illustration involving this numerical example, suppose one member of the community is especially interested in raising his income. Since b_1 is positive in the regression function, families in expensive homes tend to have large incomes. Should he move into a more expensive home? Perhaps it would raise his income, but this regression function does not say so. This function is related to the experiment of picking (X, Y) at random from the community, observing the outcome x of X, and then predicting Y. The function says nothing about the experiment of willfully fixing x to influence Y. The latter experiment is the subject of Chapter VI.

Summary. For the random variable (X, Y), Y has a conditional normal distribution with

$$E(Y|x) = \beta_0 + \beta_1 x,$$

$$V(Y|x) = \sigma^2.$$

From a random sample of size n, the unbiased estimators of β_0 and β_1 are

$$b_0 = y. - b_1 x.,$$

$$b_1 = \frac{n\sum x_j y_j - (\sum x_j)(\sum y_j)}{n\sum x_j^2 - (\sum x_j)^2}.$$

The sums of squares are

$$\text{Total SS} = \sum (y_j - y.)^2 = \sum y_j^2 - \frac{(\sum y_j)^2}{n},$$

$$\text{Regression SS} = \sum (b_0 + b_1 x_j - y.)^2 = b_1^2 \sum (x_j - x.)^2$$

$$= b_1^2 \left[\sum x_j^2 - \frac{(\sum x_j)^2}{n} \right],$$

$$\text{Error SS} = \sum (y_j - b_0 - b_1 x_j)^2 = \text{Total SS} - \text{Regression SS}.$$

The sample correlation coefficient has the sign of b_1, and its square is

$$r^2 = \frac{\text{Regression SS}}{\text{Total SS}}.$$

The unbiased estimator of σ^2 is

$$\frac{\text{Error SS}}{n - 2}.$$

The level α significance test of the hypothesis, $\beta_1 = 0$ or $\text{Cor}(X, Y) = 0$, is

$$\text{reject if } F(\alpha, 1, n - 2) \leq \text{observed} \quad \frac{\dfrac{\text{Regression SS}}{1}}{\dfrac{\text{Error SS}}{n - 2}}.$$

EXERCISES

41. Verify that the point $(x., y.)$ lies on the estimated regression line $b_0 + b_1 x$.

* 42. Derive the normal equations by minimizing $\sum_j (y_j - b_0 - b_1 x_j)^2$.

43. Under the assumptions of this subsection, analyze the following sample of ten observations of (X, Y).

x_j:	0	0	1	1	2	2	3	3	4	4
y_j:	4	7	9	12	13	16	17	22	20	20

a) Plot the 10 points (x_j, y_j) on a graph.
b) Compute $\sum x_j$, $\sum y_j$, $\sum x_j^2$, $\sum y_j^2$, and $\sum x_j y_j$.
c) Compute b_0 and b_1.
d) Draw the line $b_0 + b_1 x$ on the graph in a).
e) Compute Total SS, Regression SS, and Error SS.
f) Estimate σ^2.
g) Compute r^2 and r.
h) Compute the F-ratio.
i) Can the hypothesis that X and Y are uncorrelated be rejected at the .01 level?

44. Divina, the college registrar, wishes to use high-school performance to predict college performance for the freshman year. Using class rank and other factors, he can rate a high-school graduate from 0 to 100 according to some objective procedure. If X is the high-school rating and Y is the grade-point average in the first year, Divina is willing to assume that Y has a normal conditional distribution with

$$E(Y|x) = \beta_0 + \beta_1 x,$$

$$V(Y|x) = \sigma^2.$$

A sample of his records showed the following:

$$n = 42 \qquad\qquad \sum x_j^2 = 209{,}900$$

$$\sum x_j = 2940 \qquad\qquad \sum y_j^2 = 248$$

$$\sum y_j = 100.8 \qquad\qquad \sum x_j y_j = 7172$$

a) Estimate β_0 and β_1.
b) Estimate σ^2.
c) Find r^2 and r.
d) Carry out the F-test at the .05 level.
e) For a new student with a rating of 60 from high school, what is the probability that he will make a grade-point average of at least 2.00 in his first year?

45. Parsons and Associates have a psychological test for predicting a new employee's worth on a job. The test predicts one of five levels: 1—excellent; 2—good; 3—average; 4—below average; and 5—unsatisfactory. A company cooperates with Parsons to evaluate fifteen new employees. After 6 months, the company itself evaluates the employees on their actual performances. The results are:

employee:	1	2	3	4	5	6	7	8	9	10	11	12	13	14	15
Parsons:	1	2	3	2	1	3	3	2	4	3	1	3	2	3	2
company:	2	3	3	1	2	2	2	2	3	4	2	3	1	2	3

At first glance, Parsons feels his psychological test is a success because he is within one level on each employee. What do you think?

46. The sample analog of $Cor(X, Y)$ is r, which is defined in the linear case by

$$r^2 = \frac{\text{Regression SS}}{\text{Total SS}}.$$

From this definition, show

$$r = \frac{\frac{1}{n}\sum(x_j - x.)(y_j - y.)}{\sqrt{\frac{\sum(x_j - x.)^2}{n}}\sqrt{\frac{\sum(y_j - y.)^2}{n}}}.$$

Compare this to the definition of $Cor(X, Y)$ in subsection 2.1.

47. It is possible to simulate observations of a random variable (X, Y). To satisfy some of the assumptions of this section, construct deck I with five cards that are numbered "1", "2", "3", "4", and "5"; construct deck II with five cards that are numbered "-2", "-1", "0", "1", and "2". Randomly draw a card from deck I and let x be the outcome. Randomly draw a card from deck II and let w be the outcome. Define y by $y = 3 + 2x + w$. Then (x, y) simulates an outcome for (X, Y).
   a) The regression of Y on X is linear. Find β_0 and β_1.
   b) The conditional variance of Y given x is constant. Find $V(Y|x)$.
   c) Does Y have a normal conditional distribution?
   d) Find other parameters: $E(X)$, $E(Y)$, $V(X)$, $V(Y)$, and $Cor(X, Y)$.

48. For the situation in exercise 47, obtain 10 independent observations of (X, Y). Starting with this random sample
   a) estimate β_0 and β_1,
   b) estimate σ^2,
   c) calculate r,
   d) carry out the F-test of the hypothesis $\beta_1 = 0$ at the .05 level.

4

Prediction for the Multi-Dimensional Case

To predict one random variable Y, an experimenter may have the outcomes of several other random variables. He may know also all the probabilistic facts about all the random variables. His problem is to use the outcomes and the probabilistic facts to produce a single number which is his prediction of the variable Y. To discuss methods for this situation we must introduce multi-dimensional random variables and their parameters.

4.1 PARAMETERS

For a random experiment that requires $m + 1$ numbers to describe an outcome, a corresponding random variable is $(X_1, X_2, \ldots, X_i, \ldots, X_m, Y)$. There is a corresponding joint distribution of probability which completely describes the random aspects of the experiment. Each component variable, X_i or Y, has its marginal distribution, expected value, and variance. For each variable, say Y, there is a conditional distribution for observed outcomes of all the others—that is, for the outcomes

$$X_1 = x_1, X_2 = x_2, \ldots, X_i = x_i, \ldots, X_m = x_m.$$

Each pair, say X_1 and X_2, has its correlation coefficient $\text{Cor}(X_1, X_2)$. In addition to these direct generalizations of familiar concepts, there are many new ones. For some examples, each pair of variables has its own joint marginal distribution; each pair of variables has its own joint conditional distribution for each set of outcomes of the other variables; each variable has a correlation coefficient with each subset of the other variables, such as the correlation coefficient of Y with X_3, X_4, and X_7. There are many other new concepts.

For the $(m + 1)$-dimensional random variable $(X_1, X_2, \ldots, X_m, Y)$, the central problem of this discussion is to predict Y from the observed outcomes of the other m variables.

Method I, which ignores the outcomes of the X_i's, always predicts the expected value of Y. The measure of the worth of this method is the variance of Y. In this context, the variance of Y is again called the total variation.

Method II, which uses the outcomes of the X_i's, predicts the conditional expected value of Y, $E(Y|x_1, x_2, \ldots, x_m)$. The function that relates each outcome $(x_1, x_2, \ldots, x_m)$ with the corresponding expected value is the *regression of Y on* $X_1, X_2, \ldots, X_m$, or simply the *regression function for Y*. For each outcome, the conditional variance of Y, $V(Y|x_1, x_2, \ldots, x_m)$, measures the worth of the regression function as a predictor of Y. An overall measure of the worth of method II is the average of the conditional variance, $E[V(Y|X_1, X_2, \ldots, X_m]$, where the expectation is taken with respect to the marginal distribution of $(X_1, X_2, \ldots, X_m)$. This expected conditional variance is the error variation for method II. The improvement of method II over method I is again the regression variation. Method II is summarized by

$$\text{predictor} = E(Y|x_1, x_2, \ldots, x_m),$$

$$\text{error variation} = E[V(Y|X_1, X_2, \ldots, X_m)],$$

$$\text{regression variation} = \text{total variation} - \text{error variation}.$$

In a very important special case, the regression of Y on $X_1, X_2, \ldots, X_m$ is linear.

$$E(Y|x_1, x_2, \ldots, x_m) = \beta_0 + \beta_1 x_1 + \beta_2 x_2 + \cdots + \beta_m x_m.$$

Like the two-dimensional case, the β_i's are functions of the other parameters—the $E(X_i)$'s, the $V(X_i)$'s, the $\text{Cor}(X_i, X_{i'})$'s, and so on. The actual relations may be obtained by finding the values of the β_i's that minimize the expected squared error,

$$E(Y - \beta_0 - \beta_1 X_1 - \beta_2 X_2 - \cdots - \beta_m X_m)^2.$$

No simple relations result, and no derivation is given. This minimum is again the error variation,

$$\text{error variation} = E[V(Y|X_1, X_2, \ldots, X_m)]$$

$$= E(Y - \beta_0 - \beta_1 X_1 - \beta_2 X_2 - \cdots - \beta_m X_m)^2.$$

The ratio of the regression variation to the total variation is the square of the *multiple correlation coefficient*.

$$\text{Cor}^2(Y; X_1, X_2, \ldots, X_m) = \frac{\text{regression variation}}{\text{total variation}}.$$

Notice that $\text{Cor}(Y; X_1, X_2, \ldots, X_m)$ is defined only when $E(Y|x_1, x_2, \ldots, x_m)$ is a linear function of $x_1, x_2, \ldots, x_m$. The multiple correlation coefficient is always between zero and one; it is never negative. If method II is a perfect predictor of Y; then the error variation is zero, the regression and total variations are equal, and the multiple correlation coefficient is one. If method II is no better than method I; then the error and the total variations are equal, the regression variation is zero, and the multiple correlation coefficient is zero.

A random variable $(X_1, X_2, \ldots, X_m, Y)$ with an $(m + 1)$-dimensional normal distribution provides one illustration. The regression function for Y is always linear in $x_1, x_2, \ldots, x_m$.

Under a linear regression function for the variable $(X_1, X_2, \ldots, X_m, Y)$, the following three statements are equivalent:

1) Method I and Method II for predicting Y are the same.
2) The multiple correlation coefficient $\text{Cor}(Y; X_1, X_2, \ldots, X_m)$ equals zero.
3) The coefficients of the regression function $\beta_1, \beta_2, \ldots, \beta_m$ are all zero.

The equivalence of these statements is a direct generalization from the two-dimensional prediction problem for (X, Y).

Fortunately, the methods for a linear regression function are easily modified to apply to a large class of non-linear regression functions. To illustrate, take a three-dimensional random variable (X_1, X_2, Y) for which the conditional expected value of Y is more complicated, say quadratic in x_1 and x_2.

$$E(Y \mid x_1, x_2) = \beta_0 + \beta_1 x_1 + \beta_2 x_2 + \beta_{11} x_1^2 + \beta_{22} x_2^2 + \beta_{12} x_1 x_2.$$

Although this function is quadratic in x_1 and x_2, it is linear in the five variables x_1, x_2, x_1^2, x_2^2, and $x_1 x_2$. That is, new variables and coefficients can be defined by the following:

$$\begin{array}{lll} x_3 = x_1^2 & x_4 = x_2^2 & x_5 = x_1 x_2 \\ \beta_3 = \beta_{11} & \beta_4 = \beta_{22} & \beta_5 = \beta_{12} \end{array}$$

By this widely used device, the theory developed for the general linear model can be applied to the original non-linear model.

Table 3

$\Pr\{y \mid x_1, x_2\}$

	1	.30	.50	.85
		.40	.40	.10
		.30	.10	.05
x_2	0	.10	.167	.50
		.40	.667	.40
		.50	.167	.10
	-1	.05	.10	.30
		.10	.40	.40
		.85	.50	.30
		-1	0	1
			x_1	

For a numerical example, suppose the change in price of stock Y is related to the previous changes in price of two other stocks, X_1 and X_2. Each stock can drop only a dollar, remain unchanged, or rise a dollar. Let (X_1, X_2, Y) be the three-dimensional random variable. The conditional distribution of Y for given values of X_1 and X_2 is shown in Table 3. To explain a typical entry in this table, suppose $x_1 = x_2 = -1$. The conditional probabilities for $Y = -1, 0, 1$ are .85, .10, .05, respectively. The conditional expected values $E(Y|x_1, x_2)$ and conditional variances $V(Y|x_1, x_2)$ are derived from Table 3 as follows:

$$E(Y|-1, -1) = (-1)(.85) + (0)(.10) + (1)(.05) = -.80,$$
$$E(Y^2|-1, -1) = (-1)^2(.85) + (0)^2(.10) + (1)^2(.05) = .90,$$
$$V(Y|-1, -1) = .90 - (-.80)^2 = .26.$$

Table 4

$E(Y|x_1, x_2)$

$V(Y|x_1, x_2)$

	1	.00	.40	.80
		.60	.44	.26
x_2	0	-.40	.00	.40
		.44	.33	.44
	-1	-.80	-.40	.00
		.26	.44	.60
		-1	0	1

x_1

The nine pairs of conditional expected values and variances are indicated in Table 4. From Table 4, notice that the regression function for Y is linear in x_1 and x_2.

$$E(Y|x_1, x_2) = 0 + .4x_1 + .4x_2.$$

This function is the predictor for method II. To obtain the error variation, the marginal distribution for (X_1, X_2) must be known. Suppose it is as follows:

$\Pr\{(x_1, x_2)\}$

	1	.05	.21	.08
x_2	0	.07	.18	.07
	-1	.08	.21	.05
		-1	0	1

x_1

This marginal distribution and Table 3 determine the marginal distribution for Y:

y	-1	0	1
$\Pr\{y\}$	.30	.40	.30

The error variation for Y is

$$\text{error variation} = E[V(Y \mid X_1, X_2)] = \sum_{x_1}\sum_{x_2} V(Y \mid x_1, x_2) \Pr\{(x_1, x_2)\}$$

$$= (.26)(.08) + (.44)(.07) + \cdots + (.26)(.08)$$

$$= .4074.$$

Since the marginal distribution for Y is as in Table I (page 134), the total variation is .6000 again, and the improvement of method II over method I is

$$\text{regression variation} = \text{total variation} - \text{error variation}$$

$$= .6000 - .4074 = .1926.$$

The multiple correlation coefficient is

$$\text{Cor}^2(Y; X_1, X_2) = \frac{\text{regression variation}}{\text{total variation}} = \frac{.1926}{.6000} = .3210,$$

$$\text{Cor}(Y; X_1, X_2) = .57.$$

Summary. An $(m + 1)$-dimensional random variable $(X_1, X_2, \ldots, X_m, Y)$ has a linear regression function for Y if

$$E(Y \mid x_1, x_2, \ldots, x_m) = \beta_0 + \beta_1 x_1 + \beta_2 x_2 + \cdots + \beta_m x_m.$$

When this function is used to predict Y, the error variation is the expected conditional variance.

$$\text{error variation} = E[V(Y \mid X_1, X_2, \ldots, X_m)].$$

The contribution of the regression function for predicting Y is measured by the

$$\text{regression variation} = \text{total variation} - \text{error variation}.$$

The square of the multiple correlation coefficient measures this contribution as a per cent.

$$\text{Cor}^2(Y; X_1, X_2, \ldots, X_m) = \frac{\text{regression variation}}{\text{total variation}}.$$

$\text{Cor}(Y; X_1, X_2, \ldots, X_m) = 0$, if and only if $\beta_1 = \beta_2 = \cdots = \beta_m = 0$.

EXERCISES

49. In the numerical example of this subsection, verify the marginal distribution for Y.

Hint: $\Pr\{(x_1, x_2, y)\} = \Pr\{y \mid x_1, x_2\} \cdot \Pr\{(x_1, x_2)\}$, and

$$\Pr\{y\} = \sum_{x_1} \sum_{x_2} \Pr\{(x_1, x_2, y)\}.$$

50. In the numerical example of this subsection, find
    a) the joint marginal distribution for (X_1, Y).
    b) $E(Y \mid x_1)$.
    c) $V(Y \mid x_1)$.
    d) $\mathrm{Cor}(X_1, Y)$.

51. For the discrete random variable (X_1, X_2, Y), the X_i's take values 0, 1, and 2; the variable Y takes only values 0 and 1. The conditional distribution for Y and the marginal distribution for (X_1, X_2) are

	$\Pr\{Y = 1 \mid x_1, x_2\}$					$\Pr\{(x_1, x_2)\}$		
	2	.4	.5	.6		2	.05	.15	.25
x_2	1	.3	.4	.5	x_2	1	.05	.20	.15
	0	.2	.3	.4		0	.05	.05	.05
		0	1	2			0	1	2
			x_1					x_1

a) Verify that the marginal distribution for Y is $\Pr\{Y = 1\} = .46$.
b) Find the regression of Y on X_1 and X_2.
c) Find $\mathrm{Cor}(Y; X_1, X_2)$.

52. The discrete random variable (X_1, X_2, Y) has the space of exercise 51. The marginal distribution for (X_1, X_2) is the same, but the conditional distribution for Y is

	$\Pr\{Y = 1 \mid x_1, x_2\}$		
	2	.1	.5	.9
x_2	1	.1	.3	.5
	0	.1	.1	.1
		0	1	2
			x_1	

a) Verify that the marginal distribution for Y is $\Pr\{Y = 1\} = .46$.
b) Verify that the regression function for Y is $E(Y|x_1, x_2) = .1 + .2x_1x_2$, which is non-linear.
c) Let $X = X_1X_2$, and find $\text{Cor}(Y, X) = \text{Cor}(Y, X_1X_2)$.

53. In case D of Tables 1 and 2, the regression of Y on X is a quadratic function of x, but a linear function of x and x^2. $E(Y|x, x^2) = \beta_0 + \beta_1 x + \beta_{11} x^2$. Find $\text{Cor}(Y; X, X^2)$.

* 54. For the random variable (X_1, X_2, Y), suppose the regression function for Y is linear. $E(Y|x_1, x_2) = \beta_0 + \beta_1 x_1 + \beta_2 x_2$. Recall that the proper values of the β_i's minimize the expected squared error, $E(Y - \beta_0 - \beta_1 X_1 - \beta_2 X_2)^2$. Verify that β_0 is $E(Y) - \beta_1 E(X_1) - \beta_2 E(X_2)$.

55. If the regression of Y on X_1 and X_2 is linear and if $\beta_1 = \beta_2 = 0$, use the result of exercise 54 to prove $\text{Cor}(Y; X_1, X_2) = 0$.

* 56. Suppose the regression of Y on X_1 and X_2 is linear. $E(Y|x_1, x_2) = \beta_0 + \beta_1 x_1 + \beta_2 x_2$. The β_i's minimize the expected squared error, $E(Y - \beta_0 - \beta_1 X_1 - \beta_2 X_2)^2$. Derive the three equations for β_0, β_1, and β_2:

$$E(Y) \quad - \beta_0 \quad\quad - \beta_1 E(X_1) \quad - \beta_2 E(X_2) \quad = 0,$$

$$E(X_1 Y) - \beta_0 E(X_1) - \beta_1 E(X_1^2) \quad - \beta_2 E(X_1 X_2) = 0,$$

$$E(X_2 Y) - \beta_0 E(X_2) - \beta_1 E(X_1 X_2) - \beta_2 E(X_2^2) \quad = 0.$$

57. The regression of Y on X_1 and X_2 is linear. $E(Y|x_1, x_2) = \beta_0 + \beta_1 x_1 + \beta_2 x_2$. Suppose the multiple correlation coefficient $\text{Cor}(Y; X_1, X_2)$ is zero. Therefore, the total variation $V(Y)$ equals the error variation. $V(Y)$ may be expanded according to

$$V(Y) = E[Y - E(Y)]^2 = E\{[Y - \beta_0 - \beta_1 X_1 - \beta_2 X_2]$$

$$+ [\beta_0 + \beta_1 X_1 + \beta_2 X_2 - E(Y)]\}^2.$$

Apply the result of exercise 56 to this to obtain

$$V(Y) = \text{error variation} + E\{\beta_1[X_1 - E(X_1)] + \beta_2[X_2 - E(X_2)]\}^2.$$

From this, conclude that β_1 and β_2 are zero. Summarize the results of the last four exercises.

4.2 STATISTICAL TOPICS

Statistical problems arise when the parameters are unknown and the outcomes of a random sample are observed. There is a significance test for a hypothesis about the coefficients of the regression function. There are point estimators for all the parameters. The discussion parallels that of subsection 3.3 for the two-dimensional case.

The three probabilistic assumptions about the random variable $(X_1, X_2, \ldots, X_m, Y)$ are

1) The regression function for Y is linear.
   $E(Y \mid x_1, x_2, \ldots, x_m) = \beta_0 + \beta_1 x_1 + \beta_2 x_2 + \cdots + \beta_m x_m$.
2) The conditional variance of Y does not depend on the other component variables. $V(Y \mid x_1, x_2, \ldots, x_m) = \sigma^2$.
3) The conditional distribution of Y is normal for each outcome of $(X_1, X_2, \ldots, X_m)$.

The β_i's and σ^2 are the unknown parameters. Some of the X_i's actually may be functions of the others, such as $X_2 = X_1^2$ or $X_3 = X_1 X_2$. A random sample of size n for $(X_1, X_2, \ldots, X_m, Y)$ is observed:

$$(x_{11}, x_{21}, \ldots, x_{m1}, y_1), (x_{12}, x_{22}, \ldots, x_{m2}, y_2), \ldots, (x_{1n}, x_{2n}, \ldots, x_{mn}, y_n),$$

where x_{ij} is the jth observation of X_i and y_j is the jth observation of Y. That is, the index i runs from 1 to m, and the index j runs from 1 to n.

The experimenter first might want to conduct a significance test for a hypothesis relating Y to the other variables. If the random variable Y is completely unrelated to the other variables, the following three equivalent statements are true:

1) Method I and method II for predicting Y are the same.
2) The multiple correlation coefficient $\mathrm{Cor}(Y; X_1, X_2, \ldots, X_m)$ equals zero.
3) The coefficients of the regression function $\beta_1, \beta_2, \ldots, \beta_m$ are all zero.

We can summarize these statements by saying that the hypothesis $\beta_1 = \beta_2 = \cdots = \beta_m = 0$ is true. If the variable Y is related to at least one of the other variables, all three statements are false. That is, the statistical hypothesis $\beta_1 = \beta_2 = \cdots = \beta_m = 0$ is false. We seek a significance test for this hypothesis.

If the hypothesis is rejected, the experimenter next might want point estimators for all the parameters—$\beta_0, \beta_1, \ldots, \beta_m$, and σ^2.

Stock Market Example. The variable Y is the change in price for a particular stock or group of stocks in some time period, such as a day, week, or month. The X_i's refer to previous changes in other stocks or in other economic indices that might be related to Y. Some possibilities are retail sales, freight-car loadings, and interest rates. The hypothesis is that Y is unrelated to the X_i's. That is, knowledge of the X_i's is worthless for predicting Y. Rejection of this hypothesis would be very exciting for an investor who would then want estimators of the coefficients in the regression function.

It is easiest to discuss first the estimated regression function, $b_0 + b_1 x_1 + b_2 x_2 + \cdots + b_m x_m$. As in subsection 3.3, the best estimators minimize the sum of squared differences,

$$\sum_j (y_j - b_0 - b_1 x_1 - b_2 x_2 - \cdots - b_m x_m)^2,$$

in the actual random sample. For the calculus reader, it is easy to verify that the desired b_i's satisfy the normal equations.

$$\sum y_j \quad - b_0 n \quad - b_1 \sum x_{1j} \quad - \cdots - b_m \sum x_{mj} \quad = 0,$$

$$\sum x_{1j} y_j - b_0 \sum x_{1j} - b_1 \sum x_{1j}^2 \quad - \cdots - b_m \sum x_{1j} x_{mj} = 0,$$

$$\cdot \qquad \cdot \qquad \cdot$$

$$\sum x_{mj} y_j - b_0 \sum x_{mj} - b_1 \sum x_{1j} x_{mj} - \cdots - b_m \sum x_{mj}^2 \quad = 0.$$

This is a system of $m + 1$ linear equations in $m + 1$ unknowns, the b_i's. The coefficients are sums, sums of squares, and sums of cross products. Finding the coefficients and then solving the equations can be a big job for a desk calculator. Fortunately, digital computers do this job quickly and accurately. The sample size n can be any magnitude without reaching the capacity of a computer. The value of m is the important consideration. An m of 25 may be too large for a small computer, but a two-minute job for a large computer.

The next task is to estimate σ^2. Consider the total sum of squares.

$$\text{Total SS} = \sum_j (y_j - y.)^2.$$

This can be partitioned into two components.

$$\text{Total SS} = \text{Regression SS} + \text{Error SS},$$

where

$$\text{Regression SS} = \sum_j (b_0 + b_1 x_{1j} + b_2 x_{2j} + \cdots + b_m x_{mj} - y.)^2,$$

$$\text{Error SS} = \sum_j (y_j - b_0 - b_1 x_{1j} - b_2 x_{2j} - \cdots - b_m x_{mj})^2.$$

When considered as a random variable, the error sum of squares has an expectation of $(n - m - 1)\sigma^2$. Therefore, an unbiased estimator of σ^2 is

$$s^2 = \frac{\text{Error SS}}{n - m - 1} .$$

This is the generalization of the previous result with $m = 1$.

Define the sample multiple correlation coefficient r by

$$r^2 = \frac{\text{Regression SS}}{\text{Total SS}} ,$$

where r is always between zero and one. If every y_j lies on the estimated regression function, then the error sum of squares is zero; the regression sum of squares equals the total sum of squares; and the sample multiple correlation coefficient is one. The converse is also true. If $r = 1$, then every y_j lies on the estimated regression function. Similarly, r is zero if and only if $b_1 = b_2 = \cdots = b_m = 0$.

Finally, we discuss the test for the hypothesis $\beta_1 = \beta_2 = \cdots = \beta_m = 0$. When considered as a random variable, the regression sum of squares has an expectation of $m\sigma^2 + \Delta$. When the hypothesis is true, Δ is zero, and we have another unbiased estimator of σ^2.

$$E\left(\frac{\text{Regression SS}}{m} \right) = \sigma^2.$$

When the hypothesis is not true, Δ is positive. $\dfrac{\text{Regression SS}}{m}$ leads to a biased estimator of σ^2.

$$E\left(\frac{\text{Regression SS}}{m} \right) > \sigma^2.$$

Consider the ratio

$$\frac{\dfrac{\text{Regression SS}}{m}}{\dfrac{\text{Error SS}}{n - m - 1}} .$$

When the hypothesis is true, the ratio tends to be near one. When the hypothesis is false, the ratio tends to be greater than one. The test is to reject, when the observed value of this ratio is too much larger than one. When the hypothesis is true, the ratio has an F-distribution with m and $n - m - 1$ degrees of freedom. This supplies the cut-off point for the test of level α.

$$\text{reject if } F(\alpha, m, n - m - 1) \leq \text{observed} \; \frac{\dfrac{\text{Regression SS}}{m}}{\dfrac{\text{Error SS}}{n - m - 1}} .$$

It is at this point that the assumed conditional normal distribution of Y is used. Without the conditional normal distribution, the test is approximate.

EXERCISES

58. For $m = 2$, verify the following computing formula for the regression sum of squares:

$$\text{Regression SS} = b_1^2 \left[\sum x_{1j}^2 - \frac{(\sum x_{1j})^2}{n} \right] + b_2^2 \left[\sum x_{2j}^2 - \frac{(\sum x_{2j})^2}{n} \right]$$
$$+ 2b_1 b_2 \left[\sum x_{1j} x_{2j} - \frac{(\sum x_{1j})(\sum x_{2j})}{n} \right].$$

59. In addition to high-school performance in exercise 44, Divina can use the results of an aptitude test to predict performance in the freshman year. Suppose X_1 is the high-school rating, X_2 is the result of the aptitude test, and Y is the grade-point average in the first year. Divina is willing to assume that Y has a normal conditional distribution with

$$E(Y \mid x_1, x_2) = \beta_0 + \beta_1 x_1 + \beta_2 x_2,$$
$$V(Y \mid x_1, x_2) = \sigma^2.$$

The random sample of his records showed:

$$n = 42 \qquad \sum y_j^2 = 428$$
$$\sum x_{1j} = 2{,}940 \qquad \sum x_{1j} x_{2j} = 89{,}184$$
$$\sum x_{2j} = 1{,}260 \qquad \sum x_{1j} y_j = 7{,}172$$
$$\sum y_j = 100.8 \qquad \sum x_{2j} y_j = 3{,}062.4$$
$$\sum x_{1j}^2 = 209{,}900$$
$$\sum x_{2j}^2 = 38{,}456$$

The estimated coefficients are

$$b_0 = -.1536,$$
$$b_1 = .0319,$$
$$b_2 = .0106.$$

Some sums of squares are

$$\text{Total SS} = 6.56,$$
$$\text{Regression SS} = 4.92.$$

a) Estimate σ^2.

b) Find the sample multiple correlation coefficient.

c) What is the observed F-ratio? Is it significant at the .05 level?

d) For a new student with a rating of 60 from high school and a 38 on the aptitude test, what is the probability that he will make an average of at least 2.00 in his first year?

60. In exercise 59,

a) show that the normal equations are

$$42b_0 + 2940b_1 + 1260b_2 = 100.8,$$

$$2940b_0 + 209,900b_1 + 89,184b_2 = 7172.0,$$

$$1260b_0 + 89,184b_1 + 38,456b_2 = 3062.4.$$

b) Solve for b_0, b_1, and b_2.

c) Verify the total sum of squares.

d) Use the result of exercise 58 to verify the regression sum of squares.

ADDITIONAL READINGS

Anderson, T., *An Introduction to Multivariate Statistical Analysis.* New York: John Wiley & Sons, Inc., 1958.

Brownlee, K., *Statistical Theory and Methodology in Science and Engineering.* 2nd ed. New York: John Wiley & Sons, Inc., 1965.

Mood, A., and F. Graybill, *Introduction to the Theory of Statistics.* 2nd ed. New York: McGraw-Hill Book Company, 1963.

Mosteller, F., R. Rourke, and G. Thomas, Jr., *Probability and Statistics.* Reading, Massachusetts: Addison-Wesley Publishing Co., 1961.

Parzen, E., *Modern Probability Theory and Its Applications.* New York: John Wiley & Sons, Inc., 1960.

Regression | *VI*

In a very general statistical situation, there is a random experiment with an associated random variable of interest Y. The variation in Y is attributable, at least in part, to some identifiable factors. The central goal is to relate the variation in Y to these factors in an explicit manner. The factors themselves can be cross-classified in two ways, making four types in all.

1

Factors

The four types of factors can be introduced conveniently with four example experiments from agricultural research.

Experiment 1. The variable of interest is the yield per acre for a certain crop. In a given geographical region the crop is regularly grown on many fields. The experimenter chooses twelve fields at random and finds the intensity of planting, say in pounds of seeds per acre. He does nothing to influence this intensity; he merely records the owners' actions. Suppose the intensity of planting is different for each field. At the harvest there is a yield for every intensity.

Experiment 1 has only one factor—intensity. The factor is at twelve *levels*—the twelve pounds of seeds per acre. The factor is *quantitative*—the levels are defined numerically. The factor is *uncontrolled*—the levels are determined by a chance selection, not the experimenter's wishes.

Experiment 2. The variable of interest is again the yield per acre for the crop in the region. This time, the experimenter chooses twelve (different) levels of planting intensity at will. He then randomly chooses twelve fields from the area and plants the crop in the fields, one field for each intensity.

Experiment 2 has one factor—intensity. The factor is at twelve levels— the pre-chosen pounds of seeds per acre. The factor is quantitative—the levels are defined numerically. Experiment 2 differs from experiment 1 only because the factor is now *controlled*—the levels are determined by the experimenter, not by chance selection.

Experiment 3. There are three different varieties of the crop to be compared. The variable of interest is again the yield per acre. The experimenter randomly chooses twelve fields from the region. Each of the three varieties is assigned to four fields.

Intensity of planting is not considered in this experiment. At harvest there are twelve observations of the variable of interest.

Experiment 3 has one factor—crop. The factor is at three levels—the three varieties of the crop. It is *qualitative*—the levels are not numerically defined. It is controlled—the three varieties are chosen by the experimenter, not by chance.

Experiment 4. There are three varieties of the crop to be compared. The variable of interest is again the yield per acre. The experimenter randomly chooses four fields from the region. Each field is divided into many plots. Within each field, the three varieties are assigned randomly to three plots. At harvest there are twelve observations of the variable of interest, the yields on the twelve plots.

Experiment 4 has two factors—crop and field. The crop factor is at three levels; it is qualitative and controlled, as in experiment 3. The field factor is at four levels—the four chosen fields. It is qualitative—the levels are not numerically defined. It is uncontrolled—the four fields are chosen by chance from the many in the region. One may ask why there is a field factor in experiment 4 and not in experiment 3. The answer is that there probably is a field effect in both. However, experiment 3 is not designed to measure it, because a particular field is used with only one variety of the crop.

These four experiments illustrate the types of factors to be considered. In addition to the number of levels, two classifications were mentioned: (1) quantitative or qualitative and (2) controlled or uncontrolled. The following chart defines the names for the four combinations:

		factor is	
		controlled	uncontrolled
factor is	quantitative	*regression factor*	*correlation factor*
	qualitative	*fixed-effects factor*	*random-effects factor*

The intensity factor of experiment 1 is a correlation factor, which was discussed in Chapter V. The intensity factor of experiment 2 is a regression factor, which will be discussed in this chapter. The crop factor of experiments 3 and 4 is a fixed-effects factor, which will be discussed in Chapter VII. The field factor of experiment 4 is a random-effects factor, which will be discussed in Chapter VIII. An experiment can have any number of factors; they can form any combination of types. Those of Chapters III and IV were experiments with one factor, usually of the fixed-effects type with one level.

The mathematical analysis for the regression factor is almost identical to that for the correlation factor of the last chapter. Perhaps for this reason, there is a tendency to confuse the two cases. The following extension of experiments 1 and 2 is intended to prevent this confusion.

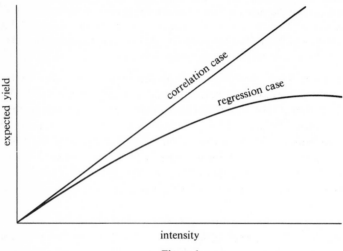

Figure 1

In Experiment 1, suppose the experimenter wants to predict the yield for a randomly chosen field. Recall that the intensity of planting is decided by the owner; the experimenter only observes. The regression function, which is the predictor, relates expected yield to observed intensity. The straight line of Figure 1 might represent this function on some convenient scale. In experiment 2, the experimenter selects a level of intensity and then applies it to a randomly chosen field. The resulting yield is still a random variable with some expected value. This defines another function which relates expected yield and intensity. There is no reason to believe that these two functions are the same. One might anticipate something like the curved line of Figure 1 for the new function. To explain the difference, consider a high level of intensity. Left to themselves in experiment 1, the owners of poor fields might never plant at this high intensity: they would waste seed. Only the owners of fertile fields would plant at this high intensity and expect high yields. In experiment 2 all fields have an equal chance to be planted at this high intensity. The expected yield is the average of the resulting high and low yields. Therefore, it is lower.

EXERCISES

1. A pharmaceutical company has a new drug that may be effective for hypertension. To find out, the company will test the new drug, a standard drug on the market, and a placebo. A patient's decrease in blood pressure from his untreated condition is the variable of interest.

   a) To this point, a treatment factor has been identified. How many levels are there? Is it a fixed-effects, random-effects, regression, or correlation factor? A corresponding one-factor experiment is to give the drug to 6 hypertensive patients, the standard drug to 6 others, and the placebo to 6 others. How many observations of the variable of interest are there?

   b) In another possible experiment, 18 randomly selected hypertensive patients receive the new drug. After two months, the same 18 patients receive the standard drug; after two more months, the same patients receive the placebo. This defines a patient factor. How many levels are there? What type of factor is it? How many observations of the variable of interest are there?

   c) In another experiment for the new drug, one hypertensive patient at age 40 is randomly selected from some population of that age, one at 42, one at 44, and so on. There are 18 patients in all. Each patient is given the new drug. The relation of change in blood pressure to age is found. The age factor is what type?

2

One-Factor Experiment

In an experiment with one regression factor, let Y be the random variable of interest and let x be the level of the one regression factor. Y has a normal distribution. The expected value of Y is a linear function of the level of the regression function, and the variance of Y is a constant. $E(Y) = \beta_0 + \beta_1 x$ and $V(Y) = \sigma^2$. The three parameters which completely describe the experiment are β_0, β_1, and σ^2. Since x is not random, the following symbols are meaningless in this discussion: $E(X)$, $V(X)$, and $\text{Cor}(X, Y)$. The function relating $E(Y)$ to x is the *regression of Y on x*, or the *regression function*. It seems unfortunate to use the same name as in the discussion of a correlation factor; occasionally, the term *response function* is used in the discussion of a regression factor.

The hypothesis $\beta = 0$ is of primary importance. If it is true, the variable of interest is not related to the regression factor. That is, the experimenter cannot influence Y by controlling the level x. If the hypothesis $\beta = 0$ is false, the variable of interest Y is related to the level x of the regression factor.

In the usual statistical situation, the three parameters are unknown, and an experiment is performed to test the hypothesis $\beta = 0$ and to estimate the parameters. In the experiment, n levels x_1, x_2, ..., x_n of the regression factor are chosen at will. The corresponding outcomes y_1, y_2, ..., y_n of the variable Y are observed. The significance test and the estimators are based on these levels and outcomes.

Analytically, the situation is identical to that of subsection 3.3 of Chapter V. That is, a good estimated response function, $b_0 + b_1 x$, minimizes the error sum of squares

$$\sum_j (y_j - b_0 - b_1 x_j)^2.$$

Recall that the b_i's are

$$b_0 = y. - b_1 x.,$$

$$b_1 = \frac{n \sum x_j y_j - (\sum x_j)(\sum y_j)}{n \sum x_j^2 - (\sum x_j)^2}.$$

With these estimators the total sum of squares is again partitioned according to

$$\text{Total SS} = \text{Error SS} + \text{Regression SS},$$

$$\sum (y_j - y.)^2 = \sum (y_j - b_0 - b_1 x_j)^2 + \sum (b_0 + b_1 x_j - y.)^2.$$

The computing formulas of the previous chapter also apply here. The estimator of σ^2 is

$$s^2 = \frac{\text{Error SS}}{n - 2}.$$

The test of the hypothesis $\beta_1 = 0$ is

$$\text{reject if } F(\alpha, 1, n-2) \le \text{observed } \frac{\dfrac{\text{Regression SS}}{1}}{\dfrac{\text{Error SS}}{n-2}}.$$

This completes the statistical analysis for the one-factor experiment. The remainder of this section gives proofs of some of the properties of these estimators.

There is another way to state the model of this section:

$$Y = \beta_0 + \beta_1 x + W,$$

where W has a normal distribution with $E(W) = 0$ and $V(W) = \sigma^2$. Since β_0, β_1, and x are constants, Y has the required normal distribution with

$$E(Y) = \beta_0 + \beta_1 x + E(W) = \beta_0 + \beta_1 x,$$

$$V(Y) = V(W) = \sigma^2.$$

The jth observation of Y may be thought of as

$$y_j = \beta_0 + \beta_1 x_j + w_j,$$

where w_j is the effect on y_j of everything in the world except x_j. In the n observations of Y, the corresponding W_j's are assumed independent.

The proofs are based on three basic facts from Chapter V:

1) $E(\sum a_j U_j) = \sum a_j E(U_j)$.
2) If the U_j's are independent, then $V(\sum a_j U_j) = \sum a_j^2 V(U_j)$.
3) If the U_j's are independent and identically distributed, then

$$E[\sum (U_j - U.)^2] = (n-1)V(U).$$

Also, the formula for b_1 can be rewritten in two ways:

$$b_1 = \frac{n\sum x_j y_j - (\sum x_j)(\sum y_j)}{n\sum x_j^2 - (\sum x_j)^2} = \frac{\sum (x_j - x.)(y_j - y.)}{\sum (x_j - x.)^2} = \frac{\sum (x_j - x.)y_j}{\sum (x_j - x.)^2}.$$

First, consider the expected value of the estimator of β_1.

$$E(B_1) = E\left[\frac{\sum (x_j - x.)(Y_j - Y.)}{\sum (x_j - x.)^2}\right] = \frac{\sum (x_j - x.)E(Y_j - Y.)}{\sum (x_j - x.)^2}$$

$$= \frac{\sum (x_j - x.)E[\beta_1(x_j - x.) + (W_j - W.)]}{\sum (x_j - x.)^2} = \beta_1.$$

Second, consider the expected value of the estimator of β_0.

$$E(B_0) = E(Y. - B_1 x.) = E(\beta_0 + \beta_1 x. + W. - B_1 x.) = \beta_0.$$

Third, consider the variance of the estimator of β_1.

$$V(B_1) = V\left[\frac{\sum(x_j - x.)Y_j}{\sum(x_j - x.)^2}\right] = \frac{\sum V[(x_j - x.)Y_j]}{[\sum(x_j - x.)^2]^2}$$

$$= \frac{\sum(x_j - x.)^2 V(Y_j)}{[\sum(x_j - x.)^2]^2} = \frac{\sigma^2}{\sum(x_j - x.)^2}.$$

Therefore,

$$E(B_1^2) = V(B_1) + \beta_1^2 = \frac{\sigma^2}{\sum(x_j - x.)^2} + \beta_1^2.$$

Fourth, consider the expected value of the regression sum of squares.

$$E(\text{Regression SS}) = E\left\{\sum(B_0 + B_1 x_j - Y.)^2\right\}$$

$$= E\left\{\sum[Y. + B_1(x_j - x.) - Y.]^2\right\}$$

$$= \sum(x_j - x.)^2 E(B_1^2)$$

$$= \sigma^2 + \beta_1^2 \sum(x_j - x.)^2.$$

Fifth, consider the expected value of the total sum of squares.

$$E(\text{Total SS}) = E\left\{\sum(Y_j - Y.)^2\right\}$$

$$= E\left\{\sum[\beta_1(x_j - x.) + (W_j - W.)]^2\right\}$$

$$= \beta_1^2 \sum(x_j - x.)^2 + 2\beta_1 \sum(x_j - x.)E(W_j - W.)$$

$$+ E[\sum(W_j - W.)^2]$$

$$= \beta_1^2 \sum(x_j - x.)^2 + (n - 1)\sigma^2.$$

Sixth, consider the expected value of the error sum of squares.

$$E(\text{Error SS}) = E(\text{Total SS}) - E(\text{Regression SS})$$

$$= (n - 2)\sigma^2.$$

Therefore,

$$E(S^2) = E\left(\frac{\text{Error SS}}{n - 2}\right) = \sigma^2.$$

In the context of this chapter, it has just been shown that B_0, B_1, and S^2 are unbiased estimators of β_0, β_1, and σ^2. If the hypothesis $\beta_1 = 0$ is true, it has also been shown that

$$\frac{\text{Regression SS}}{1} \quad \text{and} \quad \frac{\text{Error SS}}{n-2}$$

have the same expected value, namely σ^2. The proof that their ratio has an F-distribution is not given in this book.

b_1, b_0, Regression SS, Total SS, and Error SS have the same formulas in this discussion of the regression factor as they had in the discussion of the correlation factor in Chapter V. The only difference is in the interpretation of the level x. Here it is the chosen level of the regression factor; there it was the observed outcome of the random variable X. These derivations, however, show that the expected values of B_0, B_1, and S^2 do not depend on x. Therefore, these estimators were also unbiased in the correlation context of Chapter V.

Summary. Let Y be the variable of interest and let x be the level of the regression factor. Y has a normal distribution with

$$E(Y) = \beta_0 + \beta_1 x,$$

$$V(Y) = \sigma^2.$$

When β_0, β_1, and σ^2 are unknown and when n observations y_j are made at n controlled levels x_j, the unbiased estimators of β_0 and β_1 are

$$b_0 = y. - b_1 x.,$$

$$b_1 = \frac{n \sum x_j y_j - \left(\sum x_j \right) \left(\sum y_j \right)}{n \sum x_j^2 - \left(\sum x_j \right)^2}.$$

The total sum of squares, $\sum (y_j - y.)^2$, is partitioned into two components.

$$\text{Regression SS} = \sum (b_0 + b_1 x_j - y.)^2 = b_1^2 \left[\sum x_j^2 - \frac{\left(\sum x_j \right)^2}{n} \right].$$

$$\text{Error SS} = \sum (y_j - b_0 - b_1 x_j)^2 = \text{Total SS} - \text{Regression SS}.$$

The unbiased estimator of σ^2 is $\dfrac{\text{Error SS}}{n-2}$. A test for the hypothesis $\beta_1 = 0$ is

$$\text{reject if } F(\alpha, 1, n-2) \leq \text{observed} \quad \frac{\dfrac{\text{Regression SS}}{1}}{\dfrac{\text{Error SS}}{n-2}}.$$

EXERCISES

2. To simulate a regression situation, pick a number between 0 and 10. Call it x. Construct a deck of five cards numbered "-2", "-1", "0", "1", and "2". Randomly draw one card from this deck. Call it w. Let $y = 10 + 4x + w$.
   a) What are β_0, β_1, and $V(Y)$?
   b) Is Y normally distributed?

3. In the context of exercise 2, select six values of x and generate the corresponding six values of Y. Start with these pairs, and carry out the analysis.
   a) Estimate β_0, β_1, and $V(Y)$.
   b) Test the hypothesis $\beta_1 = 0$.

4. A study of a large number of wooded plots in northern Illinois shows about three white oaks for every red oak. That is, the regression function for the number of white oaks Y is $3x$, where x is the number of red oaks on a plot. On some cleared land in the area, 1000 red oaks are planted. At maturity, approximately how many white oaks will there be?

5. Show that the three expressions for b_1 in this section are equivalent.

6. If the response function is linear $E(Y) = \beta_0 + \beta_1 x$, if the variance is constant $V(Y) = \sigma^2$, and if six observations of Y are allowed for $0 \le x_j \le 10$, what values of the x_j's should be chosen to minimize the variance of B_1?

3

Multi-Factor Experiment

In an experiment with one variable of interest Y and several, say m, regression factors, let $x_1, x_2, \ldots, x_m$ be the levels of the regression factors. The basic probabilistic assumptions are:

1) The expected value of Y is a linear function of the levels. $E(Y) = \beta_0 + \beta_1 x_1 + \beta_2 x_2 + \cdots + \beta_m x_m$.

2) The variance of Y is a constant. $V(Y) = \sigma^2$.

3) Y has a normal distribution.

There are $m + 2$ parameters—β_0, β_1, β_2, ..., β_m, and σ^2. Some of the x_i's actually can be functions of the others, such as $x_2 = x_1^2$ or $x_3 = x_1 x_2$.

If the hypothesis $\beta_1 = \beta_2 = \cdots = \beta_m = 0$ is true, the variable of interest is unrelated to the regression factors. The experimenter cannot influence Y by controlling the levels x_1, x_2, ..., x_m. If the hypothesis is false, the variable of interest Y is related to at least one of the regression factors.

In the usual statistical situation, the parameters are unknown. An experiment is performed to estimate the parameters and to test the hypothesis $\beta_1 = \beta_2 = \cdots = \beta_m$. If this hypothesis is rejected, some of the regression factors are related to the variable of interest. Further tests may be needed to identify them. The estimators and the tests are based on the outcomes of the experiment. Let y_1, y_2, ..., y_n be the observations of the variable Y. Let x_{ij} be the level of the ith factor in the jth observation of Y, where $i = 1, 2, ..., m$ and $j = 1, 2, ..., n$. Recall that each level of each factor is selected by the experimenter, not by chance.

Analytically, the situation is identical to that of subsection 4.2 of Chapter V. The b_i's of a good estimated regression function minimize the sum of squares,

$$\sum_j (y_j - b_0 - b_1 x_{1j} - \cdots - b_i x_{ij} - \cdots - b_m x_{mj})^2.$$

The same normal equations result. The b_i's are the solutions of these normal equations. The total sum of squares $\sum (y_j - y.)^2$ can be partitioned again according to

$$\text{Total SS} = \text{Error SS} + \text{Regression SS}.$$

The unbiased estimator of σ^2 is

$$s^2 = \frac{\text{Error SS}}{n - m - 1}.$$

The significance test of the hypothesis $\beta_1 = \beta_2 = \cdots = \beta_m = 0$ is

$$\text{reject if } F(\alpha, m, n - m - 1) \leq \text{observed } \frac{\dfrac{\text{Regression SS}}{m}}{\dfrac{\text{Error SS}}{n - m - 1}}.$$

The usual computer program for multiple regression outputs all of these quantities.

Rejection of the hypothesis $\beta_1 = \beta_2 = \cdots = \beta_m = 0$ is usually only the beginning of the analysis. Having found this group of m factors, the experimenter frequently wants to simplify the group by eliminating the unimportant factors. There are many informal procedures for this common situation. Most of them are related to the following discussion. Consider the ith factor and the corresponding hypothesis $\beta_i = 0$, where β_i is the coefficient of x_i in the regression function. We seek a significance test for this hypothesis.

The key step in the test is to find another sum of squares, called the *sum of squares for* β_i, such that $E(\text{SS for } \beta_i) = \sigma^2 + \Delta$, where Δ must be zero when $\beta_i = 0$ and Δ must be positive when $\beta_i \neq 0$. To get this sum of squares, assume $\beta_i = 0$. The original model becomes

$$E(Y) = \beta_0 + \beta_1 x_1 + \cdots + \beta_{i-1} x_{i-1} + \beta_{i+1} x_{i+1} + \cdots + \beta_m x_m.$$

That is, the regression is now a linear function of $m - 1$ of the x's. The data in the experiment can now be re-analyzed according to this new model. The result is a new set of answers. In particular, there is a new regression sum of squares which is smaller than the original regression sum of squares. The desired sum of squares for β_i is the difference of these two.

SS for β_i = Original Regression SS − New Regression SS.

The significance test for the hypothesis $\beta_i = 0$ is

$$\text{reject if } F(\alpha, 1, n - m - 1) \leq \text{observed} \quad \frac{\dfrac{\text{SS for } \beta_i}{1}}{\dfrac{\text{Error SS}}{n - m - 1}}.$$

The error sum of squares in the denominator is the original error sum of squares.

This test is easily generalized to apply to the hypothesis that several of the coefficients are zero. For example, take the hypothesis $\beta_1 = \beta_2 = 0$, where $3 \leq m$. To obtain the sum of squares for β_1 and β_2, re-analyze the data according to a new model $E(Y) = \beta_0 + \beta_3 x_3 + \beta_4 x_4 + \cdots + \beta_m x_m$, and obtain a new regression sum of squares. The desired sum of squares for β_1 and β_2 is

SS for β_1 and β_2 = Original Regression SS − New Regression SS.

The test for the hypothesis $\beta_1 = \beta_2 = 0$ is

$$\text{reject if } F(\alpha, 2, n - m - 1) \leq \text{observed} \quad \frac{\dfrac{\text{SS for } \beta_1 \text{ and } \beta_2}{2}}{\dfrac{\text{Error SS}}{n - m - 1}}.$$

Some surprises can happen. For example, the experiment can fail to reject either $\beta_1 = 0$ or $\beta_2 = 0$, but it can reject $\beta_1 = \beta_2 = 0$.

The numerical computations for all these tests can be huge when done by hand. Computer programs are widely available. In fact, one usually can calculate on a computer more interesting sums of squares than one has theory to explain.

Finally, notice that the analysis starts from an assumed form of the regression function. The experimenter, however, may not know this form. For an example, take two regression factors with levels x_1 and x_2. As a first approximation the experimenter might assume a linear form $E(Y) = \beta_0 + \beta_1 x_1 + \beta_2 x_2$. This is very likely to be unsatisfactory, especially if the ranges for the x_i's are large. Another procedure is to start with a fairly general, non-linear form, such as

$$E(Y) = \beta_0 + \beta_1 x_1 + \beta_2 x_2 + \beta_3 x_1^2 + \beta_4 x_2^2 + \beta_5 x_1 x_2,$$

and eliminate the unimportant terms.

Table 1

j	x_{1j}	x_{2j}	x_{3j}	y_j
1	0	1	0	12.41
2	0	0	5	25.24
3	1	1	2	13.62
4	1	3	3	25.46
5	2	0	1	14.55
6	2	2	4	26.03
7	3	3	2	21.34
8	3	2	3	20.52
9	4	4	1	23.52
10	4	5	4	33.40
11	5	4	0	21.70
12	5	5	5	38.84

The data for this numerical example are fictitious, but the resulting situations are typical. With $m = 3$ and $n = 12$, let the experimental results be as in Table 1. The x_{ij}'s were chosen at will, and the y_j's were simulated from a table of random numbers (with $\beta_0 = 10$, $\beta_1 = 1$, $\beta_2 = 1$, $\beta_3 = 3$, and $\sigma = 3$). The assumed model is

$$E(Y) = \beta_0 + \beta_1 x_1 + \beta_2 x_2 + \beta_3 x_3,$$

$$V(Y) = \sigma^2.$$

Notice that chosen levels of x_1 and x_2 are approximately equal. This will lead to trouble. A typical computer program picks up the problem here and does the remaining calculations. The normal equations are

$$12b_0 + 30b_1 + 30b_2 + 30b_3 = 276.63,$$
$$30b_0 + 110b_1 + 104b_2 + 75b_3 = 776.20,$$
$$30b_0 + 104b_1 + 110b_2 + 80b_3 = 801.61,$$
$$30b_0 + 75b_1 + 80b_2 + 110b_3 = 804.05.$$

The solution is

$$b_0 = 8.808,$$
$$b_1 = 0.491,$$
$$b_2 = 2.325,$$
$$b_3 = 2.881.$$

The sums of squares are

$$\text{Total SS} = 661.684,$$
$$\text{Regression SS} = 621.506,$$
$$\text{Error SS} = 40.178.$$

The estimator of σ^2 is

$$s^2 = \frac{\text{Error SS}}{n - m - 1} = \frac{40.178}{8} = 5.022.$$

The observed F-ratio for $\beta_1 = \beta_2 = \beta_3 = 0$ is

$$\frac{\dfrac{\text{Regression SS}}{m}}{\dfrac{\text{Error SS}}{n - m - 1}} = \frac{\dfrac{621.506}{3}}{5.022} = 41.3.$$

Take $\alpha = .01$. At this significance level the cut-off point is

$$F(\alpha, m, n - m - 1) = F(.01, 3, 8) = 7.59.$$

Therefore, $\beta_1 = \beta_2 = \beta_3 = 0$ is rejected, and the group of three regression factors is related to Y. Is each factor related to Y? The sums of squares for the β_i's are

$$\text{SS for } \beta_1 = 2.525,$$
$$\text{SS for } \beta_2 = 55.456,$$
$$\text{SS for } \beta_3 = 271.665.$$

The F-ratio for the hypothesis $\beta_i = 0$ is

$$\frac{\dfrac{\text{SS for } \beta_i}{1}}{\dfrac{\text{Error SS}}{n-m-1}} = \frac{\text{SS for } \beta_i}{5.022}.$$

The observed F-ratios are

$$\text{for } \beta_1 = 0.50,$$
$$\text{for } \beta_2 = 11.04,$$
$$\text{for } \beta_3 = 54.09.$$

At $\alpha = .01$, the cut-off point is

$$F(\alpha, 1, n - m - 1) = F(.01, 1, 8) = 11.3.$$

The hypothesis $\beta_3 = 0$ is definitely rejected; hypothesis $\beta_2 = 0$ is on the borderline; and the hypothesis $\beta_1 = 0$ is definitely not rejected. Now consider the hypothesis $\beta_1 = \beta_2 = 0$. The sum of squares for β_1 and β_2 is

$$\text{SS for } \beta_1 \text{ and } \beta_2 = 260.064.$$

The observed F-ratio is

$$\frac{\dfrac{\text{SS for } \beta_1 \text{ and } \beta_2}{2}}{\dfrac{\text{Error SS}}{n-m-1}} = \frac{\dfrac{260.064}{2}}{5.022} = 51.78.$$

The cut-off point is

$$F(\alpha, 2, n - m - 1) = F(.01, 2, 8) = 8.65.$$

The hypothesis $\beta_1 = \beta_2 = 0$ is definitely rejected.

Assume that the experimenter wants to simplify the regression function for future use. He should keep the term $\beta_3 x_3$, because the hypothesis $\beta_3 = 0$ is rejected. He can not eliminate both of the other terms, $\beta_1 x_1$ and $\beta_2 x_2$, because the hypothesis $\beta_1 = \beta_2 = 0$ is rejected. He might decide to keep $\beta_2 x_2$ and drop $\beta_1 x_1$. If the data are re-analyzed according to $E(Y) = \beta_0 + \beta_2 x_2 + \beta_3 x_3$, the estimators for future use are

$$b_0 = 9.146,$$
$$b_2 = 2.741,$$
$$b_3 = 2.822.$$

This may appear very different from the actual model that generated the data.

$$E(Y) = 10 + x_1 + x_2 + 3x_3.$$

Recall from the experimental data, however, that x_{1j} and x_{2j} were approximately equal for all j. This makes it very hard for the experiment to detect the actual model from $E(Y) = 10 + 2x_2 + 3x_3$, which does not differ greatly from the result of the statistical analysis.

EXERCISES

7. With two regression factors, let the experimental results be those shown here.

j	x_{1j}	x_{2j}	y_j
1	0	1	10.2
2	1	0	10.9
3	1	3	20.7
4	2	2	16.8
5	3	0	13.5
6	4	3	25.0
7	4	4	32.6

Assume a regression function of the form

$$E(Y) = \beta_0 + \beta_1 x_1 + \beta_2 x_2.$$

The estimated coefficients are

$$b_0 = 7.06,$$
$$b_1 = 2.13,$$
$$b_2 = 3.72.$$

Some sums of squares are

$$\text{Total SS} = 400.43,$$
$$\text{Regression SS} = 385.60,$$
$$\text{SS for } \beta_1 = 51.75,$$
$$\text{SS for } \beta_2 = 157.80.$$

a) Estimate σ^2.
b) What is the observed F-ratio for the hypothesis $\beta_1 = \beta_2 = 0$? What is the cut-off point for $\alpha = .01$?

c) What is the observed F-ratio for the hypothesis $\beta_1 = 0$? What is the cut-off point for $\alpha = .01$?

d) What is the observed F-ratio for the hypothesis $\beta_2 = 0$? What is the cut-off point for $\alpha = .01$?

8. a) In exercise 7, find the normal equations and verify the results for b_0, b_1, and b_2.

   b) Verify the total sum of squares.

   c) Use exercise 58 of Chapter V to verify the regression sum of squares.

   d) Verify the sum of squares for β_1.

9. Let the results of an experiment be as follows.

j	x_j	y_j
1	0	1
2	0	2
3	1	5
4	2	10
5	2	11
6	2	12
7	3	10
8	3	12
9	4	10

a) Plot the nine points (x_j, y_j) on a graph.

Assume a regression function of the quadratic form

$$E(Y) = \beta_0 + \beta_1 x + \beta_2 x^2,$$

$$V(Y) = \sigma^2.$$

The estimated coefficients are

$$b_0 = \quad 1.18,$$

$$b_1 = \quad 6.96,$$

$$b_2 = -1.19.$$

Some sums of squares are

$$\text{Total SS} = 146.89,$$

$$\text{Regression SS} = 136.83,$$

$$\text{SS for } \beta_2 = \quad 34.09.$$

b) Draw the estimated regression function on the graph in a).

c) Estimate σ^2.

d) What is the observed F-ratio for $\beta_1 = \beta_2 = 0$? What is the cut-off point for $\alpha = .01$?

e) What is the observed F-ratio for $\beta_2 = 0$? What is the cut-off point for $\alpha = .01$?

10. a) In exercise 9, verify that the normal equations are

$$9b_0 + 17b_1 + 47b_2 = 73,$$
$$17b_0 + 47b_1 + 143b_2 = 177,$$
$$47b_0 + 143b_1 + 467b_2 = 495.$$

b) Verify the total sum of squares.

c) Use exercise 58 of Chapter V to verify the regression sum of squares.

d) Verify the sum of squares for β_2.

Analysis of Variance: One | VII

In all the experiments to be discussed in this chapter, there are a variable of interest Y and one or more fixed-effects factors. Recall that a fixed-effects factor is controlled and qualitative. That is, the levels of the factor are selected by the experimenter, not by chance. The levels are not numerically defined. This differs from the discussions of the regression and correlation factors, where the levels were numerically defined.

The first question about a fixed-effects factor usually is, "Does the random variable of interest Y have the same probability distribution for each level of the factor?" The experimenter frequently wants to conduct a significance test to establish a negative answer to this question. He also wants estimators for the parameters.

1

One-Factor Experiment

In the experiment of this section there are a variable of interest Y and one fixed-effects factor at I levels. A conventional way of laying out the data suggests *row factor* for the name of the factor in this experiment. At each of the I levels, there are J observations of Y. This makes IJ observations of Y in all. Let the outcome of the jth observation at the ith level be y_{ij}, where $i = 1, 2, \ldots, I$ and $j = 1, 2, \ldots, J$. An experiment with unequal numbers of observations at each level is not discussed in this book.

Agricultural Example. There are three (I) varieties of a crop (row factor) to be compared. The variable of interest is the yield per acre (Y). The experimenter randomly chooses twelve fields from a region. Each of the three varieties is assigned to four (J) fields. This is experiment 3 from the introduction to Chapter VI.

Table 1

case A	$j =$				case B	$j =$			
	1	2	3	4		1	2	3	4
1	80	80	80	80	1	79	79	79	79
$i = 2$	80	80	80	80	$i = 2$	85	85	85	85
3	80	80	80	80	3	76	76	76	76

case C	$j =$				case D	$j =$			
	1	2	3	4		1	2	3	4
1	90	83	75	72	1	89	82	74	71
$i = 2$	89	82	81	68	$i = 2$	94	87	86	73
3	85	81	78	76	3	81	77	74	72

Table 1 gives four different possible results to this experiment. In each case, there are three rows for the three varieties and four columns for the four replications of the experiment. The yield for the second variety on the third field is y_{23}; in case D, y_{23} is 86. The four yields for the second variety in case D are 94, 87, 86, and 73. The order of the four numbers in a row is irrelevant.

Model

In the probabilistic model, Y_{ij} is the random variable corresponding to y_{ij}. For each i, Y_{i1}, Y_{i2}, ..., Y_{iJ} are independent random variables with the same distribution of probability. That is, they form a random sample of size J for the ith level of the row factor. Let the parameters be $E(Y_{ij}) = \mu_i$ and $V(Y_{ij}) = \sigma_i^2$. To this point, we have assumed nothing about the Y_{ij}'s except independence. First, assume a common variance. $V(Y_{ij}) = \sigma_i^2 = \sigma^2$ for all i. When the σ_i's are not all equal, it frequently is easy to transform the data to make them equal. Second, assume that Y_{ij} has a normal distribution. The theory is strictly correct when this is true; otherwise it is approximate. A violation of the first assumption about a constant variance is far more likely to be serious than a violation of the second about normality.

There are now $I + 1$ parameters for the experiment: μ_1, μ_2, ..., μ_I, and σ^2. If the variable of interest Y has the same probability distribution for each level of the row factor, then the hypothesis $\mu_1 = \mu_2 = \cdots = \mu_I$ is true. If the variable of interest Y does not have the same probability distribution for each level, then the hypothesis is false. Usually the experimenter's first goal is the rejection of this hypothesis. He may also be interested in estimators of these parameters and in comparisons among them, such as $\mu_1 - \mu_2$.

The experiment is defined completely by these parameters, and the analysis could be carried out in terms of them. There is, however, a special system of notation for the analysis of variance. For one-factor experiments it may seem artificial. The point is that it generalizes well. The μ_i's have a mean value μ.

$$\mu = \frac{\mu_1 + \mu_2 + \cdots + \mu_I}{I} = \frac{\sum \mu_i}{I}.$$

Let the ith *main effect* α_i be the difference between the ith expected value and μ.

$$i\text{th main effect} = \alpha_i = \mu_i - \mu.$$

Each of the I levels has its main effect. The mean (and sum) of the main effects $\alpha.$ is always zero.

$$\alpha. = \frac{\alpha_1 + \alpha_2 + \cdots + \alpha_I}{I} = \frac{\sum \alpha_i}{I} = \frac{\sum(\mu_i - \mu)}{I} = \mu - \mu = 0.$$

The expected value of Y_{ij} may now be written $E(Y_{ij}) = \mu_i = \mu + \alpha_i$. By this device the set of I parameters, the μ_i's, is replaced by an equivalent set of $I + 1$ parameters, μ and the α_i's.

The hypothesis $\mu_1 = \mu_2 = \cdots = \mu_I$ has another form under the new system of parameters. If the hypothesis is true, $\mu_i = \mu$ for all i, and $\alpha_i = 0$ for all i. Conversely, if $\alpha_i = 0$ for all i, then all the μ_i's are equal and the hypothesis is true. Therefore, an equivalent form of the hypothesis is $\alpha_1 = \alpha_2 = \cdots = \alpha_I = 0$. This form is also equivalent to the statement $\sum \alpha_i^2 = 0$. In words, the hypothesis is now that all the main effects are zero.

The special system of notation for the analysis of variance also identifies the effects of chance. The difference between the observed outcome y_{ij} and the expected value $\mu + \alpha_i$ is a random component w_{ij}, where $y_{ij} = \mu + \alpha_i + w_{ij}$. It is helpful to think of w_{ij} as the effect on y_{ij} of everything in the world, except the one fixed-effects factor which has effect $\mu + \alpha_i$. Of course, y_{ij} is observed, not μ, α_i or w_{ij}. In the corresponding probabilistic statements the W_{ij}'s are independent, normally distributed random variables with $E(W_{ij}) = 0$ and $V(W_{ij}) = \sigma^2$ for all i and j. Then $\mu = \alpha_i + W_{ij}$ has a normal distribution with the same properties as Y.

$$E(\mu + \alpha_i + W_{ij}) = \mu + \alpha_i = E(Y_{ij}),$$
$$V(\mu + \alpha_i + W_{ij}) = \sigma^2 = V(Y_{ij}).$$

The idea of resolving a random variable like Y_{ij} into components like μ, α_i, and W_{ij} is fundamental for all of the analysis of variance.

Exercises

1. Seven random variables have the expected values given below. Find the corresponding μ and the main effects.

i:	1	2	3	4	5	6	7
μ_i:	20	25	27	21	14	19	14

2. Seven random variables have $\mu = 100$ and the main effects given below. Find the corresponding expected values, the μ_i's.

i:	1	2	3	4	5	6	7
α_i:	3	12	-5	-20	8	7	?

Sums of Squares

The fundamental step in the analysis of the one-factor experiment identifies a sum of squares for the effect of the row factor and for the effect of chance. The significance test for the hypothesis is based on these sums of squares.

First, it is necessary to introduce some new notation for familiar concepts. Let the mean of the outcomes for the ith level be the ith *row mean* $y_{i\cdot}$.

$$i\text{th row mean} = y_{i\cdot} = \frac{y_{i1} + y_{i2} + \cdots + y_{iJ}}{J} = \frac{\sum_j y_{ij}}{J}.$$

Of course, there are I row means. The *grand mean* $y_{\cdot\cdot}$ is

$$\text{grand mean} = y_{\cdot\cdot} = \frac{y_1\cdot + y_2\cdot + \cdots + y_I\cdot}{I} = \frac{\sum_i y_{i\cdot}}{I} = \frac{\sum_i \sum_j y_{ij}}{IJ},$$

where the sums are for $i = 1, 2, \ldots, I$ and $j = 1, 2, \ldots, J$. Notice that the grand mean may be thought of as the mean of the I row means $y_{i\cdot}$ or as the mean of the IJ individual outcomes y_{ij}. As in Chapters V and VI the gross variation in the data is measured by the *total sum of squares*.

$$\text{Total SS} = \sum_i \sum_j (y_{ij} - y_{\cdot\cdot})^2.$$

A convenient computing formula is given later.

The total sum of squares must be partitioned into two components, one for the row factor and one for chance. The key step introduces the row means into the total sum of squares.

$$\begin{aligned}
\text{Total SS} &= \sum_i \sum_j (y_{ij} - y_{\cdot\cdot})^2 \\
&= \sum_i \sum_j [(y_{ij} - y_{i\cdot}) + (y_{i\cdot} - y_{\cdot\cdot})]^2 \\
&= \sum_i \sum_j (y_{ij} - y_{i\cdot})^2 + \sum_i \sum_j (y_{i\cdot} - y_{\cdot\cdot})^2.
\end{aligned}$$

The middle term in the expansion is zero because

$$2\sum_i \sum_j (y_{ij} - y_{i\cdot})(y_{i\cdot} - y_{\cdot\cdot}) = 2\sum_i (y_{i\cdot} - y_{\cdot\cdot})\sum_j (y_{ij} - y_{i\cdot}),$$

and

$$\sum_j (y_{ij} - y_{i\cdot}) = 0 \text{ for all } i.$$

$\sum\limits_{j}(y_{ij} - y_{i\cdot})$ is the sum of the deviations from the mean in the ith row, which is always zero. The first sum of squares $\sum\limits_{i}\sum\limits_{j}(y_{ij} - y_{i\cdot})^2$ is the *error sum of squares*. It measures the variations within the rows. The second sum of squares $\sum\limits_{i}\sum\limits_{j}(y_{i\cdot} - y_{\cdot\cdot})^2$ is the *row sum of squares*. It measures the variation in the row means. If all the row means are equal, the row sum of squares is zero; if they differ widely, the row sum of squares is large.

As a practical matter, it is almost never a good idea to calculate these sums of squares from their definitions. There are computing formulas that are easier and more accurate. Take the total sum of squares,

$$\sum_{i}\sum_{j}(y_{ij} - y_{\cdot\cdot})^2 = \sum_{i}\sum_{j}y_{ij}^2 - 2\sum_{i}\sum_{j}y_{ij}y_{\cdot\cdot} + \sum_{i}\sum_{j}y_{\cdot\cdot}^2$$

$$= \sum_{i}\sum_{j}y_{ij}^2 - 2y_{\cdot\cdot}\sum_{i}\sum_{j}y_{ij} + IJy_{\cdot\cdot}^2$$

$$= \sum_{i}\sum_{j}y_{ij}^2 - \frac{2\left(\sum\limits_{i}\sum\limits_{j}y_{ij}\right)^2}{IJ} + \frac{\left(\sum\limits_{i}\sum\limits_{j}y_{ij}\right)^2}{IJ}$$

$$= \sum_{i}\sum_{j}y_{ij}^2 - \frac{\left(\sum\limits_{i}\sum\limits_{j}y_{ij}\right)^2}{IJ}.$$

This is a better formula, because each individual difference $y_{ij} - y_{\cdot\cdot}$ does not have to be calculated. By a similar derivation the computing formula for the row sum of squares is

$$\sum_{i}\sum_{j}(y_{i\cdot} - y_{\cdot\cdot})^2 = \frac{\sum\limits_{i}\left(\sum\limits_{j}y_{ij}\right)^2}{J} - \frac{\left(\sum\limits_{i}\sum\limits_{j}y_{ij}\right)^2}{IJ}.$$

For the error sum of squares the formula is

$$\sum_{i}\sum_{j}(y_{ij} - y_{i\cdot})^2 = \sum_{i}\sum_{j}y_{ij}^2 - \frac{\sum\limits_{i}\left(\sum\limits_{j}y_{ij}\right)^2}{J}.$$

Even with these computing formulas the calculations can be tedious. For experiments with more factors they can be very tedious. Fortunately, the calculations are fairly standard, and programs for electronic computers are readily available. A complete breakdown of the total sum of squares is one usual output of such a program. The interpretation of this breakdown can vary, and it must be supplied by the user of the program. The discussions of this chapter and the next are from the viewpoint of such a user.

Table 2

case

	A	B	C	D
1	80	79	80	79
$i = 2$	80	85	80	85
3	80	76	80	76

Table 3

case

	A	B	C	D
Row SS	0	168	0	168
Error SS	0	0	474	474
Total SS	0	168	474	642

Table 2 gives the row means for the four cases of Table 1. In each case, the grand mean is 80. Table 3 gives the sums of squares for the same four cases. Case A is the most degenerate possible result for this experiment. The row sum of squares is zero, indicating no variation in the row means. The error sum of squares is also zero, indicating no variations within the rows. Tables 1 and 2 verify these statements. In case B, the row sum of squares is 168, indicating variation in the row means. The zero error sum of squares again indicates no variations within the rows. Case C is the reverse. There is no variation in the row means, but variations exist within the rows. Case D is the most realistic and interesting. The row means vary, and the outcomes vary within rows.

Exercises

3. Verify the computing formulas for the row sum of squares and the error sum of squares.

4. When $I = 2$, verify that the row sum of squares is

$$\frac{J(y_1. - y_2.)^2}{2}.$$

5. In exercises 1 a) of Chapter VI, a pharmaceutical company wants to test a new drug ($i = 1$), a standard drug on the market ($i = 2$), and a placebo ($i = 3$). The variable of interest is the change in a patient's blood pressure. Results for 18 patients are given below. Negative numbers mean decreases.

$$j =$$

	1	2	3	4	5	6
1	-25	-30	-30	-25	-35	-5
$i = 2$	-15	-25	-30	-10	-20	-20
3	$+5$	0	-5	-5	-5	-20

a) Compute the row means.
b) Compute the Total SS.
c) Compute the Row SS.
d) Compute the Error SS.

Expected Sums of Squares

With the probability model the sums of squares are random variables with distributions and parameters of their own. In particular, the error and row sums of squares have expected values. These expected values suggest the desired significance test of the hypothesis $\sum \alpha_i^2 = 0$.

One basic fact is prerequisite for the derivations. It was first encountered in section 1 of Chapter IV in connection with the unbiasedness of the sample variance as an estimator of the variance. Let X be a random variable and n be the size of a random sample for X. Consider $E\left[\sum_h (X_h - \bar{X})^2\right]$, where $h = 1, 2, \ldots, n$. If this is divided by $n - 1$, the expected value is the variance $E(S^2) = V(X)$. Therefore,

$$E\left[\sum_h (X_h - \bar{X})^2\right] = (n - 1)V(X).$$

This is the useful basic fact.

In these derivations the object of interest is the expected value of a double sum of squares. The expectations and the sums can be taken in any order. Factors containing only Greek letters are not random, and they can be moved past the E symbol. Factors without an i (or j) can be moved past the $\sum_i$ (or $\sum_j$) symbol.

Consider the expected value of the error sum of squares.

$$E\left[\sum_i \sum_j (Y_{ij} - Y_{i.})^2\right] = \sum_i E\left[\sum_j (Y_{ij} - Y_{i.})^2\right]$$

$$= \sum_i E\left[\sum_j (\mu + \alpha_i + W_{ij} - \mu - \alpha_i - W_{i.})^2\right]$$

$$= \sum_i E\left[\sum_j (W_{ij} - W_{i.})^2\right].$$

The basic fact applies to $E\left[\sum_j (W_{ij} - W_{i.})^2\right]$ with the following correspondences:

$$W_{ij} \sim X_h,$$

$$j \sim h,$$

$$J \sim n,$$

$$\sigma^2 \text{ or } V(W_{ij}) \sim V(X_h),$$

$$W_{i.} \sim \bar{X}.$$

The result of the application is

$$E\left[\sum_j (W_{ij} - W_{i.})^2\right] = (J - 1)\sigma^2.$$

Therefore, the result for the entire error sum of squares is

$$E\left[\sum_i \sum_j (Y_{ij} - Y_{i.})^2\right] = I(J - 1)\sigma^2.$$

The quantity $I(J - 1)$ is the *degrees of freedom* for the error sum of squares. When the error sum of squares is divided by its degrees of freedom, the result is the *mean error sum of squares.*

$$\frac{\text{Error SS}}{I(J - 1)} = \frac{\sum_i \sum_j (Y_{ij} - Y_{i.})^2}{I(J - 1)}.$$

Since the expected value of this is just σ^2, the mean error sum of squares is an unbiased estimator of σ^2. Very loosely speaking, one can say that of the total IJ observations, $I(J - 1)$ go into estimating σ^2.

Next consider the expected value of the row sum of squares.

$$E\left[\sum_i \sum_j (Y_{i.} - Y_{..})^2\right] = \sum_j E\left[\sum_i (Y_{i.} - Y_{..})^2\right]$$

$$= JE\left[\sum_i (\mu + \alpha_i + W_{i.} - \mu - \alpha. - W_{..})^2\right]$$

$$= JE\left[\sum_i (\alpha_i + W_{i.} - W_{..})^2\right]$$

$$= J\sum_i \alpha_i^2 + JE\left[\sum_i (W_{i.} - W_{..})^2\right].$$

The basic fact applies to $E\left[\sum_i (W_{i.} - w_{..})^2\right]$ with the following correspondences:

$$W_{i.} \sim X_h,$$

$$i \sim h,$$

$$I \sim n,$$

$$\sigma^2/J \text{ or } V(W_{i.}) \sim V(X_h),$$

$$W_{..} \sim \bar{X}.$$

The result is

$$E\left[\sum_i (W_{i\cdot} - W_{\cdot\cdot})^2\right] = \frac{(I-1)\sigma^2}{J}.$$

Therefore, the result for the entire row sum of squares is

$$E\left[\sum_i \sum_j (Y_{i\cdot} - Y_{\cdot\cdot})^2\right] = J\sum_i \alpha_i^2 + (I-1)\sigma^2.$$

The quantity $(I - 1)$ is the *degrees of freedom* for the row sum of squares. When the row sum of squares is divided by its degrees of freedom, the result is the *mean row sum of squares*.

$$\frac{\text{Row SS}}{I-1} = \frac{\sum_i \sum_j (Y_{i\cdot} - Y_{\cdot\cdot})^2}{I-1}.$$

The expected value of this is

$$\frac{J\sum \alpha_i^2}{I-1} + \sigma^2.$$

Loosely speaking again, one can say that of the IJ observations $I - 1$ go into estimating the α_i's.

Table 4

Effect	Degrees of freedom	Sum of squares	Expected mean sum of squares
Row	$I-1$	$\sum_i \sum_j (Y_{i\cdot} - Y_{\cdot\cdot})^2$	$\sigma^2 + \dfrac{J\sum \alpha_i^2}{I-1}$
Error	$I(J-1)$	$\sum_i \sum_j (Y_{ij} - Y_{i\cdot})^2$	σ^2
Total	$IJ-1$	$\sum_i \sum_j (Y_{ij} - Y_{\cdot\cdot})^2$	

Table 4 summarizes the theoretical properties of this one-factor experiment. There will be a second table for the numerical results.

Significance Test

When the hypothesis $\sum \alpha_i^2 = 0$ is true, the expected mean row sum of squares is σ^2. The expected mean error sum of squares is always σ^2. The ratio of these two,

$$\frac{\text{mean row sum of squares}}{\text{mean error sum of squares}} = \frac{\dfrac{\text{Row SS}}{I-1}}{\dfrac{\text{Error SS}}{I(J-1)}},$$

is near one, on the average. When the hypothesis is not true, $\sum \alpha_i^2$ is positive; and the expected mean row sum of squares is greater than σ^2. The ratio is greater than one, on the average. The F-distribution, introduced in section 3.3 of Chapter V, supplies the cut-off point for the suggested test.

$$\text{reject if } F[\alpha, I-1, I(J-1)] \leq \text{observed } \frac{\dfrac{\text{Row SS}}{I-1}}{\dfrac{\text{Error SS}}{I(J-1)}}.$$

Significance tests like this usually can be constructed from the last column of a table for the analysis of variance.

Case D of Table 1 is a good numerical example, since there are variations within the rows and since Table 2 shows variation among the row means. From Table 3 the observed F-ratio is

$$\frac{\dfrac{\text{Row SS}}{I-1}}{\dfrac{\text{Error SS}}{I(J-1)}} = \frac{\dfrac{168}{2}}{\dfrac{474}{9}} = \frac{84.0}{52.7} = 1.59.$$

At $\alpha = .05$, the cut-off point is

$$F[\alpha, I-1, I(J-1)] = F[.05, 2, 9] = 4.26.$$

Therefore, the hypothesis is not rejected, and the experiment does not establish a difference in yields for the three varieties of the crop. Table 5 presents these numerical results in the conventional manner for the analysis of variance.

Table 5

Effect	Degrees of freedom	Sum of squares	Mean sum of squares	F-ratio
Crop	2	168	84.0	1.59
Error	9	474	52.7	
Total	11	642		

According to the logic of a significance test, this is as far as the analysis goes. If the experimenter wants to reject or to accept the hypothesis, he is in the decision situation. A proper procedure is based on a power function; however, the power function for the F-test is not discussed in this book.

It is valuable to explore the possibilities of a larger experiment, larger J, for the three crop varieties. The mean error sum of squares is an estimator of σ^2; it would not change (on the average) as J increased. Table VI in the Appendix shows that the cut-off point decreases as $I(J-1)$ increases. This would make rejection easier. More importantly, Table 4 shows that the mean row sum of squares would be expected to increase as J increased. This would tend to raise the observed F-ratio and to reject the hypothesis. In these two ways, a larger experiment does what is intuitively reasonable: it is more likely to detect differences among the levels and reject the hypothesis. The differences among the row means in case D of Table 2 actually may be encouraging to the experimenter. The failure of Table 5 to establish the significance of these differences may lead only to a larger experiment.

Exercise

6. For the data of exercise 5, construct the numerical table for the analysis of variance. At the .05 level, are the differences among the row means significant?

Estimators

If the hypothesis is rejected, the experimenter is usually interested in point estimators of the parameters. The mean error sum of squares is an unbiased estimator of σ^2. Let s^2 be the symbol.

$$E(S^2) = \sigma^2.$$

Each row mean $y_i.$ is an unbiased estimator of the corresponding row expected value $\mu_i.$

$$E(Y_i.) = E(\mu + \alpha_i + W_i.) = \mu + \alpha_i = \mu_i.$$

The best unbiased estimator of μ is $y...$

$$E(Y..) = E(\mu + \alpha. + W..) = \mu.$$

The corresponding unbiased estimator of α_i is $y_i. - y...$

$$E(Y_i. - Y..) = \mu_i - \mu = \alpha_i.$$

The significance test is more easily discussed with one set of parameters, μ and the α_i's. Interpretation of significant results is often easier with the other set of parameters, the μ_i's. This is also true with the more complicated models we will discuss later.

Since the F-test failed to reject the hypothesis $\sum \alpha_i^2 = 0$, or $\mu_1 = \mu_2 = \mu_3$, for case **D** of Table 1, estimators of the parameters are probably not very interesting. Nevertheless, they are

$$s^2 = 52.7 \text{ for } \sigma^2,$$
$$y_1. = 79.0 \text{ for } \mu_1,$$
$$y_2. = 85.0 \text{ for } \mu_2,$$
$$y_3. = 76.0 \text{ for } \mu_3,$$
$$y.. = 80.0 \text{ for } \mu,$$
$$y_1. - y.. = -1.0 \text{ for } \alpha_1,$$
$$y_2. - y.. = 5.0 \text{ for } \alpha_2,$$
$$y_3. - y.. = -4.0 \text{ for } \alpha_3.$$

Comparisons

An easy application of the method in subsection 2.1 of Chapter IV finds a confidence interval for one of the μ_i's. $Y_i.$ has a normal distribution with

$$E(Y_i.) = \mu_i \text{ and } V(Y_i.) = \frac{\sigma^2}{J}.$$

If σ^2 were known, the $1 - \alpha$ interval would be

$$y_i. \pm z\left(\frac{\alpha}{2}\right)\frac{\sigma}{\sqrt{J}}.$$

Since s^2 is an unbiased estimator of σ^2 with $I(J - 1)$ degrees of freedom, the desired interval is

$$y_i. \pm t\left[\frac{\alpha}{2}, I(J - 1)\right]\frac{s}{\sqrt{J}}.$$

A confidence interval for a comparison, say $\mu_i - \mu_{i'}$, will be more important. The variable $Y_i. - Y_{i'}.$ has a normal distribution with

$$E(Y_i. - Y_{i'}.) = \mu_i - \mu_{i'},$$

$$V(Y_i. - Y_{i'}.) = V(Y_i.) + V(Y_{i'}.) = \frac{2\sigma^2}{J}.$$

If σ^2 were known, subsection 2.4 of Chapter IV would apply to give a $1 - \alpha$ interval.

$$(y_{i\cdot} - y_{i'\cdot}) \pm z\left(\frac{\alpha}{2}\right)\sigma\sqrt{\frac{2}{J}}.$$

Since s^2 is an unbiased estimator of σ^2 with $I(J-1)$ degrees of freedom, the desired interval is

$$(y_{i\cdot} - y_{i'\cdot}) \pm t\left[\frac{\alpha}{2}, I(J-1)\right] s\sqrt{\frac{2}{J}}.$$

This interval is of the form $(y_{i\cdot} - y_{i'\cdot}) \pm \epsilon$, where ϵ is the same for each pair of μ_i's. For the numerical example of this discussion, a .95 confidence interval for $\mu_2 - \mu_3$ is

$$(85.0 - 76.0) \pm (2.262)\sqrt{52.7}\ \sqrt{\frac{2}{4}},$$

$$9 \pm 11.4,$$

$$-2.4 \text{ to } 20.4.$$

A confidence interval for $\mu_i - \mu_{i'}$ is worth while in itself, but it also helps answer another important question. Suppose the experiment rejects the hypothesis $\mu_1 = \mu_2 = \cdots = \mu_I$ at a significance level of α. This says that all the μ_i's are not equal, or, in other words, some of the differences among the y_i's are significant. Which μ_i's are not equal? Or which differences among the $y_{i\cdot}$'s are significant? Two particular expected values, μ_i and $\mu_{i'}$, differ, if and only if the hypothesis $\mu_i - \mu_{i'} = 0$ is false. The level α significance test rejects when $y_{i\cdot} - y_{i'\cdot}$ differs from zero by more than some number ϵ, where ϵ depends on the significance level, the sample standard deviation, and the sample sizes. In the corresponding estimation situation the confidence interval for $\mu_i - \mu_{i'}$ is $(y_{i\cdot} - y_{i'\cdot}) \pm \epsilon$, for the same ϵ. That is, the hypothesis $\mu_i - \mu_{i'} = 0$ is rejected, if and only if the confidence interval does not include zero. This appears to provide the desired method: μ_i and $\mu_{i'}$ are unequal if $y_{i\cdot}$ and $y_{i'\cdot}$ differ by more than

$$\epsilon = t\left[\frac{\alpha}{2}, I(J-1)\right] s\sqrt{\frac{2}{J}}.$$

This procedure is strictly correct for one pair of μ_i's, chosen prior to observation of the data. Frequently, the experimenter wants to examine several pairs of μ_i's, and he may not want to select the pairs before seeing the data. Why not use ϵ, which is the same for all pairs, as the measuring stick for testing these differences? Carrying the argument to its ultimate implication reveals the trouble with this proposal. To illustrate, let I be 3. The test of level α for $\mu_1 - \mu_2 = 0$ is

reject if $y_1.$ and $y_2.$ differ by more than ϵ,

where ϵ is fixed by α, J, and s. Testing all pairs of means with three applications of ϵ is equivalent to testing the composite hypothesis $\mu_1 - \mu_2 = 0$ and $\mu_1 - \mu_3 = 0$ and $\mu_2 - \mu_3 = 0$. As a significance test of this composite hypothesis, the significance level of this procedure is not α; it is larger, say α'. The composite hypothesis, however, is equivalent to the original hypothesis $\mu_1 = \mu_2 = \mu_3$, which was examined with the F-test. There is now a contradiction with the original intention to test at level α, not α'. When $I = 2$, α and α' are equal. As I increases, $\alpha' - \alpha$ increases sharply.

Multiple comparisons is a common name for this topic of comparing several means. One of the many procedures from multiple comparisons will be discussed in subsection 2.2 of this chapter. Until then, the following method can be used for the exercises in this section:

1) Test the hypothesis $\mu_1 = \mu_2 = \cdots = \mu_I$ with the F-test at level α.
2) If the test fails to reject, stop the investigation of the means.
3) If the test rejects, look for significant differences among the $y_i.$'s with

$$\epsilon = t\left[\frac{\alpha}{2}, I(J-1)\right] s\sqrt{\frac{2}{J}}.$$

Summary. In an experiment with one fixed-effects factor at I levels, the Y_{ij}'s have normal distributions with

$$E(Y_{ij}) = \mu_i = \mu + \alpha_i,$$
$$V(Y_{ij}) = \sigma^2,$$

where $i = 1, 2, \ldots, I$, $j = 1, 2, \ldots, J$, and $\alpha. = 0$. The hypothesis of no main effects is

$$\mu_1 = \mu_2 = \cdots = \mu_I \quad \text{or} \quad \sum \alpha_i^2 = 0.$$

The Total SS is the sum of the Row SS and the Error SS:

$$\text{Row SS} = \sum_i \sum_j (y_i. - y..)^2 = \frac{\sum_i \left(\sum_j y_{ij}\right)^2}{J} - \frac{\left(\sum_i \sum_j y_{ij}\right)^2}{IJ},$$

$$\text{Error SS} = \sum_i \sum_j (y_{ij} - y_i.)^2 = \sum_i \sum_j y_{ij}^2 - \frac{\sum_i \left(\sum_j y_{ij}\right)^2}{J},$$

$$\text{Total SS} = \sum_i \sum_j (y_{ij} - y..)^2 = \sum_i \sum_j y_{ij}^2 - \frac{\left(\sum_i \sum_j y_{ij}\right)^2}{IJ}.$$

The significance test of level α is

$$\text{reject if } F[\alpha, I - 1, I(J - 1)] \leq \text{observed } \frac{\dfrac{\text{Row SS}}{I - 1}}{\dfrac{\text{Error SS}}{I(J - 1)}}.$$

The unbiased estimators are

$$s^2 = \frac{\text{Error SS}}{I(J - 1)} \quad \text{for } \sigma^2,$$

$$y_{i.} \quad \text{for} \quad \mu_i,$$

$$y_{..} \quad \text{for} \quad \mu,$$

$$y_{i.} - y_{..} \quad \text{for} \quad \alpha_i.$$

A $1 - \alpha$ confidence interval for $\mu_i - \mu_{i'}$ is

$$(y_{i.} - y_{i'.}) \pm t\left[\frac{\alpha}{2}, I(J - 1)\right] s\sqrt{\frac{2}{J}}.$$

EXERCISES

7. For the experimental results of exercise 5,
   a) estimate the μ_i's, μ, the α_i's, and σ^2.
   b) A .95 confidence interval for a comparison is $(y_{i.} - y_{i'.}) \pm \epsilon$. Find ϵ.
   c) Suppose $i = 1$ for the new drug; $i = 2$ for the standard drug; and $i = 3$ for the placebo. Does the experiment establish the efficacy of the new drug for reducing blood pressure? Does the experiment establish the superiority of the new drug over the standard drug?

8. For the general one-factor experiment a linear combination of the μ_i's is $\sum c_i \mu_i$, where $i = 1, 2, \ldots, I$ and the c_i's are known constants. Show that the corresponding $1 - \alpha$ confidence interval is

$$\left(\sum c_i y_{i.}\right) \pm t\left[\frac{\alpha}{2}, I(J - 1)\right] s\sqrt{\frac{\sum c_i^2}{J}}.$$

9. Use the result of exercise 8 to find a .95 confidence interval for $\frac{1}{2}(\mu_1 + \mu_2) - \mu_3$ in the experiment of exercise 5. Suggest a use for this interval.

10. For a fixed I, the length of the confidence interval for $\mu_i - \mu_{i'}$ depends on J in two ways. What are they?

11. To construct a confidence interval for $\mu_1 - \mu_2$ when $I = 3$, how are the outcomes y_{3j} used? How is the confidence interval shortened by this use?

12. Construct a deck of five cards, numbered "-2", "-1", "0", "1", and "2". A one-factor experiment with $I = 4$ and $J = 6$ can be simulated as follows. Randomly draw a card six times from the deck and add 7 to each outcome. Let these be the six y_{1j}'s. Draw a card six times and add 5 to each outcome. Let these be the six y_{2j}'s. Draw a card six times and add 8 to each outcome. Let these be the six y_{3j}'s. Draw a card six times and add 10 to each outcome. Let these be the six y_{4j}'s.
   a) What are the four μ_i's?
   b) What is the variance of Y_{ij}?
   c) What is μ?
   d) What are the four α_i's?
   e) Does Y_{ij} have a normal distribution?

13. Perform the experiment of exercise 12. Using your results,
   a) test $\mu_1 = \mu_2 = \mu_3$ or $\sum \alpha_i^2 = 0$ at $\alpha = .01$.
   b) Estimate the μ_i's.
   c) Which differences among the row means are significant at the .01 level?

14. Four brands of gasoline are to be compared on road octane rating. Each brand is rated five times. The results are shown here.

		$j =$				
		1	2	3	4	5
	1	89	88	87	91	88
	2	87	89	88	87	86
gasoline	3	84	85	86	84	86
	4	91	91	93	91	91

Some sums of squares are

$$\text{Row SS} = 106.2,$$
$$\text{Total SS} = 127.8.$$

   a) At $\alpha = .05$, do the brands appear to have the same octane rating?
   b) Which differences among the row means appear significant for $\alpha = .05$?

2

Two-Factor Experiment

In this section, the random variable of interest Y depends on two fixed-effects factors. One factor is at I levels, and the other is at J levels. The probability distribution for Y can be different for each of the IJ combinations of levels. Various hypotheses about the parameters of these IJ probability distributions will be tested. Point estimators for the parameters will be given.

Agricultural Example. There are three varieties of a crop to be compared. This defines a crop factor at three levels. There are also four brands of fertilizer, each suitable for the three varieties of the crop. This defines a fertilizer factor at four levels. The variable of interest is the yield per acre on a randomly chosen field. For each of the twelve variety–brand combinations the yield can have a separate probability distribution.

There are two cases for two-factor experiments: a special case and the general case. The model for an experiment indicates the case. Some parts of the model are common to both cases. These parts are discussed in this introduction. Other parts of the model depend on the particular case. These parts will be discussed in separate subsections.

For all two-factor experiments, let the factor at I levels be the row factor again, and let the factor at J levels be the *column factor*. For each of the IJ combinations, the variable of interest is observed K times. That is, there are IJ random samples, each of size K. The kth outcome at the ith level of the row factor and the jth level of the column factor is y_{ijk}. The corresponding random variables, the Y_{ijk}'s, are independent and normally distributed with $E(Y_{ijk}) = \mu_{ij}$ and $V(Y_{ijk}) = \sigma^2$. This defines IJ expected values and one variance. Knowledge of these parameters is a complete description of the random experiment.

A second set of parameters is more convenient for the significance tests. The μ_{ij}'s can be arranged in a rectangular array.

$$j =$$

		1	2	. . .	J
	1	μ_{11}	μ_{12}	. . .	μ_{1J}
$i =$	2	μ_{21}	μ_{22}	. . .	μ_{2J}
		. . .	. . .	. . .	. . .
	I	μ_{I1}	μ_{I2}	. . .	μ_{IJ}

In the ith row, the μ_{ij}'s have a mean $\mu_{i\cdot}$, where

$$\mu_{i\cdot} = \frac{\mu_{i1} + \mu_{i2} + \cdots + \mu_{iJ}}{J} = \frac{\sum_j \mu_{ij}}{J}.$$

In the jth column, the μ_{ij}'s have a mean $\mu_{\cdot j}$, where

$$\mu_{\cdot j} = \frac{\mu_{1j} + \mu_{2j} + \cdots + \mu_{Ij}}{I} = \frac{\sum_i \mu_{ij}}{I}.$$

The grand mean μ of the μ_{ij}'s is

$$\mu = \frac{\mu_{1\cdot} + \mu_{2\cdot} + \cdots + \mu_{I\cdot}}{I} = \frac{\mu_{\cdot 1} + \mu_{\cdot 2} + \cdots + \mu_{\cdot J}}{J} = \frac{\sum_i \sum_j \mu_{ij}}{IJ}.$$

The *main effect* α_i for the ith row is

$$\alpha_i = \mu_{i\cdot} - \mu.$$

The *main effect* β_j for the jth column is

$$\beta_j = \mu_{\cdot j} - \mu.$$

As in the previous section, the mean $\alpha_{\cdot}$ (and sum) of the row main effects is zero.

$$\alpha_{\cdot} = \frac{\alpha_1 + \alpha_2 + \cdots + \alpha_I}{I} = \frac{\sum \alpha_i}{I} = \frac{\sum (\mu_{i\cdot} - \mu)}{I} = \mu - \mu = 0.$$

Similarly, the mean $\beta_{\cdot}$ (and sum) of the column main effects is zero.

$$\beta_{\cdot} = \frac{\beta_1 + \beta_2 + \cdots + \beta_J}{J} = \frac{\sum \beta_j}{J} = \frac{\sum (\mu_{\cdot j} - \mu)}{J} = \mu - \mu = 0.$$

One important hypothesis for all two-factor experiments is that there are no main effects for the row factor. In symbols, this hypothesis is

$$\mu_{1\cdot} = \mu_{2\cdot} = \cdots = \mu_{I\cdot} \quad \text{or} \quad \sum \alpha_i^2 = 0.$$

A second hypothesis is that there are no main effects for the column factor. In symbols, this hypothesis is

$$\mu_{\cdot 1} = \mu_{\cdot 2} = \cdots = \mu_{\cdot J} \quad \text{or} \quad \sum \beta_j^2 = 0.$$

For a numerical illustration with $I = 3$ and $J = 4$, take the following μ_{ij}'s.

	$j =$ 1	2	3	4
1	13	10	9	12
$i =$ 2	12	13	11	12
3	5	10	4	9

The $\mu_{i.}$'s are 11, 12, and 7; the $\mu_{.j}$'s are 10, 11, 8, and 11; μ is 10; the α_i's are 1, 2, and -3; the β_j's are 0, 1, -2, and 1. Notice that the α_i's and the β_j's sum to zero.

EXERCISES

15. For $I = 2$ and $J = 3$, the following charts give two sets of μ_{ij}'s. In each case, find μ, the α_i's, and the β_j's.

a)

	$j =$ 1	2	3
$i =$ 1	9	5	10
2	5	1	6

b)

	$j =$ 1	2	3
$i =$ 1	11	4	9
2	3	2	7

c) In spite of their similarities, the two sets have one fundamental difference. Can you find it?

16. For $I = 2$ and $J = 3$, let $\mu = 6$, $\alpha_1 = 2$, $\beta_1 = 1$, and $\beta_2 = -3$. In the three sets below, some of the μ_{ij}'s are also given. In which case are the remaining values uniquely determined? Fill them in.

a)

	$j =$ 1	2	3
$i =$ 1	7		
2			

b)

	$j =$ 1	2	3
$i =$ 1	7		
2		4	

c)

$$j =$$

	1	2	3
$i = 1$	7		
$ 2$		4	8

2.1 ADDITIVE MODEL

The big assumption which defines the *additive model* is that the expected value of Y_{ijk} depends only on the overall average expected value μ, the ith row main effect α_i, and the jth column main effect β_j. In symbols, the precise statement is

$$E(Y_{ijk}) = \mu_{ij} = \mu + \alpha_i + \beta_j.$$

Counting free (independent) parameters gives an insight into this strong assumption. The value for μ is one free parameter. Since the α_i's always add to zero, only $I - 1$ of them can be free parameters. Since the β_j's always add to zero, only $J - 1$ of them can be free. After these are fixed, the entire model is fixed. The total number of free parameters is $1 + (I - 1) + (J - 1) = I + J - 1$. There are, however, IJ of the μ_{ij}'s. The difference between IJ and $I + J + 1$ indicates the strength of the additivity assumption: $IJ - (I + J - 1) = (I - 1)(J - 1)$. In words, fixing $I + J - 1$ parameters in the additive model completely determines another $(I - 1)(J - 1)$ parameters.

For another insight into the assumption, consider the difference between the two expected values in the same column. Let the rows be i and i'. In the jth column, this difference is

$$\mu_{ij} - \mu_{i'j} = (\mu + \alpha_i + \beta_j) - (\mu + \alpha_{i'} + \beta_j)$$

$$= \alpha_i - \alpha_{i'} = \mu_{i\cdot} - \mu_{i'\cdot}.$$

That is, the difference does not depend on the column, only on the rows. Next, consider the difference between two expected values in the same row. Let the columns be j and j'. In the ith row, this difference is

$$\mu_{ij} - \mu_{ij'} = (\mu + \alpha_i + \beta_j) - (\mu + \alpha_i + \beta_{j'})$$

$$= \beta_j - \beta_{j'} = \mu_{\cdot j} - \mu_{\cdot j'}.$$

That is, the difference does not depend on the row, only on the columns.

To illustrate with $I = 3$ and $J = 4$, it is sufficient to specify $I + J - 1 = 6$ parameters. Let them be

$$\mu = 10, \qquad \beta_1 = 0,$$
$$\alpha_1 = 1, \qquad \beta_2 = 1,$$
$$\alpha_2 = 2, \qquad \beta_3 = -2.$$

Then α_3 is -3 and β_4 is 1. The complete set of μ_{ij}'s is shown below.

		$j =$			
		1	2	3	4
	1	11	12	9	12
$i =$	2	12	13	10	13
	3	7	8	5	8

A sample calculation is

$$\mu_{13} = \mu + \alpha_1 + \beta_3 = 10 + 1 - 2 = 9.$$

Each μ_{1j} of the first row differs from μ_{2j} of the second by 1 and from μ_{3j} of the third by 4. There is a similar relation among the columns. The main effects and μ are the same as those in the introductory numerical illustration of section 2. Some of the μ_{ij}'s of this additive model differ from the previous set. Therefore, the previous set does not follow the additive model; it is more general.

EXERCISES

17. Three sets of μ_{ij}'s are given below. Which are of the additive model?

a)

		$j =$	
		1	2
$i =$	1	3	5
	2	5	11

b)

		$j =$		
		1	2	3
$i =$	1	2	4	7
	2	6	8	3

c)

		$j =$	
		1	2
	1	2	4
$i =$	2	10	12
	3	3	5

18. For those parts of exercise 17 that are additive, find μ, the α_i's, and the β_j's.

19. For the additive model, show that

$$(\mu_{ij} + \mu_{i'j'}) - (\mu_{i'j} + \mu_{ij'}) = 0,$$

for all i, i', j, and j'.

20. Let M be a constant, and let

$$\mu_{ij} = M + i + j,$$

for $i = 1, 2, \ldots, I$ and $j = 1, 2, \ldots, J$. Show that the μ_{ij}'s follow the additive model by finding formulas for μ, α_i, and β_j.

Sums of Squares

The general procedure in the analysis of variance is to partition the total sum of squares into component sums of squares, one for each factor. All the essential ideas for the additive model can be illustrated by an experiment with only one observation of Y for each of the IJ combinations of levels—that is, for $K = 1$. Let us make this assumption for the remainder of this subsection on the additive model. The third subscript k on y now can be dropped. An outcome is now y_{ij} instead of y_{ijk} or y_{ij1}.

The first step in the partition of the total sum of squares is the definition of the necessary means.

$$\text{ith row mean} = y_{i.} = \frac{y_{i1} + y_{i2} + \cdots + y_{iJ}}{J} = \frac{\sum\limits_{j} y_{ij}}{J}.$$

$$\text{jth column mean} = y_{.j} = \frac{y_{1j} + y_{2j} + \cdots + y_{Ij}}{I} = \frac{\sum\limits_{i} y_{ij}}{I}.$$

$$\text{grand mean} = y_{..} = \frac{\sum\limits_{i} y_{i.}}{I} = \frac{\sum\limits_{j} y_{.j}}{J} = \frac{\sum\limits_{i}\sum\limits_{j} y_{ij}}{IJ}.$$

The partition of section 1 for the one-factor experiment is still valid.

Total SS $\quad\quad$ = Row SS $\quad\quad\quad$ + Error SS.

$$\sum_{i}\sum_{j}(y_{ij} - y_{..})^2 = \sum_{i}\sum_{j}(y_{i.} - y_{..})^2 + \sum_{i}\sum_{j}(y_{ij} - y_{i.})^2.$$

Since this partition does not yield a component for the column factor, it does not go far enough. The desired component is in the error sum of squares. Introduction of the column means and the grand mean brings it out.

$$\sum_i \sum_j (y_{ij} - y_{i.})^2 = \sum_i \sum_j [(y_{ij} - y_{i.} - y_{.j} + y_{..}) + (y_{.j} - y_{..})]^2$$

$$= \sum_i \sum_j (y_{ij} - y_{i.} - y_{.j} + y_{..})^2 + \sum_i \sum_j (y_{.j} - y_{..})^2.$$

The middle term is zero because

$$2\sum_i \sum_j (y_{ij} - y_{i.} - y_{.j} + y_{..})(y_{.j} - y_{..}) =$$

$$2\sum_j (y_{.j} - y_{..})\sum_i [(y_{ij} - y_{.j}) - (y_{i.} - y_{..})],$$

and

$$\sum_i (y_{ij} - y_{.j}) - \sum_i (y_{i.} - y_{..}) = 0 - 0 = 0.$$

The first sum of squares $\sum_i \sum_j (y_{ij} - y_{i.} - y_{.j} + y_{..})^2$ is now the *error sum of squares*. The second sum of squares $\sum_i \sum_j (y_{.j} - y_{..})^2$ is the *column sum of squares*.

As a practical matter, the computing formulas are as follows.

$$\text{Row SS} = \sum_i \sum_j (y_{i.} - y_{..})^2 = \frac{\sum_i \left(\sum_j y_{ij}\right)^2}{J} - \frac{\left(\sum_i \sum_j y_{ij}\right)^2}{IJ}.$$

$$\text{Column SS} = \sum_i \sum_j (y_{.j} - y_{..})^2 = \frac{\sum_j \left(\sum_i y_{ij}\right)^2}{I} - \frac{\left(\sum_i \sum_j y_{ij}\right)^2}{IJ}.$$

$$\text{Error SS} = \text{Total SS} - \text{Row SS} - \text{Column SS}.$$

$$\text{Total SS} = \sum_i \sum_j (y_{ij} - y_{..})^2 = \sum_i \sum_j y_{ij}^2 - \frac{\left(\sum_i \sum_j y_{ij}\right)^2}{IJ}.$$

In the agricultural example of this discussion, the crop (row) factor is at 3 (I) levels, and the fertilizer (column) factor is at 4 (J) levels. One field is assigned randomly to each of the 12 combinations. For numerical results, take the data from case D of Table 1 again.

		$j =$			
		1	2	3	4
	1	89	82	74	71
$i =$	2	94	87	86	73
	3	81	77	74	72

In the one-factor analysis, the four numbers in each row formed a random sample of size four for each variety of the crop. The order within a row was irrelevant. These data will now be analyzed according to the additive two-factor model. Each of the twelve numbers is now a random sample of size one for a crop–fertilizer combination. The order of the numbers within a row is now relevant. Of course, in practice the model and the analysis must correspond to the way the experiment actually is performed. The grand mean $y..$ is 80. The row means, the $y_{i.}$'s, are 79, 85, and 76. The column means, the $y_{.j}$'s, are 88, 82, 78, and 72. The sums of squares are

$$\text{Row SS} = \frac{\sum_i \left(\sum_j y_{ij}\right)^2}{J} - \frac{\left(\sum_i \sum_j y_{ij}\right)^2}{IJ} = 76968 - 76800 = 168,$$

$$\text{Column SS} = \frac{\sum_j \left(\sum_i y_{ij}\right)^2}{I} - \frac{\left(\sum_i \sum_j y_{ij}\right)^2}{IJ} = 77208 - 76800 = 408,$$

$$\text{Error SS} = \text{Total SS} - \text{Row SS} - \text{Column SS} = 66,$$

$$\text{Total SS} = \sum_i \sum_j y_{ij}^2 - \frac{\left(\sum_i \sum_j y_{ij}\right)^2}{IJ} = 77442 - 76800 = 642.$$

The row and total sums of squares are the same as in the analysis of section 1. The old error sum of squares is now partitioned into the column sum of squares and into the new error sum of squares.

Exercises

21. Verify the computing formula for the column sum of squares.

22. Calculate the error sum of squares for the following two sets of y_{ij}'s. Compare these sets to those for μ_{ij} in exercise 17 a) and c).

a)

		$j =$ 1	2
$i =$	1	3	5
	2	5	11

b)

		$j =$ 1	2
	1	2	4
$i =$	2	10	12
	3	3	5

23. Take a rectangular array of IJ numbers. Let n_{ij} be the number in the ith row and jth column. On one hand, the n_{ij}'s might be param-

eters, the μ_{ij}'s, for a two-factor experiment. On the other hand, the n_{ij}'s might be outcomes, the y_{ij}'s, for a two-factor experiment. Suppose the n_{ij}'s follow the additive model when considered parameters. Prove then that the error sum of squares is zero, when the n_{ij}'s are considered outcomes. The converse is also true; prove it.

Expected Sums of Squares

Under the assumption that Y_{ij} is a random variable, the sums of squares become random variables. We seek the expected values for some of them. To facilitate this, introduce the independent, normally distributed W_{ij}'s again, where $E(W_{ij}) = 0$ and $V(W_{ij}) = \sigma^2$, for $i = 1, 2, \ldots, I$ and $j = 1, 2, \ldots, J$. The Y_{ij}'s are

$$Y_{ij} = \mu_{ij} + W_{ij} = \mu + \alpha_i + \beta_j + W_{ij},$$

where $\alpha. = \beta. = 0$. Simple alterations of the one-factor derivations show

$$E(\text{Row SS}) = E\left[\sum_i\sum_j(Y_{i.} - Y_{..})^2\right] = J\sum\alpha_i^2 + (I - 1)\sigma^2,$$

$$E(\text{Column SS}) = E\left[\sum_i\sum_j(Y_{.j} - Y_{..})^2\right] = I\sum\beta_j^2 + (J - 1)\sigma^2.$$

$(I - 1)$ is again the degrees of freedom for the row sum of squares, and $(\text{Row SS})/(I - 1)$ is the mean row sum of squares. $(J - 1)$ is now the degrees of freedom for the column sum of squares, and $(\text{Column SS})/(J - 1)$ is the mean column sum of squares. The expected mean sums of squares are

$$E\left(\frac{\text{Row SS}}{I - 1}\right) = \frac{J\sum\alpha_i^2}{I - 1} + \sigma^2,$$

$$E\left(\frac{\text{Column SS}}{J - 1}\right) = \frac{I\sum\beta_j^2}{J - 1} + \sigma^2.$$

The derivation of the expected error sum of squares requires two introductory useful facts. If $X_1, X_2, \ldots, X_h, \ldots, X_n$ is a random sample of size n of a random variable X, then

$$E\left[\sum_h(X_h - \bar{X})^2\right] = (n - 1)V(X).$$

This first basic fact was used in the one-factor derivations. Consider next the variance of $X_h - \bar{X}$.

$$V(X_h - \bar{X}) = V\left[-\frac{X_1}{n} - \frac{X_2}{n} - \cdots + \frac{(n-1)X_h}{n} - \cdots - \frac{X_n}{n} \right]$$

$$= \frac{1}{n^2}[V(X_1) + V(X_2) + \cdots + (n-1)^2 V(X_h)$$

$$+ \cdots + V(X_n)]$$

$$= \frac{V(X)}{n^2}[(n-1) + (n-1)^2] = \frac{n-1}{n} V(X).$$

This is the second useful basic fact.

The expected error sum of squares can be expressed with the W_{ij}'s and grouped according to

$$E\left[\sum_i \sum_j (Y_{ij} - Y_{i.} - Y_{.j} + Y_{..})^2 \right] = E\left[\sum_i \sum_j (W_{ij} - W_{i.} - W_{.j} + W_{..})^2 \right]$$

$$= \sum_j E\left\{ \sum_i [(W_{ij} - W_{i.}) - (W_{.j} - W_{..})]^2 \right\}.$$

For each j, the first basic fact applies to

$E\left\{ \sum_i [(W_{ij} - W_{i.}) - (W_{.j} - W_{..})]^2 \right\}$ with the following correspondences.

$$(W_{ij} - W_{i.}) \sim X_h,$$

$$i \sim h,$$

$$I \sim n,$$

$$V(W_{ij} - W_{i.}) \sim V(X_h),$$

$$(W_{.j} - W_{..}) \sim \bar{X}.$$

The application yields

$$E\left\{ \sum_i [(W_{ij} - W_{i.}) - (W_{.j} - W_{..})]^2 \right\} = (I-1)V(W_{ij} - W_{i.}).$$

The second basic fact applies to $V(W_{ij} - W_{i.})$ with

$$W_{ij} \sim X_h,$$

$$j \sim h,$$

$$J \sim n,$$

$$\sigma^2 \text{ or } V(W_{ij}) \sim V(X_h),$$

$$W_{i.} \sim \bar{X}.$$

The result is

$$V(W_{ij} - W_{i\cdot}) = \frac{J-1}{J}\sigma^2.$$

The grand result of all this is

$$E(\text{Error SS}) = (I-1)(J-1)\sigma^2.$$

$(I-1)(J-1)$ is the degrees of freedom for the error sum of squares. $(\text{Error SS})/(I-1)(J-1)$ is the mean error sum of squares, and its expected value is

$$E\left[\frac{\text{Error SS}}{(I-1)(J-1)}\right] = \sigma^2.$$

Table 6

Effect	Degrees of freedom	Sum of squares	Expected mean sum of squares
Row	$I-1$	$\displaystyle\sum_i\sum_j(Y_{i\cdot} - Y_{\cdot\cdot})^2$	$\sigma^2 + \dfrac{J\sum a_i^2}{I-1}$
Column	$J-1$	$\displaystyle\sum_i\sum_j(Y_{\cdot j} - Y_{\cdot\cdot})^2$	$\sigma^2 + \dfrac{I\sum \beta_j^2}{J-1}$
Error	$(I-1)(J-1)$	$\displaystyle\sum_i\sum_j(Y_{ij} - Y_{i\cdot} - Y_{\cdot j} + Y_{\cdot\cdot})^2$	σ^2
Total	$IJ-1$	$\displaystyle\sum_i\sum_j(Y_{ij} - Y_{\cdot\cdot})^2$	

Table 6 summarizes the theoretical results for this two-factor experiment.

Significance Tests

The hypothesis of no main effects for the row factor is

$$\sum \alpha_i^2 = 0 \quad \text{or} \quad \mu_1. = \mu_2. = \cdots = \mu_I..$$

The significance test is a simple modification of the one-factor case. Only the degrees of freedom for the error sum of squares are different.

$$\text{reject if } F[\alpha, I-1, (I-1)(J-1)] \leq \text{observed } \frac{\dfrac{\text{Row SS}}{I-1}}{\dfrac{\text{Error SS}}{(I-1)(J-1)}}.$$

The hypothesis of no main effects for the column factor is

$$\sum \beta_j^2 = 0 \quad \text{or} \quad \mu_{.1} = \mu_{.2} = \cdots = \mu_{.J}.$$

The significance test is

$$\text{reject if } F[\alpha, J - 1, (I - 1)(J - 1)] \leq \text{observed } \frac{\dfrac{\text{Column SS}}{J - 1}}{\dfrac{\text{Error SS}}{(I - 1)(J - 1)}}.$$

The last column of Table 6 suggests both these tests.

Table 7

Effect	Degrees of freedom	Sum of squares	Mean sum of squares	F-ratio
Crop	2	168	82	7.64*
Fertilizer	3	408	136	12.36**
Error	6	66	11	
Total	11	642		

Table 7 gives the numerical results for the agricultural example in the conventional form. Since $F(.05, 2, 6) = 5.14$ and $F(.01, 2, 6) = 10.9$, the hypothesis of no crop main effects is rejected at the .05 level but not at the .01 level. Since $F(.01, 3, 6) = 9.78$, the hypothesis of no fertilizer main effects is rejected at the .01 level. The asterisk (*) indicates significance for $\alpha = .05$, but not for $\alpha = .01$; the double asterisk (**) indicates significance for $\alpha = .01$.

Exercises

24. Verify the formula for the expected mean column sum of squares.

25. Skydell Business College, which employs four instructors, is considering three methods for teaching typing. To evaluate the instructors and the methods, each instructor uses each method on a new class—twelve different classes in all. The number of words per minute attained by the class is the variable of interest. Skydell assumes the additive model for the following outcomes.

		instructor			
		1	2	3	4
	1	54	62	51	49
method	2	46	62	52	52
	3	56	62	59	55

The row, column, and total sums of squares are 56, 204, and 316, respectively. Construct the numerical table for the analysis of variance. At the .05 level, is there any difference among the methods? At the .05 level, is there any difference among the instructors?

26. Construct a deck of five cards numbered "−2", "−1", "0", "1", and "2". Let W_{ij} be the random variable associated with drawing one card. For $i = 1, 2, 3, 4, 5$ and $j = 1, 2, 3$, let $Y_{ij} = 5 + i + j + W_{ij}$. $E(Y_{ij})$ now follows the additive model.
    a) What is μ?
    b) What are the five α_i's?
    c) What are the three β_j's?
    d) What is $V(Y_{ij})$?

27. Carry out the experiment of exercise 26. With your data construct the numerical table for the analysis of variance.

Estimators

The mean error sum of squares is an unbiased estimator of σ^2. As usual, the symbol is s^2.

$$E(S^2) = \sigma^2.$$

The ith row mean $y_i.$ is an unbiased estimator of $\mu_i..$

$$E(Y_i.) = E(\mu + \alpha_i + \beta. + W_i.) = \mu + \alpha_i = \mu_i..$$

The jth column mean $y._j$ is an unbiased estimator of $\mu._j.$

$$E(Y._j) = E(\mu + \alpha. + \beta_j + W._j) = \mu + \beta_j = \mu._j.$$

The grand mean $y..$ is an unbiased estimator of μ.

$$E(Y..) = E(\mu + \alpha. + \beta. + W..) = \mu.$$

The corresponding unbiased estimator of α_i is $y_i. - y...$

$$E(Y_i. - Y..) = \mu_i. - \mu = \alpha_i.$$

The corresponding unbiased estimator of β_j is $y._j - y...$

$$E(Y._j - Y..) = \mu._j - \mu = \beta_j.$$

In the numerical example of this subsection, these results are as follows:

$$s^2 = 11 \text{ for } \sigma^2$$

$y_1.$	$=$	79 for $\mu_1.$		$y._1$	$=$	88 for $\mu._1$
$y_2.$	$=$	85 for $\mu_2.$		$y._2$	$=$	82 for $\mu._2$
$y_3.$	$=$	76 for $\mu_3.$		$y._3$	$=$	78 for $\mu._3$
$y..$	$=$	80 for $\mu_4.$		$y._4$	$=$	72 for $\mu._4$
$y_1. - y..$	$=$	-1 for α_1		$y._1 - y..$	$=$	8 for β_1
$y_2. - y..$	$=$	5 for α_2		$y._2 - y..$	$=$	2 for β_2
$y_3. - y..$	$=$	-4 for α_3		$y._3 - y..$	$=$	-2 for β_3
				$y._4 - y..$	$=$	-8 for β_4

Comparisons

After the F-test establishes differences among the main effects of a factor, the experimenter is usually interested in comparisons of the levels of that factor. Take the row factor, for example, and consider two particular rows, say i and i'. The question is, do the probability distributions of Y differ in rows i and i'? If the distributions are the same, then the expected values, μ_{ij} and $\mu_{i'j}$, are equal, and $\mu_{ij} - \mu_{i'j}$ is zero for each column j. If the distributions are different, then recall that $\mu_{ij} - \mu_{i'j}$ is a constant, $\mu_i. - \mu_{i'}. = \alpha_i - \alpha_{i'}$, which does not depend on j. That is, the constant $\mu_i. - \mu_{i'}.$ characterizes the differences between the two rows.

The best estimator of the constant $\mu_i. - \mu_{i'}.$ is $y_i. - y_{i'}..$ As a random variable, $Y_i. - Y_{i'}.$ has a normal distribution with $E(Y_i. - Y_{i'}.) = \mu_i. - \mu_{i'}.$ and $V(Y_i. - Y_{i'}.) = 2\sigma^2/J$. If σ^2 were known, a $1 - \alpha$ confidence interval would be

$$(y_i. - y_{i'}.) \pm z\left(\frac{\alpha}{2}\right)\sigma\sqrt{\frac{2}{J}}.$$

Since s^2 is an unbiased estimator of σ^2 with $(I - 1)(J - 1)$ degrees of freedom, the $1 - \alpha$ confidence interval is

$$(y_i. - y_{i'}.) \pm t\left[\frac{\alpha}{2}, (I - 1)(J - 1)\right]s\sqrt{\frac{2}{J}}.$$

Two levels of the column factor are compared in the same way. The $1 - \alpha$ confidence interval for $\mu._j - \mu._{j'}$ is

$$(y._j - y._{j'}) \pm t\left[\frac{\alpha}{2}, (I - 1)(J - 1)\right]s\sqrt{\frac{2}{J}}.$$

As in the one-factor experiment these confidence intervals are appropriate for one pair of prechosen levels of a factor. The problems of multiple comparisons arise when the experimenter attempts to identify significant differences among the y_i.'s or among the $y._j$'s. One method of multiple comparisons will be discussed in the next subsection. Until then, the following crude method can be used for the exercises of this subsection:

1) Test $\mu_1. = \mu_2. = \cdots = \mu_I.$ with the F-test at level α.
2) If the test fails to reject, stop the investigation of the row means.
3) If the test rejects, look for significant differences among the row means with

$$\epsilon = t\left[\frac{\alpha}{2}, (I-1)(J-1)\right] s\sqrt{\frac{2}{J}}.$$

4) Test $\mu._1 = \mu._2 = \cdots = \mu._J$ with the F-test at level α.
5) If the test fails to reject, stop the investigation of the column means.
6) If the test rejects, look for significant differences among the column means with

$$\epsilon = t\left[\frac{\alpha}{2}, (I-1)(J-1)\right] s\sqrt{\frac{2}{I}}.$$

At the .05 level, the F-test showed significant differences among the three varieties of the crop and among the four brands of fertilizer. The three means for the varieties are 79, 85, and 76. Which differences are significant? The .95 confidence interval for any two $\mu_i.$'s is

$$(y_i. - y_{i'}.) \pm t\left[\frac{\alpha}{2}, (I-1)(J-1)\right] s\sqrt{\frac{2}{J}}$$

$$(y_i. - y_{i'}.) \pm t(.025, 6)\sqrt{11}\ \sqrt{\frac{2}{4}}$$

$$(y_i. - y_{i'}.) \pm 5.74.$$

Two means that differ by more than 5.74 differ significantly. Therefore, the second crop variety appears to be better than both of the others. The difference between the first and third varieties is not significant. The means for the four brands of fertilizer are 88, 82, 78, and 72. The .95 confidence interval is

$$(y._j - y._{j'}) \pm t\left[\frac{\alpha}{2}, (I-1)(J-1)\right] s\sqrt{\frac{2}{I}}$$

$$(y._j - y._{j'}) \pm t(.025, 6)\sqrt{11}\ \sqrt{\frac{2}{3}}$$

$$(y._j - y._{j'}) \pm 6.63.$$

Two brand means that differ by more than 6.63 differ significantly. There-fore, the first brand appears to be better than the third and fourth; the second is better than the fourth; the other differences are not significant.

A consumer of statistical results should not forget his common sense when evaluating these differences. For example, the first two row means, 79 and 85, differ by a little more than 5.74; therefore, they differ signifi-cantly. On the other hand, the first two column means, 88 and 82, differ by a little less than 6.63; therefore, they do not differ significantly. These borderline cases are very dependent on the choice of α. Why take $\alpha = .05$ rather than $\alpha = .04$ or $\alpha = .06$? There is seldom a good answer to this question. Remember too that the methods of multiple comparisons, which apply here, tend to make significance harder to establish.

Summary. To summarize the two-factor experiment with the additive model, let the Y_{ij}'s have independent, normal distributions with $E(Y_{ij}) = \mu_{ij} = \mu + \alpha_i + \beta_j$ and $V(Y_{ij}) = \sigma^2$, where $i = 1, 2, \ldots, I$, $j = 1, 2, \ldots, J$, $\alpha. = 0$, and $\beta. = 0$. The total sum of squares is par-titioned according to

$$\text{Total SS} = \text{Row SS} + \text{Column SS} + \text{Error SS}.$$

The hypothesis of no row main effects is $\sum \alpha_i^2 = 0$. The significance test is

$$\text{reject if } F[\alpha, I - 1, (I - 1)(J - 1)] \leq \text{observed } \dfrac{\dfrac{\text{Row SS}}{I - 1}}{\dfrac{\text{Error SS}}{(I - 1)(J - 1)}}.$$

The hypothesis of no column main effects is $\sum \beta_j^2 = 0$. The significance test is

$$\text{reject if } F[\alpha, J - 1, (I - 1)(J - 1)] \leq \text{observed } \dfrac{\dfrac{\text{Column SS}}{J - 1}}{\dfrac{\text{Error SS}}{(I - 1)(J - 1)}}.$$

The unbiased estimators are

$$s^2 \text{ for } \sigma^2,$$
$$y.. \text{ for } \mu,$$
$$y_i. - y.. \text{ for } \alpha_i,$$
$$y._j - y.. \text{ for } \beta_j.$$

A $1 - \alpha$ confidence interval for $\mu_i. - \mu_{i'}.$ (and $\alpha_i - \alpha_{i'}$) is

$$(y_i. - y_{i'}.) \pm t\left[\frac{\alpha}{2}, (I - 1)(J - 1)\right] s\sqrt{\frac{2}{J}}.$$

A $1 - \alpha$ confidence interval for $\mu_{.j} - \mu_{.j'}$ (and $\beta_j - \beta_{j'}$) is

$$(y_{.j} - y_{.j'}) \pm t\left[\frac{\alpha}{2}, (I-1)(J-1)\right] s \sqrt{\frac{2}{I}}.$$

EXERCISES

28. With Skydell's results of exercise 25,
    a) give an estimate of σ^2.
    b) Estimate μ.
    c) Estimate the β_j's.
    d) Which differences among the instructors are significant at $\alpha = .05$?

29. Prove that y_{ij} and $y_{i.} + y_{.j} - y_{..}$ are unbiased estimators of μ_{ij}.

30. For the two unbiased estimators in exercise 29, show that the variances are

$$V(Y_{ij}) = \sigma^2,$$

$$V(Y_{i.} + Y_{.j} - Y_{..}) = \frac{I + J - 1}{IJ} \sigma^2.$$

Which variance is smaller?
Hint: $Y_{i.} + Y_{.j} - Y_{..} = \sum_i \sum_j c_{ij} Y_{ij}$, where there are only four different values of the c_{ij}'s.

31. Show

$$E(Y_{ij} - Y_{i.} - Y_{.j} + Y_{..}) = 0,$$

$$V(Y_{ij} - Y_{i.} - Y_{.j} + Y_{..}) = \frac{(I-1)(J-1)}{IJ} \sigma^2.$$

Hint: See exercise 30.

32. Using the results of exercise 31, show

$$E(\text{Error SS}) = \sum_i \sum_j V(Y_{ij} - Y_{i.} - Y_{.j} + Y_{..}) = (I-1)(J-1)\sigma^2.$$

33. Four brands of gasoline are to be compared, and four types of automobile engines are to be compared. The variable of interest is the road octane rating. One rating is obtained for each gasoline–engine combination. The additive model is assumed for the results indicated on page 241.

	engine 1	engine 2	engine 3	engine 4
	1	2	3	4
gasoline 1	82	87	76	79
gasoline 2	88	94	84	87
gasoline 3	86	91	85	88
gasoline 4	81	88	84	79

Some sums of squares are

$$\text{Row SS} = 147.19,$$

$$\text{Column SS} = 144.69,$$

$$\text{Total SS} = 332.94.$$

a) Construct the numerical table for the analysis of variance.
b) At $\alpha = .01$, test the hypothesis of no main effects for the gasoline factor.
c) At $\alpha = .01$, test the hypothesis of no main effects for the engine factor.
d) Summarize the results for $\alpha = .01$. Be sure to mention significant differences among the levels of each factor.

34. Dunne leaves his office at five o'clock every day and drives straight home. There are five routes available for the trip. This defines a route factor at five levels. There is also a day factor at five levels— the five days of the work week. Dunne randomly assigns a different route to each of the next five Mondays, to each of the next five Tuesdays, and so on. In minutes, the lengths of the resulting trips are

	day M	T	W	T	F
	M	T	W	T	F
route 1	7	6	7	12	8
route 2	8	7	9	9	7
route 3	3	5	13	8	5
route 4	10	4	11	9	7
route 5	6	8	6	10	12

Assume the additive model.
a) Construct the numerical table for the analysis of variance.
b) At $\alpha = .05$, test the hypothesis of no main effects for the route factor.

c) At $\alpha = .05$, test the hypothesis of no main effects for the day factor.

d) Summarize the results for $\alpha = .05$. Be sure to mention significant differences among the levels of each factor.

35. In exercise 34, suppose Dunne took only route 1 during the first week, only route 2 during the second week, and so on. Suppose the primary goal is to compare the travel times on the five routes. Compare the experiments. Which do you prefer?

2.2 GENERAL MODEL

The general model for a two-factor experiment drops the strong assumption which characterized the additive model. The probability distribution of the variable of interest Y still depends on the level of the row factor and the level of the column factor, but this dependence is now more complicated. Some new parameters are required to describe the dependence.

Model

To review the symbols, the row factor is at I levels, and the column factor is at J levels. At each of the IJ combinations of levels, there are K observations of the variable of interest. An outcome is y_{ijk}. As random variables, the Y_{ijk}'s are independent and normally distributed with $E(Y_{ijk}) = \mu_{ij}$ and $V(Y_{ijk}) = \sigma^2$, for $i = 1, 2, \ldots, I$, $j = 1, 2, \ldots, J$, $k = 1, 2, \ldots, K$. This defines IJ expected values, the μ_{ij}'s, and one variance σ^2. Knowledge of these $IJ + 1$ parameters is a complete description of the two-factor experiment. Recall that other parameters are defined from the μ_{ij}'s:

$$\mu = \frac{\sum_i \sum_j \mu_{ij}}{IJ}$$

$$\mu_{i.} = \frac{\sum_j \mu_{ij}}{J} \qquad \mu_{.j} = \frac{\sum_i \mu_{ij}}{I}$$

$$\alpha_i = \mu_{i.} - \mu \qquad \beta_j = \mu_{.j} - \mu$$

where $\alpha_. = \beta_. = 0$. The additive model of the previous subsection assumed $\mu_{ij} = \mu + \alpha_i + \beta_j$ for all i and j.

The general model assumes no relation between μ_{ij} and μ, α_i, and β_j. In particular, μ_{ij} need not equal $\mu + \alpha_i + \beta_j$. The difference between them is an *interaction*, and its symbol is γ_{ij}.

$$\gamma_{ij} = \mu_{ij} - (\mu + \alpha_i + \beta_j),$$

or

$$\mu_{ij} = \mu + \alpha_i + \beta_j + \gamma_{ij}.$$

There are IJ interactions, one for each combination of i and j. When all the interactions are zero, the μ_{ij}'s follow the additive model.

Like the main effects, the interactions are restricted. For a given i, the mean (and sum) of the interactions in that row is zero.

$$\gamma_{i\cdot} = \frac{\sum_j \gamma_{ij}}{J} = \frac{\sum_j (\mu_{ij} - \mu - \alpha_i - \beta_j)}{J} = \frac{\sum_j (\mu_{ij} - \mu_{i\cdot} - \beta_j)}{J}$$

$$= \frac{\sum_j \mu_{ij} - \sum_j \mu_{ij} - \sum_j \beta_j}{J} = \frac{0}{J} = 0.$$

For a given j, the mean (and sum) of the interactions in that column is zero.

$$\gamma_{\cdot j} = \frac{\sum_i \gamma_{ij}}{I} = \frac{\sum_i (\mu_{ij} - \mu - \alpha_i - \beta_j)}{I} = \frac{\sum_i (\mu_{ij} - \mu_{\cdot j} - \alpha_i)}{I}$$

$$= \frac{\sum_i \mu_{ij} - \sum_i \mu_{ij} - \sum_i \alpha_i}{I} = \frac{0}{I} = 0.$$

In words, the mean (and sum) of the interactions in every row and column is zero.

Counting free (independent) parameters again gives an insight into the second system of parameters—μ, the α_i's, the β_j's, and the γ_{ij}'s. The value for μ is one free parameter. Since the α_i's always add to zero, only $I-1$ of them can be free. Since the β_j's always add to zero, only $J-1$ of them can be free. Since the γ_{ij}'s of the first row always add to zero, only $J-1$ of them can be free. This is true of the γ_{ij}'s for the first $I-1$ rows. The last row is not free, because the column sums of the γ_{ij}'s must be zero. Therefore, $(I-1)(J-1)$ of the γ_{ij}'s are free. The total number of free parameters is

$$1 + (I-1) + (J-1) + (I-1)(J-1) = IJ.$$

This is the anticipated total, because there is no restriction on the IJ values of the μ_{ij}'s.

In some situations the experimenter knows or assumes that interactions are absent. The analysis of the additive model is then appropriate. In the other situations he does not know about the interactions. He frequently hopes they are absent, because the analysis and interpretation are simpler. Consider the hypothesis

$$\gamma_{ij} = 0 \text{ for all } i \text{ and } j$$

or

$$\sum_i \sum_j \gamma_{ij}^2 = 0.$$

If this is true, the additive model applies; if it is false, the general model applies. We shall discuss a test for this hypothesis and for two other familiar hypotheses: $\sum \alpha_i^2 = 0$ and $\sum \beta_j^2 = 0$.

For a numerical example with $I = 3$ and $J = 4$, take the μ_{ij}'s in the following chart.

		$j =$			
		1	2	3	4
	1	13	10	9	12
$i =$	2	12	13	11	12
	3	5	10	4	9

This example appeared earlier in the introductory remarks of section 2. The overall mean μ is 10; the α_i's are 1, 2, and -3; the β_j's are 0, 1, -2, and 1. The twelve corresponding values of $\mu + \alpha_i + \beta_j$ are

		$j =$			
		1	2	3	4
	1	11	12	9	12
$i =$	2	12	13	10	13
	3	7	8	5	8

These would be the μ_{ij}'s under the additive model. In fact, they were given in subsection 2.1. The interactions, $\gamma_{ij} = \mu_{ij} - (\mu + \alpha_i + \beta_j)$, are

		$j =$			
		1	2	3	4
	1	2	-2	0	0
$i =$	2	0	0	1	-1
	3	-2	2	-1	1

Notice that the rows and columns sum to zero.

Interpreting the general model leads to new difficulties. The difference between two levels of one factor is no longer independent of the level of the other factor. For example, take $i = 1$ and $i' = 2$ in the above chart of μ_{ij}'s. The difference $\mu_{1j} - \mu_{2j}$ is not the same in every column. These differences are 1, -3, -2, and 0. One number no longer characterizes the difference between these two levels, as in the additive model. It is still possible to take the row averages and compare them.

$$\mu_{1\cdot} = 11, \qquad \mu_{2\cdot} = 12, \qquad \text{and} \qquad \mu_{1\cdot} - \mu_{2\cdot} = -1.$$

However, this difference is not very informative.

EXERCISES

36. Find the μ_{ij}'s for $I = 2$, $J = 3$, $\mu = 15$, $\alpha_1 = 2$, $\beta_1 = -1$, $\beta_2 = -2$, $\gamma_{11} = 1$, and $\gamma_{12} = 0$.

37. Find the γ_{ij}'s for each of the three sets of μ_{ij}'s in exercise 17.

38. Find the μ_{ij}'s for $I = J = 2$, $\mu = \alpha_1 = \beta_1 = 0$, $\mu_{11} > 0$, and $\sum_i \sum_j \gamma_{ij}^2 = 16$.

39. Let $\mu_{ij} = 1 + i^2 j$ for $I = 2$ and $J = 3$. Find γ_{23}.

Sums of Squares

The experiment produces IJK outcomes, the y_{ijk}'s. Following the general procedure we seek component sums of squares for the main effects and now for the interactions. The necessary means are

$$cell\ mean = y_{ij\cdot} = \frac{\sum\limits_{k} y_{ijk}}{K},$$

$$row\ mean = y_{i\cdot\cdot} = \frac{\sum\limits_{j}\sum\limits_{k} y_{ijk}}{JK},$$

$$column\ mean = y_{\cdot j\cdot} = \frac{\sum\limits_{i}\sum\limits_{k} y_{ijk}}{IK},$$

$$grand\ mean = y_{\cdots} = \frac{\sum\limits_{i}\sum\limits_{j}\sum\limits_{k} y_{ijk}}{IJK}.$$

These means partition the total sum of squares according to

$$\text{Total SS} = \sum_i \sum_j \sum_k (y_{ijk} - y...)^2$$

$$= \sum_i \sum_j \sum_k [(y_{i..} - y...) + (y_{.j.} - y...)$$

$$+ (y_{ij.} - y_{i..} - y_{.j.} + y...) + (y_{ijk} - y_{ij.})]^2.$$

$$= \sum_i \sum_j \sum_k (y_{i..} - y...)^2 + \sum_i \sum_j \sum_k (y_{.j.} - y...)^2$$

$$+ \sum_i \sum_j \sum_k (y_{ij.} - y_{i..} - y_{.j.} + y...)^2 + \sum_i \sum_j \sum_k (y_{ijk} - y_{ij.})^2.$$

All the cross-product terms are zero. The names and computing formulas for these sums of squares are

$$\text{Row SS} = \sum_i \sum_j \sum_k (y_{i..} - y...)^2 = \frac{\sum_i (\sum_j \sum_k y_{ijk})^2}{JK} - \frac{(\sum_i \sum_j \sum_k y_{ijk})^2}{IJK},$$

$$\text{Column SS} = \sum_i \sum_j \sum_k (y_{.j.} - y...)^2 = \frac{\sum_j (\sum_i \sum_k y_{ijk})^2}{IK} - \frac{(\sum_i \sum_j \sum_k y_{ijk})^2}{IJK},$$

$$\text{Interaction SS} = \sum_i \sum_j \sum_k (y_{ij.} - y_{i..} - y_{.j.} + y...)^2$$

$$= \text{Total SS} - \text{Row SS} - \text{Column SS} - \text{Error SS},$$

$$\text{Error SS} = \sum_i \sum_j \sum_k (y_{ijk} - y_{ij.})^2 = \sum_i \sum_j \sum_k y_{ijk}^2 - \frac{\sum_i \sum_j (\sum_k y_{ijk})^2}{K},$$

$$\text{Total SS} = \sum_i \sum_j \sum_k (y_{ijk} - y...)^2 = \sum_i \sum_j \sum_k y_{ijk}^2 - \frac{(\sum_i \sum_j \sum_k y_{ijk})^2}{IJK}.$$

The row and column sums of squares are essentially those discussed earlier. The interaction sum of squares is essentially the previous error sum of squares. The new error sum of squares measures the variations within the cells.

For a numerical example, extend the experiment with three (I) varieties of the crop and four (J) brands of the fertilizer. Let two (K) observations be made for every crop–fertilizer combination. Some results are shown here.

		$j =$			
		1	2	3	4
	1	82, 77	88, 88	82, 87	80, 84
$i =$	2	65, 66	83, 84	75, 79	69, 73
	3	72, 71	87, 81	87, 93	82, 79

For example, y_{322} is 81. The cell means are in the center of Table 8; the row means are at the right; the column means are at the bottom; and the grand mean is at the lower right.

Table 8

		1	2	3	4	$y_{i..}$
				$j =$		
$i =$	1	79.5	88.0	84.5	82.0	83.50
	2	65.5	83.5	77.0	71.0	74.25
	3	71.5	84.0	90.0	80.5	81.50
$y_{.j.}$		72.17	85.17	83.03	77.83	79.75

The initial calculations for the sums of squares yield

$$\sum_i\sum_j\sum_k y_{ijk}^2 = 153{,}910.00,$$

$$\frac{\sum_i\sum_j(\sum_k y_{ijk})^2}{K} = \frac{307{,}638}{2} = 153{,}819.00,$$

$$\frac{\sum_i(\sum_j\sum_k y_{ijk})^2}{JK} = \frac{1{,}224{,}164}{8} = 153{,}020.50,$$

$$\frac{\sum_j(\sum_i\sum_k y_{ijk})^2}{IK} = \frac{919{,}708}{6} = 153{,}284.67,$$

$$\frac{(\sum_i\sum_j\sum_k y_{ijk})^2}{IJK} = \frac{3{,}663{,}396}{24} = 152{,}641.50.$$

The sum of squares are then

Row SS $= 153{,}020.50 - 152{,}641.50 = 379.00,$

Column SS $= 153{,}284.67 - 152{,}641.50 = 643.17,$

Interaction SS $= 1268.50 - 379.00 - 643.17 - 91.00 = 155.33,$

Error SS $= 153{,}910.00 - 153{,}819.00 = 91.00,$

Total SS $= 153{,}910.00 - 152{,}641.50 = 1268.50.$

Expected Sums of Squares

To facilitate the derivations introduce the independent, normally distributed W_{ijk}'s, where

$$E(W_{ijk}) = 0,$$
$$V(W_{ijk}) = \sigma^2,$$

for all i, j, and k. The Y_{ijk}'s are

$$Y_{ijk} = \mu_{ij} + W_{ijk} = \mu + \alpha_i + \beta_j + \gamma_{ij} + W_{ijk},$$

where $\alpha. = \beta. = \gamma_i. = \gamma._j = 0$.

The derivations essentially are those used in previous discussions. For one example, take the expected row sum of squares.

$$E(\text{Row SS}) = E\left[\sum_i \sum_j \sum_k (Y_{i..} - Y_{...})^2\right]$$

$$= E\left[\sum_i \sum_j \sum_k (\alpha_i + W_{i..} - W_{...})^2\right]$$

$$= \sum_j \sum_k E\left(\sum_i \alpha_i^2\right) + \sum_i \sum_j \sum_k 2\alpha_i E(W_{i..} - W_{...})$$

$$+ \sum_j \sum_k E\left[\sum_i (W_{i..} - W_{...})^2\right]$$

$$= JK \sum_i \alpha_i^2 + 0 + JK(I - 1)\frac{\sigma^2}{JK}$$

$$= JK \sum_i \alpha_i^2 + (I - 1)\sigma^2.$$

$(I - 1)$ is again the degrees of freedom for the row sum of squares, and $(\text{Row SS})/(I - 1)$ is the mean row sum of squares. Table 9 gives these theoretical results for the general two-factor experiment.

Table 9

Effect	Degrees of freedom	Sum of squares	Expected mean sum of squares
Row	$I - 1$	$\sum_i \sum_j \sum_k (Y_{i..} - Y_{...})^2$	$\sigma^2 + \dfrac{JK \sum_i \alpha_i^2}{I - 1}$
Column	$J - 1$	$\sum_i \sum_j \sum_k (Y_{.j.} - Y_{...})^2$	$\sigma^2 + \dfrac{IK \sum_j \beta_j^2}{J - 1}$
Inter-action	$(I - 1)(J - 1)$	$\sum_i \sum_j \sum_k (Y_{ij.} - Y_{i..} - Y_{.j.} + Y_{...})^2$	$\sigma^2 + \dfrac{K \sum_i \sum_j \gamma_{ij}^2}{(I - 1)(J - 1)}$
Error	$IJ(K - 1)$	$\sum_i \sum_j \sum_k (Y_{ijk} - Y_{ij.})^2$	σ^2
Total	$IJK - 1$	$\sum_i \sum_j \sum_k (Y_{ijk} - Y_{...})^2$	

Significance Tests

The last column of Table 9 suggests the significance tests. The test of zero row main effects, $\sum \alpha_i^2 = 0$, is

$$\text{reject if } F[\alpha, I - 1, IJ(K - 1)] \leq \text{observed } \dfrac{\dfrac{\text{Row SS}}{I - 1}}{\dfrac{\text{Error SS}}{IJ(K - 1)}} \cdot$$

The test of zero column main effects, $\sum \beta_j^2 = 0$, is

$$\text{reject if } F[\alpha, J - 1, IJ(K - 1)] \leq \text{observed } \dfrac{\dfrac{\text{Column SS}}{J - 1}}{\dfrac{\text{Error SS}}{IJ(K - 1)}} \cdot$$

The test of zero interactions, $\sum_i \sum_j \gamma_{ij}^2 = 0$, is reject if

$$F[\alpha, (I - 1)(J - 1), IJ (K - 1)] \leq \text{observed} \dfrac{\dfrac{\text{Interaction SS}}{(J - 1)(J - 1)}}{\dfrac{\text{Error SS}}{IJ(K - 1)}} \cdot$$

Table 10

Effect	Degrees of freedom	Sum of squares	Mean sum of squares	F-ratio
Crop	2	379.00	189.50	24.99**
Fertilizer	3	643.17	214.39	28.27**
Interaction	6	155.33	25.89	3.41*
Error	12	91.00	7.58	
Total	23	1280.50		

Table 10 gives the results for the numerical example. The two hypotheses concerning main effects are rejected at the .01 level; the hypothesis concerning interactions is rejected at the .05 level but not at the .01 level. An experimenter who operates at $\alpha = .05$ might be happy to discover the main effects, but he might be unhappy to discover the interactions. Their presence makes further analysis and interpretation more complicated. In our discussion of comparisons we shall return to this example.

Exercises

40. In the partitioning of the total sum of squares, show that the following cross-product terms are zero:

a) $\sum_i \sum_j \sum_k 2(y_{i..} - y_{...})(y_{ij.} - y_{i..} - y_{.j.} + y_{...})$.

b) $\sum_i \sum_j \sum_k 2(y_{i..} - y_{...})(y_{ijk} - y_{ij.})$.

41. Verify the computing formulas for
a) the row sum of squares,
b) the error sum of squares.

42. Verify that the expected error sum of squares is $IJ(K - 1)\sigma^2$.

43. Verify that the expected interaction sum of squares is
$(I - 1)(J - 1)\sigma^2 + K\sum_i \sum_j \gamma_{ij}^2$.

44. Consider the one hypothesis
$\sum_i \alpha_i^2 = \sum_j \beta_j^2 = \sum_i \sum_j \gamma_{ij}^2 = 0$ or $\mu_{ij} = \mu$ for all i and j.
a) Construct a significance test for this hypothesis.
b) Apply the test to the numerical example of this subsection.

45. With $I = 2$, $J = 3$, and $K = 2$, construct the numerical table for the analysis of variance for the following y_{ijk}'s.

		$j =$		
		1	2	3
$i =$	1	4, 7	1, 3	6, 7
	2	4, 1	3, 3	1, 2

Estimators

The mean error sum of squares is an unbiased estimator of σ^2. As usual, the symbol is s^2.

$$E(S^2) = E\left[\frac{\text{Error SS}}{IJ(K - 1)}\right] = \sigma^2.$$

The i, jth cell mean $y_{ij.}$ is an unbiased estimator of μ_{ij}.

$$E(Y_{ij.}) = E(\mu_{ij} + W_{ij.}) = \mu_{ij}.$$

The grand mean $y_{...}$ is the best unbiased estimator of μ.

$$E(Y_{...}) = E(\mu + \alpha. + \beta. + \gamma.. + W_{...}) = \mu.$$

The best unbiased estimator of α_i is $y_{i..} - y_{....}$.

$$E(Y_{i..} - Y_{...}) = E(\alpha_i + W_{i..} - W_{....}) = \alpha_i.$$

Similarly, the best unbiased estimator of β_j is $y_{.j.} - y_{....}$.

The best unbiased estimator of γ_{ij} is $y_{ij.} - y_{i..} - y_{.j.} + y_{....}$.

$$E(Y_{ij.} - Y_{i..} - Y_{.j.} + Y_{...}) = E(\gamma_{ij} + W_{ij.} - W_{i..} - W_{.j.} + W_{...})$$

$$= \gamma_{ij}.$$

In the numerical example, Table 10 gives 3.41 for the estimator of σ^2. In the discussion of sums of squares, Table 8 gives the estimators for μ, the $\mu_{i.}$'s, the $\mu_{.j}$'s, and the μ_{ij}'s. For the main effects, the estimators are:

3.75 for α_1	-7.58 for β_1
-5.50 for α_2	5.42 for β_2
1.75 for α_3	4.08 for β_3
	-1.92 for β_4

The estimated interactions are indicated in the chart below.

		$j =$			
		1	2	3	4
	1	3.58	-0.92	-3.08	0.42
$i =$	2	-1.17	3.83	-1.33	-1.33
	3	-2.42	-2.92	4.42	0.92

Comparisons

Comparing means in a multi-factor experiment is a very big topic. Even in this two-factor experiment there are more variations to the problem than can be covered in an introductory book. This discussion considers only one specific situation. Suppose the F-tests indicate differences among the levels of the two factors. If interactions are absent, the experimenter wants to explore differences among the I row means or among the J column means. In this case, the additive model applies, and the methods of that discussion are easily applied here. If interactions are present, the experimenter might want to explore differences among the IJ cell means. Interactions are absent if the hypothesis $\sum\sum\gamma_{ij}^2 = 0$ is true. Interactions are present, if the hypothesis $\sum\sum\gamma_{ij}^2 > 0$ is true. The experimenter is clearly in a decision situation. If he accepts the first hypothesis, he looks for differences among the row or column means. If he accepts the second hypothesis, he looks for differences among the cell means. Probably he makes his decision from the observed F-ratio for the interaction sum of squares. A low ratio suggests the first hypothesis; a high ratio suggests the second hypothesis. A proper decision procedure is based on the power function. Power for the F-test will not be discussed in this book. We must make this decision on an informal basis.

If the hypothesis of no interactions is accepted, attention turns to the differences among the row means.

$$E(Y_{i..} - Y_{i'..}) = E(\mu + \alpha_i + W_{i..} - \mu - \alpha_{i'} - W_{i'..})$$

$$= \mu_{i.} - \mu_{i'.} \text{ or } \alpha_i - \alpha_{i'},$$

$$V(Y_{i..} - Y_{i'..}) = V(W_{i..} - W_{i'..}) = \frac{2\sigma^2}{JK}.$$

A $1 - \alpha$ confidence interval for $\mu_{i.} - \mu_{i'.}$ or $\alpha_i - \alpha_{i'}$ is $(y_{i..} - y_{i'..}) \pm \epsilon$, where

$$\epsilon = t\left[\frac{\alpha}{2}, IJ(K-1)\right] s\sqrt{\frac{2}{JK}}.$$

This is a slight modification of the result in the previous subsection.

Differences among the column means are treated similarly. A $1 - \alpha$ confidence interval for $\mu_{.j} - \mu_{.j'}$ or $\beta_j - \beta_{j'}$ is $(y_{.j.} - y_{.j'.}) \pm \epsilon$, where

$$\epsilon = t\left[\frac{\alpha}{2}, IJ(K-1)\right] s\sqrt{\frac{2}{IK}}.$$

If he believes interactions are present, the experimenter turns to differences among the IJ cell means.

$$E(Y_{ij.} - Y_{i'j'.}) = \mu_{ij} - \mu_{i'j'},$$

$$V(Y_{ij.} - Y_{i'j'.}) = 2\sigma^2/K.$$

A $1 - \alpha$ confidence interval for $\mu_{ij} - \mu_{i'j'}$ is $(y_{ij.} - y_{i'j'.}) \pm \epsilon$, where

$$\epsilon = t\left[\frac{\alpha}{2}, IJ(K-1)\right] s\sqrt{\frac{2}{K}}.$$

This interval is strictly correct for one pair of cell means, chosen prior to seeing the data.

Even when I and J are small, say 3 and 4, IJ is large enough to make this ϵ a poor measuring stick for comparing all the pairs of cell means. In terms of the comparisons discussion of subsection 2.1, $\alpha' - \alpha$ is likely to be very large. We seek a new procedure for making multiple comparisons. A slight digression from the two-factor experiment is necessary.

Let $X_1, X_2, \ldots, X_k$ be independent, normal random variables with $E(X_h) = 0$, and $V(X_h) = \sigma^2$, for $h = 1, 2, \ldots, k$. A set of outcomes is $x_1, x_2, \ldots, x_k$. Let

$\max x_h$ = maximum of $x_1, x_2, \ldots, x_k$,

$\min x_h$ = minimum of $x_1, x_2, \ldots, x_k$,

$r = \max x_h - \min x_h$ = range of $x_1, x_2, \ldots, x_k$,

s^2 = a mean error sum of squares for σ^2 with ν degrees of freedom,

$$q = \frac{r}{s}.$$

The name for q is the *studentized range*. As a random variable, Q is continuous with its own distribution of probability, which depends on k and ν. The space is $\{0 \text{ to } +\infty\}$. Some critical values are given in Table VII of the appendix. These values are indicated by $q(\alpha, k, \nu)$, where

$$\Pr\{q(\alpha, k, \nu) \leq Q\} = \alpha,$$

$$\Pr\{Q < q(\alpha, k, \nu)\} = 1 - \alpha.$$

For an example with $\alpha = .05$, $k = 12$, and $\nu = 12$, Table VII gives

$$q(.05, 12, 12) = 5.615.$$

To prepare for the application of the studentized range, notice that the following statements are equivalent:

$$Q < q(\alpha, k, \nu),$$

$$\max X_h - \min X_h < q(\alpha, k, \nu)S,$$

$$|X_h - X_{h'}| < q(\alpha, k, \nu)S \text{ for all } h \text{ and } h' \text{ in } 1, 2, \ldots, k,$$

$$-q(\alpha, k, \nu)S < X_h - X_{h'} < q(\alpha, k, \nu)S \text{ for all } h \text{ and } h' \text{ in } 1, 2, \ldots, k.$$

Therefore,

$$1 - \alpha = \Pr\{Q < q(\alpha, k, \nu)\}$$

$$= \Pr\{-q(\alpha, k, \nu)S < X_h - X_{h'} < q(\alpha, k, \nu)S \text{ for all } h, h'\}$$

Return to the two-factor experiment with IJ means, where
$$E(Y_{ij.}) = \mu_{ij}, \text{ and } V(Y_{ij.}) = \sigma^2/K.$$

To apply the last statement for the studentized range, make these correspondences:

$$Y_{ij\cdot} - \mu_{ij} \sim X_h,$$

$$i, j, \text{ combination} \sim h,$$

$$IJ \sim k,$$

$$\sigma^2/K \sim \sigma^2,$$

$$S/\sqrt{K} \sim S,$$

$$IJ(K - 1) \sim \nu.$$

The result is

$$1 - \alpha = \Pr\left\{-q[\alpha, IJ, IJ(K-1)]\frac{S}{\sqrt{K}} < (Y_{ij\cdot} - \mu_{ij})\right.$$

$$\left. -(Y_{i'j'\cdot} - \mu_{i'j'}) < q[\alpha, IJ, IJ(K-1)]\frac{S}{\sqrt{K}}\right\}.$$

Solving the two inequalities for $\mu_{ij} - \mu_{i'j'}$ gives a $1 - \alpha$ confidence interval for $\mu_{ij} - \mu_{ij}$.

$$(y_{ij\cdot} - y_{i'j'\cdot}) - \epsilon < \mu_{ij} - \mu_{i'j'} < (y_{ij\cdot} - y_{i'j'\cdot}) + \epsilon,$$

$$(y_{ij\cdot} - y_{i'j'\cdot}) \pm \epsilon,$$

where

$$\epsilon = q[\alpha, IJ, IJ(K-1)]\frac{S}{\sqrt{K}}.$$

Two cell means differ significantly, if they differ by more than ϵ.

In effect, this method of multiple comparison provides a level α significance test of the hypothesis

$$\mu_{ij} - \mu_{i'j'} = 0 \text{ for all } i, j, i', \text{ and } j'.$$

This hypothesis is equivalent to

$$\mu_{ij} = \mu \text{ for all } i \text{ and } j.$$

Therefore, this method of multiple comparisons substitutes another level α significance test for the F-test of the hypothesis. The point is that the prechosen value of α is not changed. In the cruder methods mentioned before, this was not true.

This exact method is applied easily to the one-factor experiment and to the additive case for the two-factor experiment. Replace $t(\alpha, \nu)\sqrt{2}$ by $q(\alpha, k, \nu)$, where k is the number of means in the family and ν is the degrees of freedom for the error sum of squares. The following example illustrates its application to the general two-factor experiment.

In the crop-fertilizer example, I is 3, J is 4, K is 2, and s^2 is 7.58 with 12 degrees of freedom. Table 10 indicated the presence of interactions at $\alpha = .05$. For multiple comparisons among the 12 cell means, the measuring stick is

$$\epsilon = q[\alpha, IJ, IJ(K-1)]\frac{s}{\sqrt{K}} = q(.05, 12, 12)\sqrt{\frac{7.58}{2}} = 10.9.$$

Two cell means that differ by at least this value differ significantly. For example, none of the differences in the first row of Table 8 is significant. The maximum, $y_{33.} = 90.0$, is significantly larger than $y_{21.}$, $y_{23.}$, $y_{24.}$, and $y_{41.}$. For one prechosen pair of means, the critical difference is

$$\epsilon = t\left[\frac{\alpha}{2}, IJ(K-1)\right]s\sqrt{\frac{2}{K}} = t(.025, 12)\sqrt{\frac{(2)(7.58)}{2}} = 6.0.$$

Summary. In the general two-factor experiment, the Y_{ijk}'s have independent normal distributions with

$$E(Y_{ijk}) = \mu_{ij} = \mu + \alpha_i + \beta_j + \gamma_{ij},$$

$$V(Y_{ijk}) = \sigma^2,$$

where $i = 1, 2, \ldots, I$, $j = 1, 2, \ldots, J$, $k = 1, 2, \ldots, K$, and $\alpha. = \beta. = \gamma_{i.} = \gamma_{.j} = 0$. The hypothesis of no interactions is $\sum\sum\gamma_{ij}^2 = 0$. The hypotheses of no main effects are

$$\sum\alpha_i^2 = 0 \quad \text{and} \quad \sum\beta_j^2 = 0.$$

The total sum of squares is partitioned according to

Total SS = Row SS + Column SS + Interaction SS + Error SS.

The significance tests of level α are

$$\text{reject } \sum\alpha_i^2 = 0 \text{ if } F[\alpha, I-1, IJ(K-1)] \leq \text{observed} \frac{\dfrac{\text{Row SS}}{I-1}}{\dfrac{\text{Error SS}}{IJ(K-1)}},$$

$$\text{reject } \sum \beta_j^2 = 0 \text{ if } F[\alpha, J-1, IJ(K-1)] \leq \text{observed } \dfrac{\dfrac{\text{Column SS}}{J-1}}{\dfrac{\text{Error SS}}{IJ(K-1)}},$$

reject $\sum\sum \gamma_{ij}^2 = 0$ if

$$F[\alpha, (I-1)(J-1), IJ(K-1)] \leq \text{observed } \dfrac{\dfrac{\text{Interaction SS}}{(I-1)(J-1)}}{\dfrac{\text{Error SS}}{IJ(K-1)}}.$$

The unbiased estimators are

$$s^2 \text{ for } \sigma^2,$$

$$y_{ij\cdot} \text{ for } \mu_{ij},$$

$$y_{\cdots} \text{ for } \mu,$$

$$y_{i\cdot\cdot} - y_{\cdots} \text{ for } \alpha_i,$$

$$y_{\cdot j\cdot} - y_{\cdots} \text{ for } \beta_j,$$

$$y_{ij\cdot} - y_{i\cdot\cdot} - y_{\cdot j\cdot} + y_{\cdots} \text{ for } \gamma_{ij}.$$

To summarize one method of multiple comparisons, let the X_h's have independent, normal distributions with

$$E(X_h) = \mu_h,$$

$$V(X_h) = \sigma^2,$$

where $h = 1, 2, \ldots, k$. For each h, a random sample of size n is taken for X_h; let $x_h.$ be the sample mean. Let s^2 be a mean sum of squares for σ^2 with ν degrees of freedom. A $1 - \alpha$ confidence interval for $\mu_h - \mu_{h'}$ is

$$(x_h. - x_{h'}.) \pm q(\alpha, k, \nu)\dfrac{s}{\sqrt{k}}.$$

Two means that differ by more than $q(\alpha, k, \nu)\dfrac{s}{\sqrt{n}}$ differ significantly.

Exercises

46. Cofoid–Bruce produces pickles for a small, local market, but now it wants to move into a larger market. Three types of newspaper advertising campaigns are being considered. C–B divides the nation into four possible markets which may react differently to advertising. For each of the 12 advertising–market combinations, three

cities are picked at random to carry that type of advertising in that market. The variable of interest is the per cent of the pickle market in a city after six months. Each number in the table below is the mean of the three observations at that combination.

		market			
		1	2	3	4
advertising	1	7	9	6	10
	2	10	8	1	1
	3	4	7	5	4

(For small per cents like these, the variance is not constant. A simple transformation of the data usually corrects this. Ignore this point in your analysis.) Complete the table for the analysis of variance. Take $\alpha = .05$ for all the parts of this exercise.

Effect	Sum of squares	Degrees of freedom	Mean sum of squares	F-ratio
advertising	72			
market	90			
interaction	156			
error	96			
total	414			

a) Are the observed F-ratios significant?
b) Suppose C–B's original intention was to choose one type of advertising and enter all four markets with it. Make the appropriate comparisons. Assume markets are the same size.
c) Suppose C–B's original intention was to choose only one type of advertising and only one market. Make the appropriate comparisons. Is the third type of advertising significantly inferior to the better of the other two in this context?
d) Suppose C–B's original intention was to enter markets 1 and 4 with the same type of advertising. The other markets were explored for future use. Make the appropriate comparisons.
e) Suppose the situation in d) exists, but the markets are not the same size. Twice as many people live in market 1 as in market 4.

Hint: Let $y_i = \frac{2}{3}y_{i1.} + \frac{1}{3}y_{i4.}$ and look for differences among the three y_i's.

47. The $X_h.$'s form a family of independent, normally distributed means, where

$$E(X_h.) = \mu_h \quad \text{and} \quad V(X_h.) = \frac{\sigma^2}{n}$$

for $h = 1, 2, \ldots, k$. Consider all comparisons of the form $\sum c_h \mu_h$, where $\sum c_h = 0$ and the sum of the positive c_h's is one. Again, s^2 is a mean sum of squares for σ^2 with ν degrees of freedom. Prove that a $1 - \alpha$ confidence interval for $\sum c_h \mu_h$ is

$$\sum c_h x_h. - \epsilon < \sum c_h \mu_h < \sum c_h x_h. + \epsilon,$$

$$\left(\sum c_h x_h. \right) \pm \epsilon,$$

where

$$\epsilon = q(\alpha, k, \nu) \frac{s}{\sqrt{n}}.$$

48. For the one-factor experiment, show that a level α test of the hypothesis $\mu_1 = \mu_2 = \cdots = \mu_I$ is

$$\text{reject if } q[\alpha, I, I(J - 1)] \leq \frac{\max y_i. - \min y_i.}{s/\sqrt{J}}.$$

49. For a one-factor experiment with $I = 3$ and $J = 2$, the y_{ij}'s are

		$j =$	
		1	2
	1	$a + 2$	$a - 2$
$i =$	2	$b - 1$	$b + 1$
	3	1	-1

where $0 \leq b \leq a$. The hypothesis of interest is $\mu_1 = \mu_2 = \mu_3$. Take $\alpha = .05$.

a) Find an a and b that reject with the F-test, but fail to reject with the test of exercise 48. Try $b = 0$, $a = ?$

b) Find an a and b that reject with the test of exercise 48, but fail to reject with the F-test. Try $a = 2b = ?$

3
Multi-Factor Experiments

This section gives a brief discussion of multi-factor experiments—their advantages, their limitations, and some reactions to their limitations.

There are three principal advantages. To illustrate the advantages, compare two one-factor experiments with one two-factor experiment. Suppose the first factor has 3 levels. At each level of a corresponding one-factor experiment, take 8 observations of the variable of interest. This makes 24 observations in all. The variance of a difference of means is $\frac{2\sigma^2}{8}$. Suppose the second factor has 4 levels. At each level of a corresponding one-factor experiment, take 6 observations of the variable of interest, 24 again in all. The variance of a difference of means is $\frac{2\sigma^2}{6}$. Now consider one two-factor experiment with the first factor at 3 levels and the second at 4 levels. For each of these 12 combinations, take 2 observations of the variable of interest. The variance of a difference of means for the first factor is still $\frac{2\sigma^2}{8}$; the variance of a difference of means for the second factor is still $\frac{2\sigma^2}{6}$. That is, one two-factor experiment with 24 observations is as good as two one-factor experiments, each with 24 observations. This illustrates the first principal advantage. As the number of factors increases, the advantage increases.

A second advantage concerns interactions. If they are present, the one-factor-at-a-time approach will probably never find them. A comprehensive experiment which explores each combination of levels is the efficient method to find them.

A third advantage concerns the variance of the variable of interest. Frequently it is profitable to introduce new factors, although they are of no importance in themselves. They may reduce the variance for comparing levels of an important factor. In the next chapter we shall return to this point.

The general two-factor experiment already illustrates most of the essential ideas. With more factors, more interactions are possible. For example, take a three-factor experiment. Each pair of factors has a set of two-factor interactions, as before. In addition, there is a set of three-factor interactions. The analysis-of-variance table has a row for each of the three main effects, for each of the three two-factor interactions, for the three-factor interaction, for error, and for the totals. The generalization to a higher number of factors follows this pattern.

Experiments with many factors become very large very quickly. This is the chief limitation. For example, take three factors at 3, 4, and 5 levels. This makes 60 different combinations of levels. An experiment of this size can estimate all the main effects and interactions, but not the variance σ^2. To obtain this as well, the process could be repeated, making 120 observations in all. In many contexts, this is too big. Worse yet, situations with more factors are common. Clearly, some simplification is needed.

The most common simplifications result from assumptions that higher order interactions are absent. Thus, fewer parameters must be estimated. If it is done carefully, the size of the experiment can be reduced without complicating the necessary analysis. Subsections 2.1 and 2.2 illustrated this point. With interactions, IJK observations (with $K \geq 2$) are necessary to estimate the main effects, the interactions, and σ^2. Without interactions only IJ observations are necessary to estimate the mains effects and σ^2.

ADDITIONAL READINGS

Brownlee, K., *Statistical Theory and Methodology in Science and Engineering.* 2nd ed. New York: John Wiley & Sons, Inc., 1965.

Cochran, W., and G. Cox, *Experimental Designs.* New York: John Wiley & Sons, Inc., 1957.

Cox, D., *Planning of Experiments.* New York: John Wiley & Sons, Inc., 1958.

Finney, D., *Experimental Design and Its Statistical Basis.* Chicago: University of Chicago Press, 1955.

———, *The Theory of Experimental Design.* Chicago: University of Chicago Press, 1960.

Fisher, R., *The Design of Experiments.* 7th ed. New York: Hafner Publishing Company, 1960.

Kempthorne, O., *The Design and Analysis of Experiments.* New York: John Wiley & Sons, Inc., 1952.

Miller, R., *Simultaneous Statistical Inference.* New York: McGraw-Hill Book Company, 1966.

Scheffé, H., *The Analysis of Variance.* New York: John Wiley & Sons, Inc., 1959.

Analysis of Variance: Two | VIII

The primary purpose of this chapter is to discuss the analysis of an experiment with a random-effects factor. That is, the probability distribution of the variable of interest Y can depend on the level of the random-effects factor. Recall that a random-effects factor is qualitative like the fixed-effects factor, because the levels in the experiment are not numerically defined. A random-effects factor is also uncontrolled like the correlation factor, because the actual levels in the experiment are chosen at random.

1

One-Factor Experiment

A random-effects factor is evaluated according to its effect on the variance of the variable of interest. The variance $V(Y)$ is partitioned into two components: one for the factor, and one for chance. Compare this to the evaluation of a fixed-effects factor. In that case the expected value $E(Y)$ is partitioned into two components: one for the overall expected value μ and one for the main effect of each level of the factor.

In the presence of a random-effects factor, the variable of interest Y can be written $Y = \mu + A + W$, where μ is a constant. A is a random variable corresponding to the random-effects factor. A has a normal distribution with $E(A) = 0$ and $V(A) = \sigma_A^2$. W is a random variable corresponding to the effects of chance. W has a normal distribution with $E(W) = 0$ and $V(W) = \sigma^2$. A and W are independent. Therefore, Y has a normal distribution with $E(Y) = \mu$ and $V(Y) = V(A) + V(W) = \sigma_A^2 + \sigma^2$.

Agricultural Example. In a geographical region there are many fields suitable for a particular crop. Each field is large enough to be divided into many plots. Randomly selecting a plot within the hth field, planting the crop, and observing the yield is one random experiment. Suppose the distribution of yields for this field is normal with expected value μ_h and variance σ^2, where the variance does not depend on the field. The yield can be written

$$\text{yield} = \mu_h + W,$$

where W is normal with $E(W) = 0$ and $V(W) = \sigma^2$. Now consider the μ_h's themselves. Let μ be their grand mean. For the random experiment of picking an expected value at random, suppose the distribution is normal with expected value μ and variance $\sigma_A{}^2$. This can be written

$$\text{selected expected value} = \mu + A,$$

where the random variable A is normal with $E(A) = 0$ and $V(A) = \sigma_A{}^2$. Finally, consider a sequential random experiment: pick a field at random; pick a plot within the field; plant the crop on the plot; measure the yield for the plot. If Y is the corresponding variable, then $Y = \mu + A + W$. Assume that A and W are independent. Then Y is normal with $E(Y) = \mu$ and $V(Y) = V(A + W) = \sigma_A{}^2 + \sigma^2$. For a particular trial of this experiment, y is the actual yield; $\mu + a$ is the expected yield for the chosen field; and w is the deviation from $\mu + a$ for the chosen plot. Of course, μ, a, and w are not observed, only their sum y.

Physiological Example. An experimenter is interested in the blood pressures of some population of persons. Each person's blood pressure can be measured on many days. Randomly selecting a day for the hth person and measuring his blood pressure is one random experiment. Suppose the distribution of pressures for this person is normal with expected value μ_h and variance σ^2, where the variance does not depend on the person. The pressure can be written

$$\text{blood pressure} = \mu_h + W,$$

where W is normal with $E(W) = 0$ and $V(W) = \sigma^2$. Now consider the μ_h's themselves. Let μ be their grand mean. For the random experiment of picking an expected value at random, suppose the distribution is normal with expected value μ and variance $\sigma_A{}^2$. This can be written

$$\text{selected expected value} = \mu + A,$$

where the random variable A is normal with $E(A) = 0$ and $V(A) = \sigma_A{}^2$. Finally, consider a sequential random experiment: pick a person at random; pick a day for that person; read his blood pressure on that day. If Y is the corresponding variable, then $Y = \mu + A + W$. Assume that A and W are independent. Then Y is normal with $E(Y) = \mu$ and $V(Y) = V(A + W) = \sigma_A{}^2 + \sigma^2$.

Model

When the parameters are unknown, they can be estimated from the outcomes of a suitable experiment. I levels of the random-effects factor A are chosen at random. Let the outcomes be $a_1, a_2, \ldots, a_I$. At the ith level of the random-effects factor, there are J outcomes for the effects of chance. Let these be $w_{i1}, w_{i2}, \ldots, w_{iJ}$. A corresponding outcome of the variable of interest is y_{ij}, where $y_{ij} = \mu + a_i + w_{ij}$. The experimenter observes y_{ij}; he does not observe μ, a_i, or w_{ij}.

In terms of random variables,

$$Y_{ij} = \mu + A_i + W_{ij},$$

where $i = i, 2, \ldots, I$ and $j = 1, 2, \ldots, J$. The A_i's and the W_{ij}'s are completely independent. A_i is normal with $E(A_i) = 0$ and $V(A_i) = \sigma_A^2$. W_{ij} is normal with $E(W_{ij}) = 0$ and $V(W_{ij}) = \sigma^2$. Therefore, Y_{ij} is normal with $E(Y_{ij}) = \mu$ and $V(Y_{ij}) = \sigma_A^2 + \sigma^2$. The central problem is to estimate μ, σ_A^2, and σ^2 from the observed y_{ij}'s. A test for the hypothesis $\sigma_A^2 = 0$ is also of minor interest.

Agricultural Example. The above simple agricultural experiment can be expanded as follows. Five (*I*) fields are randomly picked in the region. Within each field, four (*J*) plots are randomly chosen. The particular crop is raised on the twenty plots. The yields (y_{ij}) are shown here.

	$j =$			
	1	2	3	4
1	57	58	74	66
2	101	98	115	99
$i =$ 3	94	86	78	88
4	78	77	70	80
5	81	81	84	95

$y_{43} = 70$, for example, is the yield on the third plot in the fourth field. The order of the four numbers in any row is not important. This numerical example will be used throughout this discussion of the one-factor experiment.

Exercises

1. Deck I contains seven cards that are numbered "2", "4", "6", "8", "10", "12", and "14". Deck II contains five cards that are numbered "-2", "-1", "0", "1", and "2". An experiment is to draw a card from deck I; draw a card from deck II; and compute the sum Y of the numbers on the two cards. This random experiment can be put into the context of this section.

$$Y = E(Y) + A + W,$$

where W is associated with deck II. Find
a) $E(Y)$,
b) the space for A,
c) $V(A)$,
d) $V(W)$.

2. Use the decks of exercise 1 to generate outcomes for a one-factor experiment with $I = 6$ and $J = 3$. Save the results for later analysis.

3. In the general model of this section $Y_{ij} = \mu + A_i + W_{ij}$, the variables Y_{ij} and $Y_{ij'}$ are not independent. Prove

$$\mathrm{Cor}(Y_{ij}, Y_{ij'}) = \frac{\sigma_A^2}{\sigma_A^2 + \sigma^2}.$$

4. For the general model of this section, $Y_{ij} = \mu + A_i + W_{ij}$, let

$$Y_{i \cdot} = \frac{\sum_j Y_{ij}}{J}.$$

Prove $\qquad\qquad V(Y_{i \cdot}) \neq \dfrac{V(Y_{ij})}{J}.$

5. In the physiological example in the text, suppose $\mu = 170$, $\sigma_A^2 = 100$ and $\sigma^2 = 25$ for some population of persons. One person is selected randomly, and his blood pressure is measured on 10 days. What are the expected value and the variance of the mean of the 10 readings?

6. In the context of exercise 5, 10 persons are randomly selected from the population. Each person's blood pressure is measured on only one day. What are the expected value and the variance of the mean of the 10 readings?

Sums of Squares

There are IJ outcomes, the y_{ij}'s. The row means and the grand mean are as in the experiment with one fixed-effects factor.

$$\text{row mean} = y_{i \cdot} = \frac{\sum_j y_{ij}}{J},$$

$$\text{grand mean} = y_{\cdot \cdot} = \frac{\sum_i \sum_j y_{ij}}{IJ}.$$

The total sum of squares also is partitioned as before. These are algebraic results which are independent of the model.

$$\text{Row SS} = \sum_i \sum_j (y_{i \cdot} - y_{\cdot \cdot})^2 = \frac{\sum_i \left(\sum_j y_{ij} \right)^2}{J} - \frac{\left(\sum_i \sum_j y_{ij} \right)^2}{IJ},$$

$$\text{Error SS} = \sum_i \sum_j (y_{ij} - y_{i \cdot})^2 = \sum_i \sum_j y_{ij}^2 - \frac{\sum_i \left(\sum_j y_{ij} \right)^2}{J},$$

$$\text{Total SS} = \sum_i \sum_j (y_{ij} - y_{\cdot \cdot})^2 = \sum_i \sum_j y_{ij}^2 - \frac{\left(\sum_i \sum_j y_{ij} \right)^2}{IJ}.$$

In the agricultural numerical example, the grand mean $y..$ is 83. The sums of squares are

$$\text{Row SS} = 141{,}154 - 137{,}780 = 3{,}374,$$

$$\text{Error SS} = 141{,}852 - 141{,}154 = 698,$$

$$\text{Total SS} = 141{,}154 - 137{,}780 = 4{,}072.$$

Expected Sums of Squares

The derivation of the expected error sum of squares is almost identical to that of the fixed-effects factor. The expectation is again $I(J-1)\sigma^2$. $I(J-1)$ is the degrees of freedom, and $(\text{Error SS})/I(J-1)$ is the mean error sum of squares.

The expected row sum of squares is

$$E\left[\sum_i \sum_j (Y_i. - Y..)^2\right] = E\left\{\sum_i \sum_j [(A_i - A.) + (W_i. - W..)]^2\right\}$$

$$= \sum_j E\left[\sum_i (A_i - A.)^2\right]$$

$$+ \sum_i \sum_j 2E(A_i - A.)(W_i. - W..)$$

$$+ \sum_j E\left[\sum_i (W_i. - W..)^2\right]$$

$$= \sum_j (I-1)\sigma_A^2 + 0 + \sum_j (I-1)\frac{\sigma^2}{J}$$

$$= J(I-1)\sigma_A^2 + (I-1)\sigma^2.$$

The independence of the A_i's and the W_{ij}'s makes the middle term zero. There are $I-1$ degrees of freedom again, and $(\text{Row SS})/(I-1)$ is the mean row sum of squares. Table 1 gives these theoretical results.

Table 1

Effect	Degrees of freedom	Sum of squares	Expected mean sum of squares
Row	$I-1$	$\sum_i \sum_j (Y_i. - Y..)^2$	$\sigma^2 + J\sigma_A^2$
Error	$I(J-1)$	$\sum_i \sum_j (Y_{ij} - Y_i)^2$	σ^2
Total	$IJ-1$	$\sum_i \sum_j (Y_{ij} - Y..)^2$	

Significance Test

Table 1 suggests the significance test of the hypothesis $\sigma_A^2 = 0$. It is

$$\text{reject if } F[\alpha, I - 1, I(J - 1)] \leq \text{observed } \dfrac{\dfrac{\text{Row SS}}{I - 1}}{\dfrac{\text{Error SS}}{I(J - 1)}}$$

This is identical to the test for the fixed-effects factor.

Table 2

Effect	Degrees of freedom	Sum of squares	Mean sum of squares	F-ratio
field	4	3374	843.50	18.13**
error	15	698	46.53	
total	19	4072		

Table 2 gives the numerical results for the agricultural example. Since $F(.01, 4, 15) = 4.89$, the hypothesis of no field effect is rejected at the .01 level.

Estimators

There are only three parameters for this experiment. The best unbiased estimator of μ is the grand mean $y...$. As usual, the mean error sum of squares is an unbiased estimator of σ^2. Table 1 also suggests an unbiased estimator for σ_A^2. From the last column,

$$E\left(\frac{\text{Row SS}}{I - 1} \right) = \sigma^2 + J\sigma_A^2,$$

$$E\left(\frac{\text{Row SS}}{I - 1} \right) = E\left[\frac{\text{Error SS}}{I(J - 1)} \right] + J\sigma_A^2,$$

$$E\left[\frac{\text{Row SS}}{I - 1} - \frac{\text{Error SS}}{I(J - 1)} \right] = J\sigma_A^2.$$

That is, an unbiased estimator of σ_A^2 is

$$\frac{1}{J}\left[\frac{\text{Row SS}}{I - 1} - \frac{\text{Error SS}}{I(J - 1)} \right].$$

One embarrassing consequence is that this is sometimes negative. An experimenter may want to use zero when this happens.

In the example the estimators are

$$y.. = 83 \text{ for } \mu,$$

$$\frac{\text{Error SS}}{I(J-1)} = 46.53 \text{ for } \sigma^2,$$

$$\frac{1}{J} \left[\frac{\text{Row SS}}{I-1} - \frac{\text{Error SS}}{I(J-1)} \right] = 199.24 \text{ for } \sigma_A{}^2.$$

Summary. For the experiment with one random-effects factor, the model is

$$Y_{ij} = \mu + A_i + W_{ij},$$

where $i = 1, 2, \ldots, I$ and $j = 1, 2, \ldots, J$. The A_i's are normal with

$$E(A_i) = 0,$$

$$V(A_i) = \sigma_A{}^2.$$

The W_{ij}'s are normal with

$$E(W_{ij}) = 0,$$

$$V(W_{ij}) = \sigma^2.$$

All the A_i's and the W_{ij}'s are independent. The sums of squares are

$$\text{Row SS} = \sum_i \sum_j (y_i. - y..)^2 = \frac{\sum_i (\sum_j y_{ij})^2}{J} - \frac{(\sum_i \sum_j y_{ij})^2}{IJ},$$

$$\text{Error SS} = \sum_i \sum_j (y_{ij} - y_i.)^2 = \sum_i \sum_j y_{ij}{}^2 - \frac{\sum_i (\sum_j y_{ij})^2}{J},$$

$$\text{Total SS} = \sum_i \sum_j (y_{ij} - y..)^2 = \sum_i \sum_j y_{ij}{}^2 - \frac{(\sum_i \sum_j y_{ij})^2}{IJ}.$$

A level α test of the hypothesis $\sigma_A{}^2 = 0$ is

$$\text{reject if } F[\alpha, I - 1, I(J - 1)] \leq \text{observed} \frac{\dfrac{\text{Row SS}}{I-1}}{\dfrac{\text{Error SS}}{I(J-1)}}.$$

$y..$ is an unbiased estimator of μ; (Error SS)/$I(J-1)$ is an unbiased estimator of σ^2; an unbiased estimator of $\sigma_A{}^2$ is

$$\frac{1}{J} \left[\frac{\text{Row SS}}{I-1} - \frac{\text{Error SS}}{I(J-1)} \right].$$

EXERCISES

7. Analyze your data from exercise 2 of this chapter. Specifically, estimate μ, σ_A^2, and σ^2.

8. Consider a modified hypothesis about σ_A^2 and σ^2: $\sigma_A^2 \leq \theta\sigma^2$, where θ is known.

   a) If $\sigma_A^2 = \theta\sigma^2$, show that the expected mean row sum of squares is $(1 + J\theta)\sigma^2$.
   b) A test for the hypothesis is

   $$\text{reject if } c \leq \text{observed } \frac{\dfrac{\text{Row SS}}{I-1}}{\dfrac{\text{Error SS}}{J(I-1)}}.$$

   Show that $c = (1 + J\theta)F[\alpha, I-1, I(J-1)]$ is a reasonable cut-off point for a level α test.

9. Use the result of exercise 8 to test the hypothesis $\sigma_A^2 \leq \sigma^2$ for the numerical example of the test. Use $\alpha = .05$.

10. Ellickson Supply Co. is one of the leading producers of snow shovels. Sales to the public are made through independent hardware stores. The sales department at Ellickson has divided the country into many regions of approximately equal size. Within each region there are many hardware stores. To study the market eight regions are randomly selected. Within each region two hardware stores are randomly selected. Each of these 16 stores is visited, and Ellickson's per cent of that store's snow shovel market is determined. Some results are

		\multicolumn{8}{c}{regions}

		1	2	3	4	5	6	7	8
stores	1	29	43	31	32	38	28	48	34
	2	27	38	27	37	44	31	37	44

The sum of these 16 numbers is 568. The sum of squares for regions is 504, and the error sum of squares is 168. Estimate Ellickson's per cent of the national market, the variance between regions, and the variance within a market.

11. For the company of exercise 10, consider the following situation: (1) A region is randomly selected, and the market size for one hardware store of the region is determined; (2) A second region is selected, and the market sizes in two stores are determined; (3) A third region is selected, and the market sizes in three stores are determined. The mean of the six numbers is calculated. What is the probability that the mean will be greater than 40? Use the estimates for parameters of exercise 10 to approximate the answer.

12. In an experiment with two random-effects factors the additive model is

$$Y_{ij} = \mu + A_i + B_j + W_{ij}.$$

All the A_i's, the B_j's, and the W_{ij}'s are independent, normally distributed with

$$E(A_i) = E(B_j) = E(W_{ij}) = 0$$

$$V(A_i) = \sigma_A^2 \qquad V(B_j) = \sigma_B^2 \qquad V(W_{ij}) = \sigma^2$$

Verify the last column of the following analysis-of-variance table.

Effect	Degrees of freedom	Sum of squares	Expected mean sum of squares
Row	$I - 1$	$\sum_i \sum_j (Y_{i.} - Y_{..})^2$	$\sigma^2 + J\sigma_A^2$
Column	$J - 1$	$\sum_i \sum_j (Y_{.j} - Y_{..})^2$	$\sigma^2 + I\sigma_B^2$
Error	$(I - 1)(J - 1)$	$\sum_i \sum_j (Y_{ij} - Y_{i.} - Y_{.j} + Y_{..})^2$	σ^2
Total	$IJ - 1$	$\sum_i \sum_j (Y_{ij} - Y_{..})^2$	

13. In an experiment with two random-effects factors the general model is

$$Y_{ijk} = \mu + A_i + B_j + C_{ij} + W_{ijk}.$$

All the A_i's, the B_j's, the C_{ij}'s, and the W_{ijk}'s are independent, normally distributed with

$$E(A_i) = E(B_j) = E(C_{ij}) \qquad E(W_{ijk}) = 0$$

$$V(A_i) = \sigma_A^2 \qquad V(B_j) = \sigma_B^2 \qquad V(C_{ij}) = \sigma_C^2 \qquad V(W_{ijk}) = \sigma^2$$

Verify the last column of the following analysis-of-variance table:

Effect	Degrees of freedom	Sum of squares	Expected mean sum of squares
Row	$I - 1$	$\sum_i \sum_j \sum_k (Y_i.. - Y...)^2$	$\sigma^2 + JK\sigma_A^2 + K\sigma_C^2$
Column	$J - 1$	$\sum_i \sum_j \sum_k (Y._j. - Y...)^2$	$\sigma^2 + IK\sigma_B^2 + K\sigma_C^2$
Inter-action	$(I - 1)(J - 1)$	$\sum_i \sum_j \sum_k (Y_{ij}. - Y_i.. - Y._j. + Y...)^2$	$\sigma^2 + K\sigma_C^2$
Error	$IJ(K - 1)$	$\sum_i \sum_j \sum_k (Y_{ijk} - Y_{ij}.)^2$	σ^2
Total	$IJK - 1$	$\sum_i \sum_j \sum_k (Y_{ijk} - Y...)^2$	

14. For the general experiment of exercise 13, suggest significance tests for the two hypotheses, $\sigma_A^2 = 0$ and $\sigma_C^2 = 0$. The test for $\sigma_A^2 = 0$ differs from previous F-tests in what way?

15. For the context of this section, verify that

$$E(Y..) = \mu,$$

$$V(Y..) = \frac{\sigma^2}{IJ} + \frac{\sigma_A^2}{I}.$$

16. Using exercise 15, suggest a $1 - \alpha$ confidence interval for μ. Remember that $V(Y..)$ must be estimated.

2

Mixed Two-Factor Experiment

In one of the most widely used experiments, the distribution of the variable of interest Y depends on two factors: one of the fixed-effects type, and one of the random-effects type. A mixed two-factor experiment can follow the additive model without interactions, or it can follow the general model with interactions. We shall discuss only the additive model.

Model

The fixed-effects factor, row factor, is at I levels, and the random-effects factor, column factor, is at J levels. y_{ij} is the outcome at the ith level of the row factor and the jth level of the column factor. The random variable Y_{ij} has components for the two factors.

$$Y_{ij} = \mu + \alpha_i + B_j + W_{ij}.$$

The α_i's are again the main effects of the row factor with $\alpha. = 0$. The B_j's are the random effects of the column factor. They are independent and normally distributed with $E(B_j) = 0$ and $V(B_j) = \sigma_B{}^2$. The W_{ij}'s are the random effects of chance. They are independent and normally distributed with $E(W_{ij}) = 0$ and $V(W_{ij}) = \sigma^2$. Therefore, Y_{ij} has a normal distribution with

$$E(Y_{ij}) = \mu + \alpha_i = \mu_i,$$

$$V(Y_{ij}) = \sigma_B{}^2 + \sigma^2.$$

Agricultural Example. There are three varieties of a crop to be compared. This identifies a crop factor. It is a fixed-effects factor at three (I) levels. Four fields are randomly selected in some region. Within each field three plots are randomly selected, and each crop variety is planted on a plot. This identifies a field factor. It is a random-effects factor at four (J) levels. The variable of interest is the yield (Y).

Physiological Example. There are three drugs to be compared for their effects on blood pressure. This identifies a fixed-effects factor, treatment, with three (I) levels. Six persons are randomly selected from some population. Each of the six is given the first drug. After several days on the drug, the blood pressures of the six persons are read on one day. Each of the six is then given the second drug, and the process is repeated. Finally, each of the six is given the third drug. This identifies a random-effects factor, person, with six (J) levels. The variable of interest is the blood pressure (Y). There are 18 observations of it.

In each of these two examples, comparing the levels of the fixed-effects factor is the primary goal. The experimenter wants a good chance to detect any differences that exist. Equivalently, he wants short confidence intervals for differences of expected values. Essentially, there are only two ways to get shorter confidence intervals: (1) get more data; or (2) reduce the variance of a comparison. The random-effects factor is introduced to reduce a variance; each level of the factor is a *block*, and the entire experiment follows a *randomized-blocks design*. In the agricultural example each field is a block. Each variety appears within each field. Comparisons of varieties are made within a field, and the field-to-field variations are eliminated from the variance. In the physiological example each person is a block.

The treatments are compared on the same person, and the person-to-person variations are eliminated from the variance.

The levels of the fixed-effects factor can be compared without blocks. The one-factor experiment discussed in Chapter VII did just that. For the three varieties of the crop the comparable one-factor experiment selects twelve fields at random and assigns four to each variety. That is, each field is used with only one variety. Field-to-field variations are now part of the variance in a comparison of two varieties.

Sums of Squares

The necessary sums of squares and their computing formulas are as before.

$$\text{Row SS} = \sum_i \sum_j (y_i. - y..)^2 = \frac{\sum_i \left(\sum_j y_{ij}\right)^2}{J} - \frac{\left(\sum_i \sum_j y_{ij}\right)^2}{IJ}.$$

$$\text{Column SS} = \sum_i \sum_j (y._j - y..)^2 = \frac{\sum_j \left(\sum_i y_{ij}\right)^2}{I} - \frac{\left(\sum_i \sum_j y_{ij}\right)^2}{IJ}.$$

$$\text{Error SS} = \text{Total SS} - \text{Row SS} - \text{Column SS}.$$

$$\text{Total SS} = \sum_i \sum_j (y_{ij} - y..)^2 = \sum_i \sum_j y_{ij}^2 - \frac{\left(\sum_i \sum_j y_{ij}\right)^2}{IJ}.$$

Expected Sums of Squares

Table 3 gives the expected mean sums of squares. The derivations require nothing new.

Table 3

Effect	Degrees of freedom	Sum of squares	Expected mean sum of squares
Row	$I - 1$	$\sum_i \sum_j (Y_i. - Y..)^2$	$\sigma^2 + \dfrac{J \sum \alpha_i^2}{I - 1}$
Column	$J - 1$	$\sum_i \sum_j (Y._j - Y..)^2$	$\sigma^2 + I \sigma_B^2$
Error	$(I - 1)(J - 1)$	$\sum_i \sum_j (Y_{ij} - Y_i. - Y._j + Y..)^2$	σ^2
Total	$IJ - 1$	$\sum_i \sum_j (Y_{ij} - Y..)^2$	

Significance Tests

The hypothesis of no main effects for the row factor is $\sum \alpha_i^2 = 0$. The significance test of level α is

$$\text{reject if } F[\alpha, I - 1, (I - 1)(J - 1)] \leq \text{observed} \quad \frac{\dfrac{\text{Row SS}}{I - 1}}{\dfrac{\text{Error SS}}{(I - 1)(J - 1)}}.$$

The hypothesis of no variation in the column factor is $\sigma_B^2 = 0$. The significance test of level α is

$$\text{reject if } F[\alpha, J - 1, (I - 1)(J - 1)] \leq \text{observed} \quad \frac{\dfrac{\text{Column SS}}{J - 1}}{\dfrac{\text{Error SS}}{(I - 1)(J - 1)}}.$$

Estimators

The unbiased estimators are

$$y_{..} \text{ for } \mu,$$

$$y_{i.} \text{ for } \mu_i,$$

$$y_{i.} - y_{..} \text{ for } \alpha_i,$$

$$s^2 = \frac{\text{Error SS}}{(I - 1)(J - 1)} \text{ for } \sigma^2,$$

$$\frac{1}{I} \left[\frac{\text{Column SS}}{J - 1} - \frac{\text{Error SS}}{(I - 1)(J - 1)} \right] \text{ for } \sigma_B^2.$$

Comparisons

For a pair of levels of the row factor, i and i', an unbiased estimator of $\mu_i - \mu_{i'}$ is $y_{i.} - y_{i'..}$. The variance is

$$V(Y_{i.} - Y_{i'.}) = V(W_{i.} - W_{i'.}) = \frac{2\sigma^2}{J}.$$

For one prechosen pair, a $1 - \alpha$ confidence interval is

$$(y_{i.} - y_{i'.}) \pm \epsilon,$$

where

$$\epsilon = t\left[\frac{\alpha}{2}, (I - 1)(J - 1) \right] s\sqrt{\frac{2}{J}}.$$

The multiple comparisons procedure based on the studentized range does not apply here. The $Y_{i.}$'s are not independent. Other procedures exist for this situation.

EXERCISES

17. In the physiological example of the text, suppose the results are those indicated below.

		$j =$					
		1	2	3	4	5	6
	1	199	195	221	219	188	194
$i =$	2	183	192	213	196	188	185
	3	187	190	208	196	193	156

a) Verify that Row SS = 644.78, Column SS = 2330.95, Error SS = 750.55.

b) Test $\sum \alpha_i^2 = 0$ and $\sigma_B^2 = 0$ at $\alpha = .05$.

c) Estimate μ_1, μ_2, μ_3, σ^2, and σ_B^2.

d) Using the only comparisons procedure of this section, which differences among the drugs appear significant?

18. With a fixed-effects factor at two levels and a random-effects factor at five levels, some y_{ij}'s are:

		$j =$				
		1	2	3	4	5
$i =$	1	10	5	10	20	25
	2	4	2	8	15	21

a) Verify Row SS = 40, Column SS = 515, Error SS = 5.

b) Estimate μ_1, μ_2, σ^2, and σ_B^2.

c) Construct a .95 confidence interval for $\mu_1 - \mu_2$.

d) Let $x_j = y_{1j} - y_{2j}$, and find the five x_j's. Compute their mean, sample standard deviation, and a .95 confidence interval for $E(X)$.

e) Compare the interval in d) to the interval in c).

19. With $I = 2$, the model of this section is an example of *paired comparisons*. Prove that the F-test of the hypothesis $\sum \alpha_i^2 = 0$ is equivalent to the two-sided t-test of the hypothesis $E(X) = 0$, where $x_j = y_{1j} - y_{2j}$ for $j = 1, 2, \ldots, J$. Use the fact that

$$t\left(\frac{\alpha}{2}, \nu\right) = [F(\alpha, 1, \nu)]^{1/2}.$$

20. In the mixed model, $Y_{i.}$ and $Y_{i'.}$ are not independent. Show that

$$\text{Cor}(Y_{i.},\ Y_{i'.}) = \frac{\sigma_B^2}{\sigma^2 + \sigma_B^2}.$$

21. There are two levels of a fixed-effects factor to be compared. Resources limit J at 5. Two experimental programs are under consideration: (1) The one-factor experiment of section 1 in Chapter VII can be used. (2) The observational units (plots, persons, and so on) can be grouped into blocks of size two. If the variance among these blocks σ_B^2 is large, the variance for a comparison will be greatly reduced. Suppose σ_B^2 is actually zero. What is the loss from using the blocks? Answer this question again for $J = 30$.

Appendices

TABLE I SQUARE ROOTS

n	$\sqrt{n}$	$\sqrt{10n}$	n	$\sqrt{n}$	$\sqrt{10n}$	n	$\sqrt{n}$	$\sqrt{10n}$
1	1.000	3.16	41	6.403	20.25	81	8.000	28.46
2	1.414	4.47	42	6.481	20.49	82	9.055	28.64
3	1.732	5.48	43	6.557	20.74	83	9.110	28.81
4	2.000	6.32	44	6.633	20.98	84	9.165	28.98
5	2.236	7.07	45	6.708	21.21	85	9.220	29.16
6	2.449	7.75	46	6.782	21.45	86	9.274	29.33
7	2.646	8.37	47	6.856	21.70	87	9.327	29.40
8	2.828	8.94	48	6.928	21.91	88	9.381	29.66
9	3.000	9.49	49	7.000	22.14	89	9.434	29.83
10	3.162	10.00	50	7.071	22.36	90	9.487	30.00
11	3.317	10.49	51	7.141	22.58	91	9.539	30.17
12	3.464	10.95	52	7.211	22.80	92	9.592	30.33
13	3.606	11.40	53	7.280	23.02	93	9.644	30.50
14	3.742	11.83	54	7.348	23.24	94	9.695	30.66
15	3.873	12.25	55	7.416	23.45	95	9.747	30.82
16	4.000	12.65	56	7.483	23.66	96	9.798	30.98
17	4.123	13.04	57	7.550	23.87	97	9.849	31.14
18	4.243	13.42	58	7.616	24.08	98	9.899	31.30
19	4.359	13.78	59	7.681	24.29	99	9.950	31.46
20	4.472	14.14	60	7.746	24.49	100	10.000	31.62
21	4.583	14.49	61	7.810	24.70			
22	4.690	14.83	62	7.874	24.90			
23	4.796	15.17	63	7.937	25.10			
24	4.899	15.49	64	8.000	25.30			
25	5.000	15.81	65	8.062	25.50			
26	5.099	16.12	66	8.124	25.69			
27	5.196	16.43	67	8.185	25.88			
28	5.292	16.73	68	8.246	26.08			
29	5.385	17.03	69	8.307	26.27			
30	5.477	17.32	70	8.367	26.46			
31	5.568	17.61	71	8.426	26.65			
32	5.657	17.89	72	8.485	26.83			
33	5.745	18.17	73	8.544	27.02			
34	5.831	18.44	74	8.602	27.20			
35	5.916	18.71	75	8.660	27.39			
36	6.000	18.97	76	8.718	27.57			
37	6.083	19.24	77	8.775	27.75			
38	6.164	19.49	78	8.832	27.93			
39	6.245	19.75	79	8.888	28.11			
40	6.325	20.00	80	8.944	28.28			

TABLE II RANDOM NORMAL NUMBERS

		$\mu = 0$	$\sigma = 1$		
−1.752	−0.329	−1.256	0.318	1.531	0.349
−0.291	0.085	1.701	−1.087	−0.443	−0.292
−0.933	0.130	0.634	0.899	1.409	−0.883
−0.450	−0.244	0.072	1.028	1.730	−0.056
0.512	−0.882	0.490	−1.304	−0.266	0.757
−0.702	0.472	0.429	−0.664	−0.592	1.443
0.284	0.039	−0.518	1.351	1.473	0.889
−0.509	1.420	−0.782	−0.429	−1.266	0.627
−1.776	−1.003	1.977	0.014	0.702	−0.435
−0.044	1.807	0.342	−2.510	1.071	−1.220
0.263	−0.578	1.612	−0.148	−0.383	−1.007
0.986	0.439	−0.192	−0.192	−0.132	0.883
−0.441	−0.852	−1.446	−0.605	−0.348	1.018
−0.866	0.489	0.097	0.379	0.192	−0.842
−1.215	0.675	1.621	0.394	−1.447	2.199
−0.475	−1.210	0.183	0.526	0.495	1.297
1.200	0.131	2.502	0.344	−1.060	−0.909
−0.498	−1.202	−0.057	−1.354	−1.441	−1.590
−0.743	0.894	−0.028	1.119	−0.598	0.279
0.779	−0.780	−0.954	0.705	−0.361	−0.734
−0.206	−0.195	1.017	−1.167	−0.079	−0.452
−0.092	−0.927	−0.439	−0.256	0.503	0.338
−1.222	−1.582	1.786	−0.517	−1.080	−0.409
0.068	0.075	−1.383	−0.084	0.159	1.276
0.183	1.600	−0.335	1.553	0.889	0.896
−0.811	−2.904	0.618	0.588	0.533	0.803
−1.010	1.148	1.033	0.336	1.306	0.835
1.453	1.210	−0.043	0.220	−0.256	−1.161
0.759	−0.838	−0.877	−0.177	1.183	−0.218
0.287	0.278	−0.454	0.897	−0.122	0.013
−0.669	0.035	−2.077	1.077	0.525	−0.154
0.392	0.106	−1.430	−0.204	−0.326	0.825
−0.337	0.199	−0.160	0.625	−0.891	−1.464
0.369	−1.990	−1.190	0.666	−1.614	0.082
−1.694	0.710	−0.655	−0.546	1.654	0.466

From *A Million Random Digits with 100,000 Normal Deviates*. Beverly Hills, California: Glencoe Free Press (1955). Reprinted by permission of The RAND Corporation.

TABLE III NORMAL DISTRIBUTION

For a variable Z with a unit normal distribution, this table gives $z(\alpha)$ and α in $\Pr\{z(\alpha) \leq Z\} = \alpha$. The values of α are in the center of the table.

$Z(\alpha)$	0	1	2	3	4	5	6	7	8	9
0.0	.5000	.4960	.4920	.4880	.4840	.4801	.4761	.4721	.4681	.4641
0.1	.4602	.4562	.4522	.4483	.4443	.4404	.4364	.4325	.4286	.4247
0.2	.4207	.4168	.4129	.4090	.4052	.4013	.3974	.3936	.3897	.3859
0.3	.3821	.3783	.3745	.3707	.3669	.3632	.3594	.3557	.3520	.3483
0.4	.3446	.3409	.3372	.3336	.3300	.3264	.3228	.3192	.3156	.3121
0.5	.3085	.3050	.3015	.2981	.2946	.2912	.2877	.2843	.2810	.2776
0.6	.2743	.2709	.2676	.2643	.2611	.2578	.2546	.2514	.2483	.2451
0.7	.2420	.2389	.2358	.2327	.2296	.2266	.2236	.2206	.2177	.2148
0.8	.2119	.2090	.2061	.2033	.2005	.1977	.1949	.1922	.1894	.1867
0.9	.1841	.1814	.1788	.1762	.1736	.1711	.1685	.1660	.1635	.1611
1.0	.1587	.1562	.1539	.1515	.1492	.1469	.1446	.1423	.1401	.1379
1.1	.1357	.1335	.1314	.1292	.1271	.1251	.1230	.1210	.1190	.1170
1.2	.1151	.1131	.1112	.1093	.1075	.1056	.1038	.1020	.1003	.0985
1.3	.0968	.0951	.0934	.0918	.0901	.0885	.0869	.0853	.0838	.0823
1.4	.0808	.0793	.0778	.0764	.0749	.0735	.0721	.0708	.0694	.0681
1.5	.0668	.0655	.0643	.0630	.0618	.0606	.0594	.0582	.0571	.0559
1.6	.0548	.0537	.0526	.0516	.0505	.0495	.0485	.0475	.0465	.0455
1.7	.0446	.0436	.0427	.0418	.0409	.0401	.0392	.0384	.0375	.0367
1.8	.0359	.0351	.0344	.0336	.0329	.0322	.0314	.0307	.0301	.0294
1.9	.0287	.0281	.0274	.0268	.0262	.0256	.0250	.0244	.0239	.0233
2.0	.0228	.0222	.0217	.0212	.0207	.0202	.0197	.0192	.0188	.0183
2.1	.0179	.0174	.0170	.0166	.0162	.0158	.0154	.0150	.0146	.0143
2.2	.0139	.0136	.0132	.0129	.0125	.0122	.0119	.0116	.0113	.0110
2.3	.0107	.0104	.0102	.0099	.0096	.0094	.0091	.0089	.0087	.0084
2.4	.0082	.0080	.0078	.0075	.0073	.0071	.0069	.0068	.0066	.0064
2.5	.0062	.0060	.0059	.0057	.0055	.0054	.0052	.0051	.0049	.0048
2.6	.0047	.0045	.0044	.0043	.0041	.0040	.0039	.0038	.0037	.0036
2.7	.0035	.0034	.0033	.0032	.0031	.0030	.0029	.0028	.0027	.0026
2.8	.0026	.0025	.0024	.0023	.0023	.0022	.0021	.0021	.0020	.0019
2.9	.0019	.0018	.0018	.0017	.0016	.0016	.0015	.0015	.0014	.0014
3.0	.0013	.0013	.0013	.0012	.0012	.0011	.0011	.0011	.0010	.0010

TABLE IV t-DISTRIBUTION

For a variable T with a t-distribution, this table gives $t(\alpha,\nu)$, ν, and α in $\Pr\{t(\alpha,\nu) \leq T\} = \alpha$. The values of $t(\alpha,\nu)$ are in the center of the table.

α ν	.100	.050	.025	.010	.005
1	3.078	6.314	12.706	31.821	63.657
2	1.886	2.920	4.303	6.965	9.925
3	1.638	2.353	3.182	4.541	5.841
4	1.533	2.132	2.776	3.747	4.604
5	1.476	2.015	2.571	3.365	4.032
6	1.440	1.943	2.447	3.143	3.707
7	1.415	1.895	2.365	2.998	3.499
8	1.397	1.860	2.306	2.896	3.355
9	1.383	1.833	2.262	2.821	3.250
10	1.372	1.812	2.228	2.764	3.169
11	1.363	1.796	2.201	2.718	3.106
12	1.356	1.782	2.179	2.681	3.055
13	1.350	1.771	2.160	2.650	3.012
14	1.345	1.761	2.145	2.624	2.977
15	1.341	1.753	2.131	2.602	2.947
16	1.337	1.746	2.120	2.583	2.921
17	1.333	1.740	2.110	2.567	2.898
18	1.330	1.734	2.101	2.552	2.878
19	1.328	1.729	2.093	2.539	2.861
20	1.325	1.725	2.086	2.528	2.845
21	1.323	1.721	2.080	2.518	2.831
22	1.321	1.717	2.074	2.508	2.819
23	1.319	1.714	2.069	2.500	2.807
24	1.318	1.711	2.064	2.492	2.797
25	1.316	1.708	2.060	2.485	2.787
26	1.315	1.706	2.056	2.479	2.779
27	1.314	1.703	2.052	2.473	2.771
28	1.313	1.701	2.048	2.467	2.763
29	1.311	1.699	2.045	2.462	2.756
30	1.310	1.697	2.042	2.457	2.750
∞	1.282	1.645	1.960	2.326	2.576

TABLE V χ^2 DISTRIBUTION

For a variable K with a χ^2 distribution, this table gives $\chi^2(\alpha,\nu)$ and α in $\Pr\{\chi^2(\alpha,\nu) \leq K\} = \alpha$. The values of $\chi^2(\alpha,\nu)$ are in the center of the table.

ν \ α	.995	.975	.950	.050	.025	.005
1	.00004	.00098	.00393	3.84	5.02	7.88
2	.0100	.0506	.103	5.99	7.38	10.60
3	.0717	.216	.352	7.81	9.35	12.84
4	.207	.484	.711	9.49	11.14	14.86
5	.412	.831	1.15	11.07	12.83	16.75
6	.676	1.24	1.64	12.59	14.45	18.55
7	.989	1.69	2.17	14.07	16.01	20.28
8	1.34	2.18	2.73	15.51	17.53	21.96
9	1.74	2.70	3.33	16.92	19.02	23.59
10	2.16	3.25	3.94	18.31	20.48	25.19
11	2.60	3.82	4.57	19.68	21.92	26.76
12	3.07	4.40	5.23	21.03	23.34	28.30
13	3.57	5.01	5.89	22.36	24.74	29.82
14	4.07	5.63	6.57	23.68	26.12	31.32
15	4.60	6.26	7.26	25.00	27.49	32.80
16	5.14	6.91	7.96	26.30	28.85	34.27
17	5.70	7.56	8.67	27.59	30.19	35.72
18	6.26	8.23	9.39	28.87	31.53	37.16
19	6.84	8.91	10.12	30.14	32.85	38.58
20	7.43	9.59	10.85	31.41	34.17	40.00
21	8.03	10.28	11.59	32.67	35.48	41.40
22	8.64	10.98	12.34	33.92	36.78	42.80
23	9.26	11.69	13.09	35.17	38.08	44.18
24	9.89	12.40	13.85	36.42	39.36	45.56
25	10.52	13.12	14.61	37.65	40.65	46.93
26	11.16	13.85	15.38	38.89	41.92	48.29
27	11.81	14.57	16.15	40.11	43.19	49.64
28	12.46	15.31	16.93	41.34	44.46	50.99
29	13.12	16.05	17.71	42.56	45.72	52.34
30	13.79	16.79	18.49	43.77	46.98	53.67
40	20.71	24.43	26.51	55.76	59.34	66.77
50	27.99	32.36	34.76	67.50	71.42	79.49
60	35.53	40.48	43.19	79.08	83.30	91.95
70	43.28	48.76	51.74	90.53	95.02	104.22
80	51.17	57.15	60.39	101.88	106.63	116.32

From E. S. Pearson and H. O. Hartley, *Biometrika Tables for Statisticians*, Volume I. Cambridge: Cambridge University Press (1958). Reprinted by permission of the Biometrika Trustees.

TABLE VI F-DISTRIBUTION

For a variable F with an F-distribution, this table gives $F(\alpha,\nu_1,\nu_2)$, ν_1, ν_2, and α in $\Pr\{F(\alpha,\nu_1,\nu_2)\le F\}=\alpha$. The values of $F(\alpha,\nu_1,\nu_2)$ are in the center of the table.

$\alpha = .05$

ν_2 \ ν_1	1	2	3	4	5	6	7	8	9	10	12	15	20	24	30	40	60	120	∞
1	161.4	199.5	215.7	224.6	230.2	234.0	236.8	238.9	240.5	241.9	243.9	245.9	248.0	249.1	250.1	251.1	252.2	253.3	254.3
2	18.51	19.00	19.16	19.25	19.30	19.33	19.35	19.37	19.38	19.40	19.41	19.43	19.45	19.45	19.46	19.47	19.48	19.49	19.50
3	10.13	9.55	9.28	9.12	9.01	8.94	8.89	8.85	8.81	8.79	8.74	8.70	8.66	8.64	8.62	8.59	8.57	8.55	8.53
4	7.71	6.94	6.59	6.39	6.26	6.16	6.09	6.04	6.00	5.96	5.91	5.86	5.80	5.77	5.75	5.72	5.69	5.66	5.63
5	6.61	5.79	5.41	5.19	5.05	4.95	4.88	4.82	4.77	4.74	4.68	4.62	4.56	4.53	4.50	4.46	4.43	4.40	4.36
6	5.99	5.14	4.76	4.53	4.39	4.28	4.21	4.15	4.10	4.06	4.00	3.94	3.87	3.84	3.81	3.77	3.74	3.70	3.67
7	5.59	4.74	4.35	4.12	3.97	3.87	3.79	3.73	3.68	3.64	3.57	3.51	3.44	3.41	3.38	3.34	3.30	3.27	3.23
8	5.32	4.46	4.07	3.84	3.69	3.58	3.50	3.44	3.39	3.35	3.28	3.22	3.15	3.12	3.08	3.04	3.01	2.97	2.93
9	5.12	4.26	3.86	3.63	3.48	3.37	3.29	3.23	3.18	3.14	3.07	3.01	2.94	2.90	2.86	2.83	2.79	2.75	2.71
10	4.96	4.10	3.71	3.48	3.33	3.22	3.14	3.07	3.02	2.98	2.91	2.85	2.77	2.74	2.70	2.66	2.62	2.58	2.54
11	4.84	3.98	3.59	3.36	3.20	3.09	3.01	2.95	2.90	2.85	2.79	2.72	2.65	2.61	2.57	2.53	2.49	2.45	2.40
12	4.75	3.89	3.49	3.26	3.11	3.00	2.91	2.85	2.80	2.75	2.69	2.62	2.54	2.51	2.47	2.43	2.38	2.34	2.30
13	4.67	3.81	3.41	3.18	3.03	2.92	2.83	2.77	2.71	2.67	2.60	2.53	2.46	2.42	2.38	2.34	2.30	2.25	2.21
14	4.60	3.74	3.34	3.11	2.96	2.85	2.76	2.70	2.65	2.60	2.53	2.46	2.39	2.35	2.31	2.27	2.22	2.18	2.13
15	4.54	3.68	3.29	3.06	2.90	2.79	2.71	2.64	2.59	2.54	2.48	2.40	2.33	2.29	2.25	2.20	2.16	2.11	2.07
16	4.49	3.63	3.24	3.01	2.85	2.74	2.66	2.59	2.54	2.49	2.42	2.35	2.28	2.24	2.19	2.15	2.11	2.06	2.01
17	4.45	3.59	3.20	2.96	2.81	2.70	2.61	2.55	2.49	2.45	2.38	2.31	2.23	2.19	2.15	2.10	2.06	2.01	1.96
18	4.41	3.55	3.16	2.93	2.77	2.66	2.58	2.51	2.46	2.41	2.34	2.27	2.19	2.15	2.11	2.06	2.02	1.97	1.92
19	4.38	3.52	3.13	2.90	2.74	2.63	2.54	2.48	2.42	2.38	2.31	2.23	2.16	2.11	2.07	2.03	1.98	1.93	1.88
20	4.35	3.49	3.10	2.87	2.71	2.60	2.51	2.45	2.39	2.35	2.28	2.20	2.12	2.08	2.04	1.99	1.95	1.90	1.84
21	4.32	3.47	3.07	2.84	2.68	2.57	2.49	2.42	2.37	2.32	2.25	2.18	2.10	2.05	2.01	1.96	1.92	1.87	1.81
22	4.30	3.44	3.05	2.82	2.66	2.55	2.46	2.40	2.34	2.30	2.23	2.15	2.07	2.03	1.98	1.94	1.89	1.84	1.78
23	4.28	3.42	3.03	2.80	2.64	2.53	2.44	2.37	2.32	2.27	2.20	2.13	2.05	2.01	1.96	1.91	1.86	1.81	1.76
24	4.26	3.40	3.01	2.78	2.62	2.51	2.42	2.36	2.30	2.25	2.18	2.11	2.03	1.98	1.94	1.89	1.84	1.79	1.73
25	4.24	3.39	2.99	2.76	2.60	2.49	2.40	2.34	2.28	2.24	2.16	2.09	2.01	1.96	1.92	1.87	1.82	1.77	1.71
26	4.23	3.37	2.98	2.74	2.59	2.47	2.39	2.32	2.27	2.22	2.15	2.07	1.99	1.95	1.90	1.85	1.80	1.75	1.69
27	4.21	3.35	2.96	2.73	2.57	2.46	2.37	2.31	2.25	2.20	2.13	2.06	1.97	1.93	1.88	1.84	1.79	1.73	1.67
28	4.20	3.34	2.95	2.71	2.56	2.45	2.36	2.29	2.24	2.19	2.12	2.04	1.96	1.91	1.87	1.82	1.77	1.71	1.65
29	4.18	3.33	2.93	2.70	2.55	2.43	2.35	2.28	2.22	2.18	2.10	2.03	1.94	1.90	1.85	1.81	1.75	1.70	1.64
30	4.17	3.32	2.92	2.69	2.53	2.42	2.33	2.27	2.21	2.16	2.09	2.01	1.93	1.89	1.84	1.79	1.74	1.68	1.62
40	4.08	3.23	2.84	2.61	2.45	2.34	2.25	2.18	2.12	2.08	2.00	1.92	1.84	1.79	1.74	1.69	1.64	1.58	1.51
60	4.00	3.15	2.76	2.53	2.37	2.25	2.17	2.10	2.04	1.99	1.92	1.84	1.75	1.70	1.65	1.59	1.53	1.47	1.39
120	3.92	3.07	2.68	2.45	2.29	2.17	2.09	2.02	1.96	1.91	1.83	1.75	1.66	1.61	1.55	1.50	1.43	1.35	1.25
∞	3.84	3.00	2.60	2.37	2.21	2.10	2.01	1.94	1.88	1.83	1.75	1.67	1.57	1.52	1.46	1.39	1.32	1.22	1.00

From E. S. Pearson and H. O. Hartley, *Biometrika Tables for Statisticians*, Volume I. Cambridge: Cambridge University Press (1958). Reprinted by permission of the Biometrika Trustees.

TABLE VI F-DISTRIBUTION

$\alpha = .01$

ν_2 \ ν_1	1	2	3	4	5	6	7	8	9	10	12	15	20	24	30	40	60	120	∞
1	4052	4999.5	5403	5625	5764	5859	5928	5982	6022	6056	6106	6157	6209	6235	6261	6287	6313	6339	6366
2	98.50	99.00	99.17	99.25	99.30	99.33	99.36	99.37	99.39	99.40	99.42	99.43	99.45	99.46	99.47	99.47	99.48	99.49	99.50
3	34.12	30.82	29.46	28.71	28.24	27.91	27.67	27.49	27.35	27.23	27.05	26.87	26.69	26.60	26.50	26.41	26.32	26.22	26.13
4	21.20	18.00	16.69	15.98	15.52	15.21	14.98	14.80	14.66	14.55	14.37	14.20	14.02	13.93	13.84	13.75	13.65	13.56	13.46
5	16.26	13.27	12.06	11.39	10.97	10.67	10.46	10.29	10.16	10.05	9.89	9.72	9.55	9.47	9.38	9.29	9.20	9.11	9.02
6	13.75	10.92	9.78	9.15	8.75	8.47	8.26	8.10	7.98	7.87	7.72	7.56	7.40	7.31	7.23	7.14	7.06	6.97	6.88
7	12.25	9.55	8.45	7.85	7.46	7.19	6.99	6.84	6.72	6.62	6.47	6.31	6.16	6.07	5.99	5.91	5.82	5.74	5.65
8	11.26	8.65	7.59	7.01	6.63	6.37	6.18	6.03	5.91	5.81	5.67	5.52	5.36	5.28	5.20	5.12	5.03	4.95	4.86
9	10.56	8.02	6.99	6.42	6.06	5.80	5.61	5.47	5.35	5.26	5.11	4.96	4.81	4.73	4.65	4.57	4.48	4.40	4.31
10	10.04	7.56	6.55	5.99	5.64	5.39	5.20	5.06	4.94	4.85	4.71	4.56	4.41	4.33	4.25	4.17	4.08	4.00	3.91
11	9.65	7.21	6.22	5.67	5.32	5.07	4.89	4.74	4.63	4.54	4.40	4.25	4.10	4.02	3.94	3.86	3.78	3.69	3.60
12	9.33	6.93	5.95	5.41	5.06	4.82	4.64	4.50	4.39	4.30	4.16	4.01	3.86	3.78	3.70	3.62	3.54	3.45	3.36
13	9.07	6.70	5.74	5.21	4.86	4.62	4.44	4.30	4.19	4.10	3.96	3.82	3.66	3.59	3.51	3.43	3.34	3.25	3.17
14	8.86	6.51	5.56	5.04	4.69	4.46	4.28	4.14	4.03	3.94	3.80	3.66	3.51	3.43	3.35	3.27	3.18	3.09	3.00
15	8.68	6.36	5.42	4.89	4.56	4.32	4.14	4.00	3.89	3.80	3.67	3.52	3.37	3.29	3.21	3.13	3.05	2.96	2.87
16	8.53	6.23	5.29	4.77	4.44	4.20	4.03	3.89	3.78	3.69	3.55	3.41	3.26	3.18	3.10	3.02	2.93	2.84	2.75
17	8.40	6.11	5.18	4.67	4.34	4.10	3.93	3.79	3.68	3.59	3.46	3.31	3.16	3.08	3.00	2.92	2.83	2.75	2.65
18	8.29	6.01	5.09	4.58	4.25	4.01	3.84	3.71	3.60	3.51	3.37	3.23	3.08	3.00	2.92	2.84	2.75	2.66	2.57
19	8.18	5.93	5.01	4.50	4.17	3.94	3.77	3.63	3.52	3.43	3.30	3.15	3.00	2.92	2.84	2.76	2.67	2.58	2.49
20	8.10	5.85	4.94	4.43	4.10	3.87	3.70	3.56	3.46	3.37	3.23	3.09	2.94	2.86	2.78	2.69	2.61	2.52	2.42
21	8.02	5.78	4.87	4.37	4.04	3.81	3.64	3.51	3.40	3.31	3.17	3.03	2.88	2.80	2.72	2.64	2.55	2.46	2.36
22	7.95	5.72	4.82	4.31	3.99	3.76	3.59	3.45	3.35	3.26	3.12	2.98	2.83	2.75	2.67	2.58	2.50	2.40	2.31
23	7.88	5.66	4.76	4.26	3.94	3.71	3.54	3.41	3.30	3.21	3.07	2.93	2.78	2.70	2.62	2.54	2.45	2.35	2.26
24	7.82	5.61	4.72	4.22	3.90	3.67	3.50	3.36	3.26	3.17	3.03	2.89	2.74	2.66	2.58	2.49	2.40	2.31	2.21
25	7.77	5.57	4.68	4.18	3.85	3.63	3.46	3.32	3.22	3.13	2.99	2.85	2.70	2.62	2.54	2.45	2.36	2.27	2.17
26	7.72	5.53	4.64	4.14	3.82	3.59	3.42	3.29	3.18	3.09	2.96	2.81	2.66	2.58	2.50	2.42	2.33	2.23	2.13
27	7.68	5.49	4.60	4.11	3.78	3.56	3.39	3.26	3.15	3.06	2.93	2.78	2.63	2.55	2.47	2.38	2.29	2.20	2.10
28	7.64	5.45	4.57	4.07	3.75	3.53	3.36	3.23	3.12	3.03	2.90	2.75	2.60	2.52	2.44	2.35	2.26	2.17	2.06
29	7.60	5.42	4.54	4.04	3.73	3.50	3.33	3.20	3.09	3.00	2.87	2.73	2.57	2.49	2.41	2.33	2.23	2.14	2.03
30	7.56	5.39	4.51	4.02	3.70	3.47	3.30	3.17	3.07	2.98	2.84	2.70	2.55	2.47	2.39	2.30	2.21	2.11	2.01
40	7.31	5.18	4.31	3.83	3.51	3.29	3.12	2.99	2.89	2.80	2.66	2.52	2.37	2.29	2.20	2.11	2.02	1.92	1.80
60	7.08	4.98	4.13	3.65	3.34	3.12	2.95	2.82	2.72	2.63	2.50	2.35	2.20	2.12	2.03	1.94	1.84	1.73	1.60
120	6.85	4.79	3.95	3.48	3.17	2.96	2.79	2.66	2.56	2.47	2.34	2.19	2.03	1.95	1.86	1.76	1.66	1.53	1.38
∞	6.63	4.61	3.78	3.32	3.02	2.80	2.64	2.51	2.41	2.32	2.18	2.04	1.88	1.79	1.70	1.59	1.47	1.32	1.00

From E. S. Pearson and H. O. Hartley, *Biometrika Tables for Statisticians*, Volume I. Cambridge: Cambridge University Press (1958). Reprinted by permission of the Biometrika Trustees.

TABLE VII STUDENTIZED RANGE DISTRIBUTION

For a variable Q with a studentized range distribution, this table gives $q(\alpha,k,\nu)$, k, ν, and α in $\Pr\{q(\alpha,k,\nu) \le Q\} = \alpha$. The values of $q(\alpha,k,\nu)$ are in the center of the table.

$\alpha = .05$

ν \ k	2	3	4	5	6	7	8	9	10	11	12	13	14	15	16	17	18	19	20
1	18.0	27.0	32.8	37.1	40.4	43.1	45.4	47.4	49.1	50.6	52.0	53.2	54.3	55.4	56.3	57.2	58.0	58.8	59.6
2	6.09	8.3	9.8	10.9	11.7	12.4	13.0	13.5	14.0	14.4	14.7	15.1	15.4	15.7	15.9	16.1	16.4	16.6	16.8
3	4.50	5.91	6.82	7.50	8.04	8.48	8.85	9.18	9.46	9.72	9.95	10.15	10.35	10.52	10.69	10.84	10.98	11.11	11.24
4	3.93	5.04	5.76	6.29	6.71	7.05	7.35	7.60	7.83	8.03	8.21	8.37	8.52	8.66	8.79	8.91	9.03	9.13	9.23
5	3.64	4.60	5.22	5.67	6.03	6.33	6.58	6.80	6.99	7.17	7.32	7.47	7.60	7.72	7.83	7.93	8.03	8.12	8.21
6	3.46	4.34	4.90	5.31	5.63	5.89	6.12	6.32	6.49	6.65	6.79	6.92	7.03	7.14	7.24	7.34	7.43	7.51	7.59
7	3.34	4.16	4.68	5.06	5.36	5.61	5.82	6.00	6.16	6.30	6.43	6.55	6.66	6.76	6.85	6.94	7.02	7.09	7.17
8	3.26	4.04	4.53	4.89	5.17	5.40	5.60	5.77	5.92	6.05	6.18	6.29	6.39	6.48	6.57	6.65	6.73	6.80	6.87
9	3.20	3.95	4.42	4.76	5.02	5.24	5.43	5.60	5.74	5.87	5.98	6.09	6.19	6.28	6.36	6.44	6.51	6.58	6.64
10	3.15	3.88	4.33	4.65	4.91	5.12	5.30	5.46	5.60	5.72	5.83	5.93	6.03	6.11	6.20	6.27	6.34	6.40	6.47
11	3.11	3.82	4.26	4.57	4.82	5.03	5.20	5.35	5.49	5.61	5.71	5.81	5.90	5.99	6.06	6.14	6.20	6.26	6.33
12	3.08	3.77	4.20	4.51	4.75	4.95	5.12	5.27	5.40	5.51	5.62	5.71	5.80	5.88	5.95	6.03	6.09	6.15	6.21
13	3.06	3.73	4.15	4.45	4.69	4.88	5.05	5.19	5.32	5.43	5.53	5.63	5.71	5.79	5.86	5.93	6.00	6.05	6.11
14	3.03	3.70	4.11	4.41	4.64	4.83	4.99	5.13	5.25	5.36	5.46	5.55	5.64	5.72	5.79	5.85	5.92	5.97	6.03
15	3.01	3.67	4.08	4.37	4.60	4.78	4.94	5.08	5.20	5.31	5.40	5.49	5.58	5.65	5.72	5.79	5.85	5.90	5.96
16	3.00	3.65	4.05	4.33	4.56	4.74	4.90	5.03	5.15	5.26	5.35	5.44	5.52	5.59	5.66	5.72	5.79	5.84	5.90
17	2.98	3.63	4.02	4.30	4.52	4.71	4.86	4.99	5.11	5.21	5.31	5.39	5.47	5.55	5.61	5.68	5.74	5.79	5.84
18	2.97	3.61	4.00	4.28	4.49	4.67	4.82	4.96	5.07	5.17	5.27	5.35	5.43	5.50	5.57	5.63	5.69	5.74	5.79
19	2.96	3.59	3.98	4.25	4.47	4.65	4.79	4.92	5.04	5.14	5.23	5.32	5.39	5.46	5.53	5.59	5.65	5.70	5.75
20	2.95	3.58	3.96	4.23	4.45	4.62	4.77	4.90	5.01	5.11	5.20	5.28	5.36	5.43	5.49	5.55	5.61	5.66	5.71
24	2.92	3.53	3.90	4.17	4.37	4.54	4.68	4.81	4.92	5.01	5.10	5.18	5.25	5.32	5.38	5.44	5.50	5.54	5.59
30	2.89	3.49	3.84	4.10	4.30	4.46	4.60	4.72	4.83	4.92	5.00	5.08	5.15	5.21	5.27	5.33	5.38	5.43	5.48
40	2.86	3.44	3.79	4.04	4.23	4.39	4.52	4.63	4.74	4.82	4.91	4.98	5.05	5.11	5.16	5.22	5.27	5.31	5.36
60	2.83	3.40	3.74	3.98	4.16	4.31	4.44	4.55	4.65	4.73	4.81	4.88	4.94	5.00	5.06	5.11	5.16	5.20	5.24
120	2.80	3.36	3.69	3.92	4.10	4.24	4.36	4.48	4.56	4.64	4.72	4.78	4.84	4.90	4.95	5.00	5.05	5.09	5.13
∞	2.77	3.31	3.63	3.86	4.03	4.17	4.29	4.39	4.47	4.55	4.62	4.68	4.74	4.80	4.85	4.89	4.93	4.97	5.01

From E. S. Pearson and H. O. Hartley, *Biometrika Tables for Statisticians*, Volume I. Cambridge: Cambridge University Press (1958). Reprinted by permission of the Biometrika Trustees.

TABLE VII STUDENTIZED RANGE DISTRIBUTION

$\alpha = .01$

v \ k	2	3	4	5	6	7	8	9	10	11	12	13	14	15	16	17	18	19	20
1	90.0	135	164	186	202	216	227	237	246	253	260	266	272	277	282	286	290	294	298
2	14.0	19.0	22.3	24.7	26.6	28.2	29.5	30.7	31.7	32.6	33.4	34.1	34.8	35.4	36.0	36.5	37.0	37.5	37.9
3	8.26	10.6	12.2	13.3	14.2	15.0	15.6	16.2	16.7	17.1	17.5	17.9	18.2	18.5	18.8	19.1	19.3	19.5	19.8
4	6.51	8.12	9.17	9.96	10.6	11.1	11.5	11.9	12.3	12.6	12.8	13.1	13.3	13.5	13.7	13.9	14.1	14.2	14.4
5	5.70	6.97	7.80	8.42	8.91	9.32	9.67	9.97	10.24	10.48	10.70	10.89	11.08	11.24	11.40	11.55	11.68	11.81	11.93
6	5.24	6.33	7.03	7.56	7.97	8.32	8.61	8.87	9.10	9.30	9.49	9.65	9.81	9.95	10.08	10.21	10.32	10.43	10.54
7	4.95	5.92	6.54	7.01	7.37	7.68	7.94	8.17	8.37	8.55	8.71	8.86	9.00	9.12	9.24	9.35	9.46	9.55	9.65
8	4.74	5.63	6.20	6.63	6.96	7.24	7.47	7.68	7.87	8.03	8.18	8.31	8.44	8.55	8.66	8.76	8.85	8.94	9.03
9	4.60	5.43	5.96	6.35	6.66	6.91	7.13	7.32	7.49	7.65	7.78	7.91	8.03	8.13	8.23	8.32	8.41	8.49	8.57
10	4.48	5.27	5.77	6.14	6.43	6.67	6.87	7.05	7.21	7.36	7.48	7.60	7.71	7.81	7.91	7.99	8.07	8.15	8.22
11	4.39	5.14	5.62	5.97	6.25	6.48	6.67	6.84	6.99	7.13	7.25	7.36	7.46	7.56	7.65	7.73	7.81	7.88	7.95
12	4.32	5.04	5.50	5.84	6.10	6.32	6.51	6.67	6.81	6.94	7.06	7.17	7.26	7.36	7.44	7.52	7.59	7.66	7.73
13	4.26	4.96	5.40	5.73	5.98	6.19	6.37	6.53	6.67	6.79	6.90	7.01	7.10	7.19	7.27	7.34	7.42	7.48	7.55
14	4.21	4.89	5.32	5.63	5.88	6.08	6.26	6.41	6.54	6.66	6.77	6.87	6.96	7.05	7.12	7.20	7.27	7.33	7.39
15	4.17	4.83	5.25	5.56	5.80	5.99	6.16	6.31	6.44	6.55	6.66	6.76	6.84	6.93	7.00	7.07	7.14	7.20	7.26
16	4.13	4.78	5.19	5.49	5.72	5.92	6.08	6.22	6.35	6.46	6.56	6.66	6.74	6.82	6.90	6.97	7.03	7.00	7.15
17	4.10	4.74	5.14	5.43	5.66	5.85	6.01	6.15	6.27	6.38	6.48	6.57	6.66	6.73	6.80	6.87	6.94	7.00	7.05
18	4.07	4.70	5.09	5.38	5.60	5.79	5.94	6.08	6.20	6.31	6.41	6.50	6.58	6.65	6.72	6.79	6.85	6.91	6.96
19	4.05	4.67	5.05	5.33	5.55	5.73	5.89	6.02	6.14	6.25	6.34	6.43	6.51	6.58	6.65	6.72	6.78	6.84	6.89
20	4.02	4.64	5.02	5.29	5.51	5.69	5.84	5.97	6.09	6.19	6.29	6.37	6.45	6.52	6.59	6.65	6.71	6.76	6.82
24	3.96	4.54	4.91	5.17	5.37	5.54	5.69	5.81	5.92	6.02	6.11	6.19	6.26	6.33	6.39	6.45	6.51	6.56	6.61
30	3.89	4.45	4.80	5.05	5.24	5.40	5.54	5.65	5.76	5.85	5.93	6.01	6.08	6.14	6.20	6.26	6.31	6.35	6.41
40	3.82	4.37	4.70	4.93	5.11	5.27	5.39	5.50	5.60	5.69	5.77	5.84	5.90	5.96	6.02	6.07	6.12	6.17	6.21
60	3.76	4.28	4.60	4.82	4.99	5.13	5.25	5.36	5.45	5.53	5.60	5.67	5.73	5.79	5.84	5.89	5.93	5.98	6.02
120	3.70	4.20	4.50	4.71	4.87	5.01	5.12	5.21	5.30	5.38	5.44	5.51	5.56	5.61	5.66	5.71	5.75	5.79	5.83
∞	3.64	4.12	4.40	4.60	4.76	4.88	4.99	5.08	5.16	5.23	5.29	5.35	5.40	5.45	5.49	5.54	5.57	5.61	5.65

Answers to Selected Exercises

Chapter II

Section 1.1
1) $\{1, 2, 3, 4\}$; 2^4; 4; .3, .3, .4, .8, .9. **2)** .60; .85; .15; .50. **3)** $1/14$. **4)** $\dfrac{2}{n(n+1)}$.
5) $\{300, 400\}$; $\Pr\{300\} = .8$, $\Pr\{400\} = .2$.

Section 1.2
6) 2.3; \$23. **8)** 2.57. **9)** $(2n + 1)/3$. **11)** \$675. **12)** \$42.50; 1 more to raise to \$45.00.

Section 1.3
13) .81, .90. **14)** $2\theta - 1$, $4\theta(1 - \theta)$.

Section 1.4
16) .40. **17)** $(n^2 + n - 2)/18$. **18)** 459.84. **19)** 8; 30.8. **20)** $\{-1, 1\}$; $\Pr\{y\} = \Pr\{w\}$; $2\theta - 1$; no. **21)** 6.1, .81; —; 23, 81, 9. **22)** 7.00, .39. **23)** $n(n + 1)/2$; $(n^2 + n - 2)/18$. **25)** 12,000; 3794.

Section 1.5
26) 30; 21. **28)** 2525, 291.

Section 2.1
29) .50; .75; .69; 0. **30)** 1.5; .10; .10. **31)** 0.14. **32)** θ. **33)** $1 - e^{-\theta x}$. **34)** e^{-2}; $e^{-1} - e^{-2}$.

Section 2.2
40) $1/\theta$, $1/\theta^2$.

Section 2.3
41) .5000; .0495; .2119; .7386; .0500; .1869; 0. **42)** .84; 1.96; .67; 1.65; −2.58. **43)** 1.65 and 2.33; 1.96 and 2.58; −1.96 and −2.58. **44)** .5000; .1587; .7865; .0228; 59.8; 37.1 and 62.9. **45)** .96. **46)** .04.

Section 3
50) 2.4, 1.67. **51)** 1240, 167. **53)** 28,800, 11,043. **54)** 27,300, 11,043.

Section 4
55) .31; 100; 40; 6.325; .06. **56)** .18. **57)** .01. **58)** .90; .05. **61)** .20.

Chapter III

Section 1
1) No; yes; yes; no; yes.

Section 1.1
2) .32; .05. **3)** .40. **4)** 116.5; 103.3. **5)** 1.8. **6)** .024. **7)** $c_1 = 79.4$ and $c_2 = 120.6$; no. **9)** $c = 26,347$. **10)** Yes, since $c_1 = 21,379$ and $c_2 = 28,621$. **11)** $\alpha = .01$ or higher. **12)** Yes, since $c = 114.7$. **13)** No, since $c = 1110$. **14)** $c_1 = 11.48$ and $c_2 = 12.52$.

Section 1.2

16) .86. **17)** Yes, since $c = .27$. **18)** $c_1 = .18$ and $c_2 = .48$. **19)** $\alpha = .02$ or higher.
20) Less than 5 or more than 15.

Section 1.3

21) .10. **22)** $c = 11.1$. **23)** $c_1 = .062$ and $c_2 = .826$ for s. **24)** $c = 43.7$ for s.

Section 1.4

25) $c_1 = -7.1$ and $c_2 = 7.1$ for $x_1 - x_2$; $c = -.95$ for $x_1 - x_2$; $c = 15.2$ for $x_1 - 3x_2$;
$c_1 = 26.4$ and $c_2 = 73.6$ for $4x_1 + 3x_2$. **26)** $c_1 = -6.82$ and $c_2 = 6.82$ for $\bar{x}_1 - \bar{x}_2$.
27) Yes, since $c = 14.8$. **29)** No, since $c_1 = -13.9$ and $c_2 = 13.9$.

Section 2

31) $-$; $-$; .27. **32)** .84; .52, .32, .52, and .84. **33)** .98, .50, .05, .50, and .98.
34) 1.00, .80, and .60. **35)** $\alpha = .40$; .80, .40, and .60; inferior. **36)** .01; .23; .77.
37) .38; .03; .08; .17. **38)** 155 and .125. **39)** 49 and -2.00.

Section 3

40) .75; .625, .250; 1.25. **41)** .125; .20 and .03; $600. **42)** Yes, since $c = 98.3$.

Section 4

43) $c = 0$, so do not bother to observe X; 1.00 and 0; 1.2. **45)** No, since $c = 96.8$.

Chapter IV

Section 1

4) $3/2$; $\theta^2/8$; superior. **6)** .83; .57; .65. **7)** $9800; $171,333.

Section 2

8) .68. **9)** .62. **11)** .66. **13)** .84. **14)** .77. **15)** .89. **16)** .75. **17)** .95.

Section 2.1

18) 446 to 754; 509 to 691; 558 to 642. **19)** 246. **20)** 6.6 to 13.4. **22)** 28.8 to 31.6.

Section 2.2

23) .11 to .35. **24)** 385; 196. **25)** .74 to .93; .46 to .69.

Section 2.3

29) .90. **30)** 1.1 to 157; 1.0 to 12.5.

Section 2.4

31) 64 to 176. **32)** 277. **34)** 3.0 to 6.6; yes. **35)** $-.07$ to .27. **36)** -9.1 to 35.1.
38) .56 to .74.

Chapter V

Section 2.1

2) .20, .20, .26, .35; $-$; $-$; $-$; $-$; .22, $-.22$, .00, .00; .50, .50, .60, 1.00. **3)** .24, .12,
.05, .73; $-$; $-$; 1.7, .24, 1.01, .1824; $-$; $-$; .50; .30; .61, .48; $-$; 165. **4)** $-$; .60.
5) .85; .85; .1; 1.4; 2.1.

Section 2.2

12) $f(x, y) = 1$; .40; .16; .08. **13)** $-$; .22; .50; $f(x) = 1$; $f(y) = 1$; .5, .5, .08, .08;
.40; $-$; .59; .28, .33.

Section 2.3

18) .75; .49; .84; .35; .49; .75. **19)** .65; .78; 16.7. **20)** .32; .94; 21.5. **21)** .81; .66.
22) .73.

Section 3.1

24) .1824; .1, .3, .5, .7; .09, .21, .25, .21; .1420; .0404. **25)** 1.01; 1.44, 2.54; .63, 1.33;
.79; .22. **27)** .0833; $\dfrac{1}{3} + \dfrac{x}{3}$; $\dfrac{1 + 2x - 2x^2}{18}$; .0741; .0092. **28)** .61; 0.3, 1.1, 1.1,
0.3; .41, .49, .49, .41; .45; .16. **29)** .45. **30)** .025.

Section 3.3

43) $-$; 20, 140, 60, 2288, 356; 6.4, 3.8; $-$; 328, 288.8, 39.2; 4.9; .88, .94; 58.94; yes.
44) .42, .028; .082; .54, .73; $-$; .63. **47)** 3, 2; 2; no; 3, 9, 2, 10, .89.

Section 4.1

50) $-$; $E(Y|x_1) = .46x_1$; .4064, .5200, .4064; .46. **51)** $-$; $E(Y|x_1, x_2) = .2 + .1x_1 +$
$.1x_2$; .22. **51)** $-$; $E(Y|x_1, x_2) = .2 + .1x_1 + .1x_2$; .22. **52)** $-$; $-$; .59. **53)** .79.

Section 4.2

59) .0420; .87; 70.4; .79.

Chapter VI

Section 2

2) 10, 4, 2; no.

Section 3

7) 3.71; 51.8, 18.0; 13.9, 21.2; 42.5, 21.2. **9)** $-$; $-$; 1.68; 40.8, 10.9; 20.3, 13.7.

Chapter VII

Section 1

5) -25, -20, -5; 2450; 1300; 1150. **6)** Yes, since observed F-ratio = 8.48. **7)** $-$;
10.78; yes, no. **9)** -17.5 ± 14.8. **12)** 7, 5, 8, 10; 2; 7.5; -0.5, -2.5, 0.5, 2.5; no.
14) No, since observed F-ratio = 26.2; all except $y_1. - y_2.$.

Section 2.1

22) 4; 0. **25)** Observed F-ratios are 3.00 and 7.29. **26)** 9; -2, -1, 0, 1, 2; -1, 0, 1; 2.
28) 9.33; 55; -3, 7, -1; -3; second is better than the others. **33)** Observed
F-ratios are 10.8 and 10.6. **34)** Observed F-ratios are .32 and 1.93.

Section 2.2

39) 1.5. **44)** $-$; observed F-ratio is 14.1. **45)** Observed F-ratios are 8.17, 1.50, and
3.06.   **46)** Yes, since they are 9.0, 7.5, 6.5; $\epsilon = q(.05, 3, 24)\dfrac{s}{\sqrt{12}} = 2.0$;

$\epsilon = q(.05, 12, 24)\dfrac{s}{\sqrt{3}} = 5.9$, no; $\epsilon = q(.05, 3, 24)\dfrac{s}{\sqrt{6}} = 2.9$;

$\epsilon = q(.05, 3, 24)\sqrt{\dfrac{5}{27}}s = 3.0$.   **49)** $a = 8.0$; $a = 8.5$.

Chapter VIII

Section 1

1) 8; $\{-6, -4, -2, 0, 2, 4, 6\}$; 16; 2. **5)** 170 and 102.5. **6)** 170 and 12.5. **9)** Reject, since $c = 15.3$. **10)** 35.5, 25.5, 21.0. **11)** 0.11. **16)** $y \pm \epsilon$, where

$$\epsilon = t\left(\frac{\alpha}{2}, I - 1\right)\sqrt{\frac{\text{Row SS}}{IJ(I-1)}}.$$

Section 2

17) $-$; observed F-ratios are 4.29 and 6.20; 202.5, 192.8, 188.3, 75.06, 130.38; $\epsilon = 11.1$. **18)** $-$; 14, 10, 1.25, 63.75; 0.44 to 7.56; 4, 1.58, 0.44 to 7.56.

Index